Robert Lee Morton • Merle Gray
Elizabeth Springstun • William L. Schaaf

Making Sure of Arithmetic

SILVER BURDETT COMPANY

New York   Chicago   Dallas   San Francisco

FOREWORD

In preparing the New Edition of MAKING SURE OF ARITHMETIC, the goal has been to keep this series the finest learning tool in the field. Each book has been extensively revised, redesigned, and completely reillustrated.

As in the earlier edition, first attention is given to the way the child learns. How can we give him the security of understanding which he needs and wants? How can we help him develop a sense of sureness and confidence in his own everyday uses of arithmetic?

The authors of MAKING SURE OF ARITHMETIC believe these things can be done only by the most careful development of each new idea; by immediately providing rich and extensive experience in using the idea; by maintaining skill and facility in using it; by constantly calling attention to relationships; and perhaps most important of all, by recognizing that the child does not learn "all at once" but must be consistently given the opportunity to re-learn and to deepen understanding.

This means re-teaching the basic ideas of arithmetic at each grade level. It means the maintaining, enriching, and extending of earlier learnings as well as the beginning of new learnings. Only in this way can we make sure of the child's continuous growth in understanding and skill.

Robert L. Morton
College of Education
Ohio University
Athens, Ohio

Merle Gray
Director of Elementary Education
Hammond Public Schools
Hammond, Indiana

Elizabeth Springstun
Supervisor of Student Teaching
National College of Education
Evanston, Illinois

William L. Schaaf
Department of Education
Brooklyn College
Brooklyn, New York

COPYRIGHT, 1946, 1952, BY SILVER BURDETT COMPANY

This makes it illegal to copy or reproduce any part of the contents of this book without written permission from the publisher.

Printed in the United States of America

CONTENTS

1. Whole Numbers and Fractions.............. 1-59
2. Percentage............................. 60-105
3. Money and Interest..................... 106-129
4. Sharing Risks and Benefits................ 130-157
5. Measuring Surfaces....................... 158-189
6. Measuring Solids........................ 190-217
7. The World We Live In.................... 218-267
8. Earning a Living........................ 268-287
9. Borrowing and Investing Money............ 288-317
10. Simple Ways of Using Geometry........... 318-344
11. A New Way of Using Arithmetic........... 345-357

REMEDIAL PRACTICE............................ 358-370

TABLES FOR REFERENCE 371-372

INDEX.. 373-379

REFERENCES TO LIFE SITUATIONS 380

Illustrated by Paul Busch and others

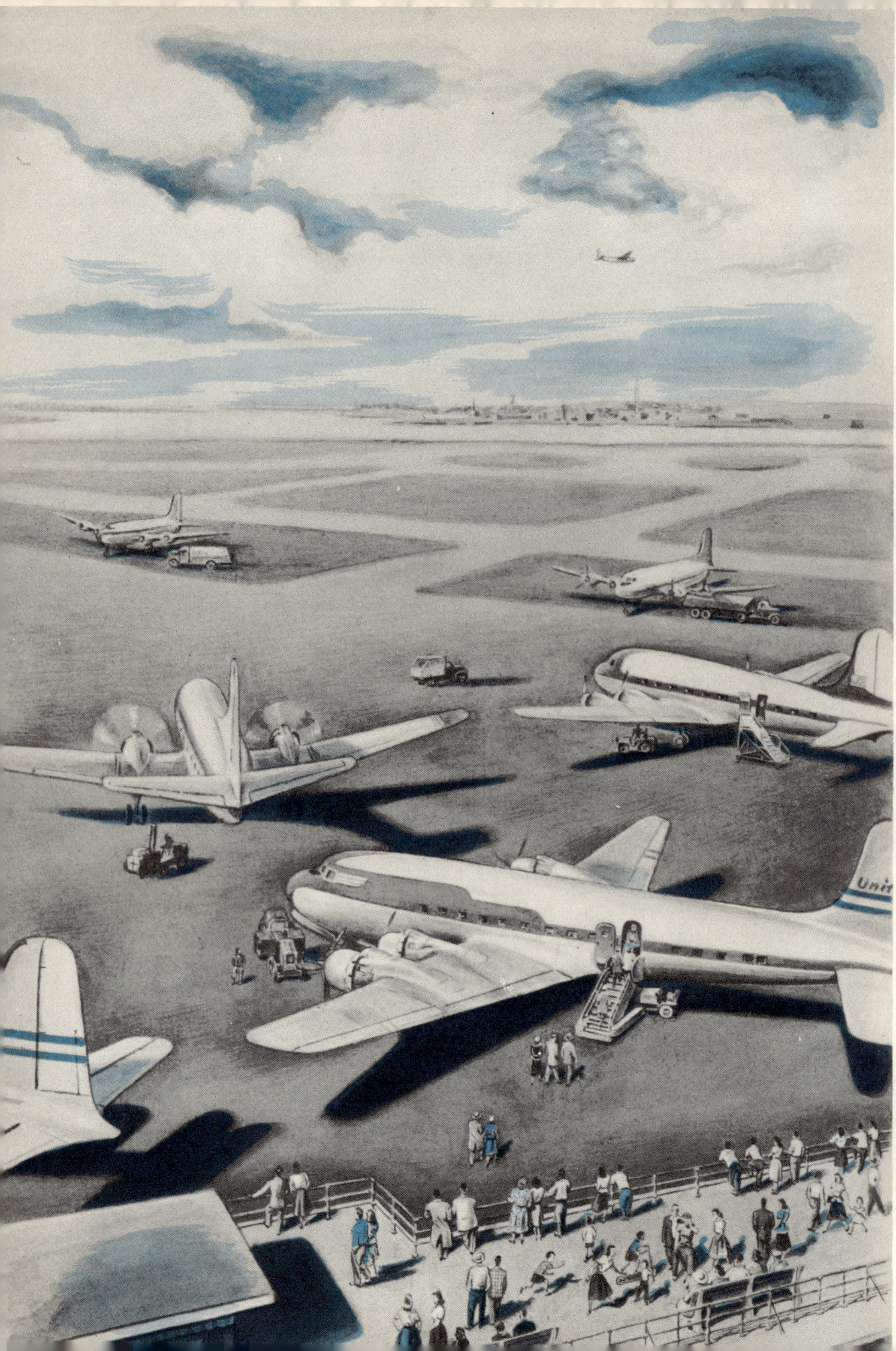

I

WHOLE NUMBERS AND FRACTIONS

Air Age

In the first fifty years of the 20th century, aviation made great advances. Airplanes, for example, progressed from slow, crude "flying machines" to giant, swift airliners. The second half of the century may see equally great changes in air transportation.

1. In 1927, a tiny plane made the first non-stop flight from New York to Paris. Often flying only a few hundred feet above the waves of the Atlantic, it covered the distance of more than 3600 miles in about 33 hours. On the average, about what was the plane's speed in miles per hour (m.p.h.)?

2. Today, transatlantic airliners fly above the weather at a height of 20,000 feet. About how many miles high would this be?

3. A certain airliner flew non-stop from New York International Airport to London Airport in $11\frac{1}{2}$ hours. If the average speed of the airliner was 300 m.p.h., how many miles apart are the airports?

4. Rapid growth of aviation in the United States is shown by the number of airports. In 1940, there were 2,331 airports. By 1950, there were 6,484. How many more were there in 1950 than in 1940?

5. A businessman flew 724 miles from New York to Chicago. He then flew 1,856 miles from Chicago to San Francisco and 2,400 miles from San Francisco to Honolulu. How many miles had he traveled in all?

Understanding What Numbers Mean

In the number 638, the 8 means 8 ones, or units; the 3 means 3 tens; the 6 means 6 hundreds. We can also say that the number 638 means 63 tens and 8 units, or 638 units.

1. In the number 792, what does the 2 mean? What does the 9 mean? the 7?

▶ In any number, the meaning of each figure depends not only upon what the figure is but also upon the place which it occupies in the number, that is, its **place value**.

2. What does the zero mean in 790? in 7092? Do you see that zero is a **place-holder** in both 790 and 7092? Can you also think of other figures as place-holders?

3. In writing numbers with 5 or more places, the figures are usually grouped by three's, beginning at the right. The groups, or **periods,** are separated by commas. Study the chart below.

hundred-billions	ten-billions	billions	hundred-millions	ten-millions	millions	hundred-thousands	ten-thousands	thousands	hundreds	tens	units
3	4	2,	5	1	9,	8	6	7,	4	6	5

We read this number, "342 billion, 519 million, 867 thousand, 465."

What does the 342 mean? the 519? the 867? the 465?

In reading very large numbers we think of the periods as a whole. For example, we read 12,475,090,800 as "12 billion, 475 million, 90 thousand, 800."

```
      billions    millions   thousands   units
    ⎧‾‾‾‾‾⎫   ⎧‾‾‾‾‾⎫   ⎧‾‾‾‾‾⎫   ⎧‾‾‾‾‾⎫
       1  2 , 4  7  5 , 0  9  0 , 8  0  0
```

Read these numbers; tell what each group of figures in each number means.

4. A. 73,526,815   B. 8,462,350   C. 24,060,500
5. A. 132,479,568   B. 10,750,000   C. 401,008,075
6. A. 2,375,450,000   B. 4,500,000,000
7. A. 27,040,200,000   B. 115,708,000,000

8. The Milky Way, a band of light extending all the way around the sky, contains about 200,000,000,000 stars. This number is read: "200 billion." Do you understand how many a billion really is? Study the figures at the right; do you see that it takes ten 100,000,000's, or 1000 million, to make a billion?

100,000,000
100,000,000
100,000,000
100,000,000
100,000,000
100,000,000
100,000,000
100,000,000
100,000,000
100,000,000
1 000,000,000

The Milky Way
Mount Wilson-Palomar Observatory Photo

How Well Can You Add and Subtract?

There are many practical problems in this book. To solve them, you must know how to add, subtract, multiply, and divide quickly and accurately. Here is a review of addition and subtraction. How well can you do these examples? If you need practice, turn to pages 358-359 and do the examples given there.

Add:

	A	B	C	D	E
1.	329	237	6798	685	26
	865	956	349	2943	144
	741	524	765	374	3068
	908	361	1824	38	12
	123	645	32	401	531
	487	958	124	3255	1045
2.	436	2068	67	269	$12,460.90
	1285	77	896	2899	825.45
	669	355	1840	887	38.22
	32	1905	69	5003	3,057.00
	4825	4	541	736	289.15
	623	488	9634	1561	

Subtract:

	A	B	C	D	E
3.	5623	$79.30	$63.08	28,932	$754.00
	819	42.08	5.26	9,347	625.94
4.	42,947	71,025	32,000	$50,804	$8000.20
	8,036	67,687	29,435	50,579	4932.50
5.	120,425	300,427	845,063	859,137	$125,644.00
	74,368	159,438	758,897	68,999	86.25

Adding and Subtracting Horizontally

Sometimes we need to add or subtract numbers written in rows across the page instead of in columns.

Without copying the following examples, add both horizontally and vertically, and write the sums. How can you tell if your addition is correct?

A	B	C
1. 72 + 46 = ?	65 + 38 = ?	77 + 28 + 65 = ?
35 + 98 = ?	74 + 86 = ?	45 + 63 + 29 = ?
88 + 25 = ?	49 + 37 = ?	34 + 26 + 83 = ?
49 + 93 = ?	64 + 68 = ?	75 + 18 + 49 = ?
? + ? = ?	? + ? = ?	? + ? + ? = ?

Add or subtract without copying the examples:

2. $.75 + $2.00 + $.50 = ?   **5.** $5 − $1.35 = ?
3. $1.25 + $4.00 + $.30 = ?   **6.** $10 − $3.75 = ?
4. $.45 + $1.19 + $.79 = ?   **7.** $10 − $2.89 = ?

For many centuries devices and machines have been used for calculating.

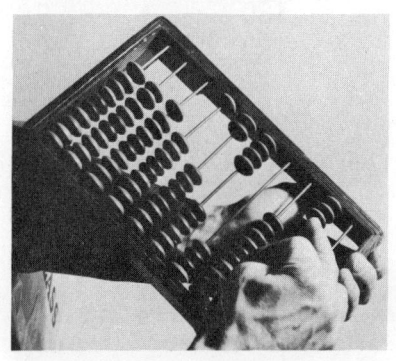

Courtesy General Electric Co.

The abacus is a primitive calculating device which has existed for over 2000 years and is still used in the Orient.

Courtesy Monroe Calculating Machine Co.

In the Western World, modern calculating machines are widely used; they perform calculations speedily and accurately.

How Well Can You Multiply and Divide?

Copy the examples below and multiply.

Check your multiplication in one of these ways:
1. multiply again in the same way;
2. interchange the numbers and multiply;
3. divide the product by the smaller number.

If you need more practice, turn to page 360 and do the multiplication examples given there.

Multiply:

	A	B	C	D
1.	39 8	$45 7	$2.96 4	3085 6
2.	83 42	462 35	$67.01 27	$56.40 19
3.	$5.09 25	$49 60	906 73	180 150
4.	$813 300	607 204	189 780	78 90
5.	4500 800	$3.75 12	$2.73 48	762 600
6.	$38.95 29	5481 74	$5.60 36	$23.70 75
7.	421 902	570 492	308 560	796 183
8.	2905 3247	2831 6008	4035 1096	7004 3587

You know how to check a division example by dividing again. Another way is to find the product of the quotient and the divisor, and add the remainder to this product.

When you do the examples below, check the division by either method, or as directed by your teacher. If you need more practice, do the division examples on pages 361 and 362.

```
        364 R 13      Check:
    29)10569            364
       87                29
       ---             ----
       186            3276
       174             728
       ---            -----
       129           10556
       116              13
       ---           -----
        13           10569
```

	A	B	C	D
9.	40)392	70)6510	90)556	80)1923
10.	12)383	42)3108	52)1298	71)39020
11.	31)2113	62)3678	91)9009	82)7220
12.	29)728	58)3747	39)2304	49)18228
13.	69)209	28)2290	89)8099	78)3199
14.	26)2290	83)1624	54)5000	37)7924
15.	14)629	15)7011	17)981	16)59035
16.	85)5983	63)2521	56)11777	35)21020
17.	74)8000	13)2686	44)26490	19)15244
18.	826)63822	123)222831	433)21584	656)521378

Understanding Fractions

1. Does the first rectangle show that $\frac{1}{3} = \frac{2}{6}$?
2. Study the first rectangle; complete the following:
   A. $\frac{1}{3} = \frac{?}{6}$ B. $\frac{2}{3} = \frac{?}{6}$ C. $\frac{1}{2} = \frac{?}{6}$
3. Does the second rectangle show that $\frac{1}{4} = \frac{2}{8}$?
4. Study the second rectangle; complete the following:
   A. $\frac{1}{4} = \frac{?}{8}$ B. $\frac{3}{4} = \frac{?}{8}$ C. $\frac{?}{8} = \frac{1}{4}$ D. $\frac{?}{8} = \frac{1}{2}$

▶ When both the numerator and the denominator of any fraction are multiplied or divided by the same number, the new fraction has the same value as the original fraction. The two fractions are **equivalent**, or equal in value.

Copy and complete the following, telling in each case by what number you multiplied or divided:

	A	B	C	D	E
5.	$\frac{6}{9} = \frac{?}{3}$	$\frac{8}{12} = \frac{?}{3}$	$\frac{6}{10} = \frac{?}{5}$	$\frac{12}{16} = \frac{?}{4}$	$\frac{3}{5} = \frac{?}{25}$
6.	$\frac{6}{18} = \frac{3}{?}$	$\frac{10}{15} = \frac{2}{?}$	$\frac{9}{12} = \frac{3}{?}$	$\frac{12}{32} = \frac{6}{?}$	$\frac{5}{6} = \frac{15}{?}$
7.	$\frac{3}{4} = \frac{18}{?}$	$\frac{2}{3} = \frac{?}{18}$	$\frac{7}{8} = \frac{?}{32}$	$\frac{1}{6} = \frac{?}{24}$	$\frac{4}{5} = \frac{24}{?}$

▶ When the two terms of a fraction are divided by the same number until there is no number by which both terms can be divided evenly, the fraction is reduced to **lowest terms**.

8. Reduce to lowest terms:
   A. $\frac{24}{30}$ B. $\frac{15}{18}$ C. $\frac{16}{48}$ D. $\frac{14}{28}$ E. $\frac{12}{36}$ F. $\frac{8}{32}$

How Well Can You Add Fractions?

You cannot add the fractions 3 fourths and 7 eighths as they stand, but you can add them if you change the 3 fourths to 6 eighths:

$$6 \text{ eighths} + 7 \text{ eighths} = 13 \text{ eighths}$$
$$\tfrac{6}{8} + \tfrac{7}{8} = \tfrac{13}{8} = 1\tfrac{5}{8}$$

Before two or more fractions can be added, their denominators must be the same. When all the fractions to be added have the same denominator, this denominator is called the **common denominator.**

Study the examples below:

A. $\tfrac{3}{4} + \tfrac{5}{8} = \tfrac{6}{8} + \tfrac{5}{8} = \tfrac{11}{8} = 1\tfrac{3}{8}$

In this case, the larger of the given denominators is evenly divisible by the smaller; we use it as the common denominator.

B. $\tfrac{2}{3} + \tfrac{3}{4} = \tfrac{8}{12} + \tfrac{9}{12} = \tfrac{17}{12} = 1\tfrac{5}{12}$

Here, the common denominator is found by taking the product of the two denominators.

C. $\tfrac{1}{4} + \tfrac{5}{6} = \tfrac{3}{12} + \tfrac{10}{12} = \tfrac{13}{12} = 1\tfrac{1}{12}$

This time the product of the denominators is 24, but we can use a smaller common denominator. Try the larger denominator, 6. It is not evenly divisible by the other denominator, 4. Try two times 6, or 12. It is evenly divisible by 4. We use 12 as the common denominator. Sometimes you must multiply the larger denominator by 3 or more than 3 to find a common denominator.

Adding Fractions

1. Answer the following without using pencil and paper:
   A. To add halves and thirds, change them to ? .
   B. To add eighths and halves, change the halves to ? .
   C. To add halves and 4ths, change the halves to ? .
   D. To add 4ths and 6ths, change them to ? .
   E. To add 8ths and 5ths, change them to ? .

   Copy the examples below and write the correct numerators in place of the question marks. If you make mistakes, turn to page 8 and practice those examples.

	A	B	C	D
2.	$\frac{3}{8} = \frac{?}{16}$	$\frac{5}{6} = \frac{?}{24}$	$\frac{3}{10} = \frac{?}{20}$	$\frac{2}{3} = \frac{?}{12}$
3.	$\frac{1}{4} = \frac{?}{8}$	$\frac{7}{12} = \frac{?}{36}$	$\frac{3}{4} = \frac{?}{32}$	$\frac{5}{3} = \frac{?}{24}$

   Reduce each of the following to whole numbers, or to mixed numbers with the fractions in lowest terms:

   4. $\frac{20}{16} = ?$ $\frac{18}{12} = ?$ $\frac{24}{18} = ?$ $\frac{14}{4} = ?$
   5. $\frac{72}{24} = ?$ $\frac{45}{30} = ?$ $\frac{26}{20} = ?$ $\frac{56}{14} = ?$

   Add the following fractions. If any sum is an improper fraction, change it to a mixed number or a whole number. Be sure all fractions in the sums are in lowest terms.

	A	B	C
6.	$\frac{1}{3} + \frac{1}{12} = ?$	$\frac{3}{5} + \frac{3}{4} = ?$	$\frac{7}{12} + \frac{2}{3} = ?$
7.	$\frac{5}{8} + \frac{7}{8} = ?$	$\frac{3}{16} + \frac{1}{4} = ?$	$\frac{1}{6} + \frac{3}{4} = ?$

	A	B	C	D	E	F	G
8.	$\frac{5}{8}$	$\frac{5}{8}$	$\frac{5}{6}$	$\frac{3}{8}$	$\frac{1}{2}$	$\frac{1}{6}$	$\frac{2}{3}$
	$\frac{3}{4}$	$\frac{1}{6}$	$\frac{1}{4}$	$\frac{3}{4}$	$\frac{7}{10}$	$\frac{3}{8}$	$\frac{4}{5}$
9.	$\frac{3}{8}$	$\frac{2}{3}$	$\frac{7}{8}$	$\frac{5}{12}$	$\frac{5}{6}$	$\frac{3}{4}$	$\frac{3}{10}$
	$\frac{5}{12}$	$\frac{3}{4}$	$\frac{1}{6}$	$\frac{7}{12}$	$\frac{1}{8}$	$\frac{5}{12}$	$\frac{1}{4}$
10.	$\frac{1}{2}$	$\frac{1}{3}$	$\frac{3}{4}$	$\frac{2}{3}$	$\frac{1}{3}$	$\frac{3}{10}$	$\frac{5}{12}$
	$\frac{1}{4}$	$\frac{1}{6}$	$\frac{5}{8}$	$\frac{1}{4}$	$\frac{3}{8}$	$\frac{3}{5}$	$\frac{3}{4}$
	$\frac{3}{8}$	$\frac{1}{2}$	$\frac{1}{4}$	$\frac{5}{12}$	$\frac{3}{4}$	$\frac{5}{6}$	$\frac{7}{8}$

Carrying When Adding Mixed Numbers

In adding mixed numbers, we often carry, as shown at the right.

$\frac{17}{12} = 1\frac{5}{12}$; $12 + 1\frac{5}{12} = 13\frac{5}{12}$

$4\frac{2}{3} = 4\frac{8}{12}$
$8\frac{3}{4} = 8\frac{9}{12}$
$12\frac{17}{12} = 13\frac{5}{12}$

	A	B	C	D	E	F
1.	$3\frac{3}{4}$	$2\frac{5}{6}$	$6\frac{3}{8}$	$5\frac{3}{16}$	$8\frac{5}{6}$	$9\frac{5}{6}$
	$5\frac{3}{8}$	$8\frac{2}{9}$	$5\frac{3}{4}$	$7\frac{7}{8}$	$9\frac{3}{4}$	$6\frac{7}{10}$
2.	$4\frac{3}{8}$	$3\frac{1}{6}$	$8\frac{2}{3}$	$2\frac{1}{4}$	$6\frac{1}{4}$	$7\frac{2}{3}$
	$5\frac{1}{2}$	$4\frac{5}{12}$	$2\frac{7}{8}$	$5\frac{3}{5}$	$1\frac{1}{6}$	$8\frac{1}{2}$
	$2\frac{7}{8}$	$1\frac{3}{4}$	$4\frac{1}{2}$	$3\frac{1}{2}$	$3\frac{2}{3}$	$3\frac{5}{6}$

3. $12\frac{1}{2} + 18\frac{3}{4} = ?$
4. $45\frac{2}{3} + 35\frac{1}{3} = ?$
5. $24\frac{7}{8} + 10\frac{1}{2} = ?$
6. $40\frac{4}{5} + 28\frac{1}{2} = ?$
7. $22\frac{3}{10} + 13\frac{5}{12} = ?$

8. $32\frac{7}{8} + 54\frac{3}{10} = ?$
9. $8\frac{2}{3} + 6 + 9\frac{3}{5} = ?$
10. $28\frac{4}{5} + 16\frac{2}{3} + 20 = ?$
11. $15\frac{3}{4} + 20\frac{3}{8} + 14\frac{3}{16} = ?$
12. $16\frac{7}{12} + 8 + 21\frac{5}{18} = ?$

If you need more practice, turn to page 363.

Subtracting Fractions

Remember that fractions must have a common denominator before you can subtract. Copy and subtract:

1.
A	B	C	D	E	F	G
$\frac{5}{6}$	$\frac{7}{8}$	$\frac{7}{9}$	$\frac{3}{4}$	$\frac{3}{4}$	$\frac{2}{3}$	$\frac{11}{12}$
$\frac{1}{2}$	$\frac{3}{4}$	$\frac{4}{9}$	$\frac{5}{16}$	$\frac{2}{3}$	$\frac{3}{5}$	$\frac{3}{4}$

2.
$\frac{7}{10}$	$\frac{5}{6}$	$\frac{7}{12}$	$\frac{3}{4}$	$\frac{5}{6}$	$\frac{7}{8}$	$\frac{5}{6}$
$\frac{3}{8}$	$\frac{4}{5}$	$\frac{1}{4}$	$\frac{3}{10}$	$\frac{3}{4}$	$\frac{5}{16}$	$\frac{1}{8}$

Borrowing When Subtracting Mixed Numbers

In subtracting mixed numbers, we often borrow, as shown at the right.

$$48\tfrac{1}{6} = 48\tfrac{4}{24} = 47\tfrac{28}{24}$$
$$24\tfrac{5}{8} = 24\tfrac{15}{24} = 24\tfrac{15}{24}$$
$$\overline{\phantom{24\tfrac{5}{8} = 24\tfrac{15}{24} = }\,23\tfrac{13}{24}}$$

Subtract:

1.
A	B	C	D	E
$8\tfrac{3}{4}$	$5\tfrac{1}{2}$	$6\tfrac{5}{6}$	$10\tfrac{1}{2}$	$8\tfrac{1}{4}$
$2\tfrac{1}{5}$	$3\tfrac{2}{3}$	$6\tfrac{7}{9}$	$5\tfrac{3}{5}$	$7\tfrac{5}{6}$

2.
A	B	C	D	E
8	6	1	5	4
$3\tfrac{3}{8}$	$4\tfrac{3}{5}$	$\tfrac{5}{12}$	$4\tfrac{3}{4}$	$2\tfrac{9}{16}$

	A	B	C
3.	$4\tfrac{1}{2} - 1\tfrac{3}{4} = ?$	$5\tfrac{3}{8} - 2\tfrac{5}{12} = ?$	$10\tfrac{1}{6} - 3\tfrac{3}{8} = ?$
4.	$6\tfrac{1}{4} - 3\tfrac{1}{2} = ?$	$8\tfrac{1}{3} - 4\tfrac{2}{3} = ?$	$12\tfrac{1}{2} - 2\tfrac{3}{4} = ?$

If you need more practice, turn to page 364.

Multiplying Fractions and Whole Numbers

1. You will remember that $3 \times \frac{5}{6}$ means $\frac{5}{6} + \frac{5}{6} + \frac{5}{6}$.

$$3 \times \frac{5}{6} = \frac{3 \times 5}{6} = \frac{15}{6} = \frac{5}{2} = 2\frac{1}{2}$$

To multiply a fraction by a whole number, we multiply the numerator by the whole number, and divide the result by the denominator.

2. You will also remember that the product of two numbers is the same, regardless of which one is the multiplier. Then, $\frac{5}{6} \times 3$ must give the same product as $3 \times \frac{5}{6}$.

$$\frac{5}{6} \times 3 = \frac{5 \times 3}{6} = \frac{15}{6} = \frac{5}{2} = 2\frac{1}{2}$$

To multiply a whole number by a fraction, we multiply the whole number by the numerator, and divide the result by the denominator.

3. When a numerator and a denominator can be evenly divided by the same number, we can divide before we multiply.

$$18 \times \frac{5}{8} = \frac{\overset{9}{\cancel{18}} \times 5}{\underset{4}{\cancel{8}}} = \frac{45}{4} = 11\frac{1}{4}$$

When we do this we are **cancelling**.

Find the products:

	A	B	C	D	E
4.	$4 \times \frac{2}{3}$	$8 \times \frac{3}{4}$	$10 \times \frac{4}{5}$	$7 \times \frac{3}{8}$	$\frac{2}{3} \times 4$
5.	$\frac{3}{4} \times 8$	$\frac{5}{6} \times 9$	$\frac{1}{2} \times 11$	$\frac{1}{3} \times 20$	$14 \times \frac{7}{8}$
6.	$18 \times \frac{7}{12}$	$\frac{2}{5} \times 13$	$\frac{4}{5} \times 15$	$3 \times \frac{2}{3}$	$40 \times \frac{5}{6}$
7.	$\frac{5}{8} \times 36$	$\frac{5}{12} \times 21$	$\frac{3}{10} \times 45$	$\frac{1}{8} \times 8$	$12 \times \frac{3}{5}$

Multiplying Fractions and Mixed Numbers

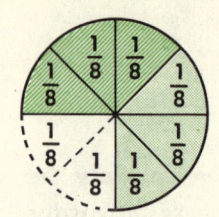

This diagram shows that $\frac{1}{2}$ of $\frac{3}{4} = \frac{3}{8}$; $\frac{1}{2}$ of $\frac{3}{4}$ means $\frac{1}{2} \times \frac{3}{4}$ just as $\frac{1}{2}$ of 4 means $\frac{1}{2} \times 4$. Then,

$$\frac{1}{2} \times \frac{3}{4} = \frac{1 \times 3}{2 \times 4} = \frac{3}{8}$$

The product of two fractions equals the product of the numerators divided by the product of the denominators.

A. $\frac{2}{3} \times \frac{4}{7} = \frac{2 \times 4}{3 \times 7} = \frac{8}{21}$ B. $\overset{1}{\cancel{\underset{5}{10}}} \times \overset{2}{\cancel{\underset{3}{9}}} = \frac{1 \times 2}{5 \times 3} = \frac{2}{15}$

Find the products; cancel if you can:

	A	B	C	D	E
1.	$\frac{7}{8} \times \frac{2}{3}$	$\frac{1}{5} \times \frac{3}{4}$	$\frac{5}{6} \times \frac{4}{5}$	$\frac{1}{2} \times \frac{1}{6}$	$\frac{1}{3} \times \frac{3}{4}$
2.	$\frac{1}{2} \times \frac{1}{2}$	$\frac{1}{2} \times \frac{3}{8}$	$\frac{1}{3} \times \frac{2}{3}$	$\frac{2}{5} \times \frac{3}{8}$	$\frac{2}{3} \times \frac{2}{3}$
3.	$\frac{1}{4} \times \frac{1}{2}$	$\frac{3}{8} \times \frac{5}{8}$	$\frac{5}{6} \times \frac{4}{9}$	$\frac{3}{4} \times \frac{3}{8}$	$\frac{2}{3} \times \frac{5}{9}$

Before multiplying with mixed numbers, we may change the mixed numbers to improper fractions.

C. $6 \times 2\frac{2}{3} = \overset{2}{\cancel{6}} \times \frac{8}{\underset{1}{\cancel{3}}} = 16$

D. $3\frac{1}{4} \times 2\frac{1}{2} \times \frac{4}{5} = \frac{13}{\underset{1}{\cancel{4}}} \times \frac{\overset{1}{\cancel{5}}}{2} \times \frac{\overset{1}{\cancel{4}}}{\underset{1}{\cancel{5}}} = \frac{13}{2} = 6\frac{1}{2}$

	A	B	C	D	E
4.	$1\frac{1}{2} \times 8$	$4 \times 1\frac{1}{3}$	$1\frac{1}{3} \times 5$	$2\frac{1}{2} \times 2\frac{1}{2}$	$3 \times 1\frac{3}{4}$
5.	$7 \times 1\frac{2}{3}$	$\frac{1}{2} \times 1\frac{2}{3}$	$\frac{4}{5} \times 1\frac{1}{2}$	$2\frac{1}{4} \times 6$	$2\frac{1}{2} \times 12$
6.	$1\frac{1}{4} \times 1\frac{1}{4}$	$2\frac{3}{4} \times \frac{1}{2}$	$3\frac{1}{2} \times 2\frac{1}{4}$	$\frac{5}{3} \times 2$	$2\frac{2}{3} \times 4\frac{1}{2}$

~ 14 ~

Practice in Multiplying with Fractions

1. At a certain winter resort, the ski lift is $\frac{2}{5}$ mile long. If a skier makes 35 trips a day, how many miles has he traveled on the ski lift?

2. If the ski run is operated $6\frac{3}{4}$ hours a day, how many hours is it operated in a week?

Find the products:

	A	B	C	D
3.	$\frac{2}{3} \times 27$	$2\frac{1}{3} \times 18$	$24 \times \frac{3}{4}$	$\frac{1}{4} \times \frac{1}{4}$
4.	$16 \times \frac{3}{5}$	$\frac{3}{8} \times 15$	$\frac{3}{4} \times \frac{1}{8} \times \frac{2}{3}$	$\frac{3}{4} \times 21$
5.	$1\frac{1}{2} \times 1\frac{1}{2}$	$12 \times 2\frac{1}{4}$	$\frac{3}{8} \times 24$	$1\frac{1}{2} \times \frac{3}{16}$
6.	$8\frac{1}{2} \times 11$	$1\frac{1}{2} \times 2\frac{1}{2}$	$18 \times 2\frac{1}{4}$	$\frac{3}{4} \times 1\frac{1}{2}$
7.	$36 \times \frac{2}{3}$	$\frac{5}{6} \times 72$	$\frac{1}{2} \times 8\frac{1}{4}$	$\frac{5}{12} \times 64$
8.	$3\frac{1}{4} \times 4\frac{1}{4} \times \frac{1}{2}$	$3\frac{1}{7} \times 28$	$\frac{3}{4} \times 1\frac{1}{3} \times \frac{1}{5}$	$64 \times 2\frac{3}{4}$

Sometimes you will have to multiply unusual numbers and fractions such as the following:

	A	B	C
9.	$124 \times 3\frac{1}{2}$	$\frac{3}{8} \times 5280$	$1728 \times 1\frac{1}{4}$
10.	$\frac{3}{4} \times \frac{3}{4} \times 18$	$2 \times 3\frac{1}{7} \times 9$	$400 \times \frac{2}{3} \times \frac{9}{200}$

If you need more practice, turn to page 365.

Dividing a Fraction by a Whole Number

Helen ate $\frac{1}{4}$ of a chocolate bar. She divided the remaining $\frac{3}{4}$ into 2 equal pieces. What part of the whole bar was each of these pieces?

Since she divided the $\frac{3}{4}$ into 2 equal pieces, each of these pieces is $\frac{1}{2}$ of $\frac{3}{4}$, or $\frac{1}{2} \times \frac{3}{4} = \frac{3}{8}$.

You may also think: $\frac{3}{4}$ divided into 2 equal pieces equals $\frac{3}{4} \div 2 = \frac{1}{2} \times \frac{3}{4} = \frac{3}{8}$.

$$\frac{3}{4} \div 2 = \frac{1}{2} \times \frac{3}{4} = \frac{3}{8}$$

Study these examples:

Example 1. Divide $\frac{8}{9}$ by 4.

$$\frac{8}{9} \div 4 \text{ means } \frac{1}{4} \text{ of } \frac{8}{9}; \text{ or, } \frac{1}{\cancel{4}_1} \times \frac{\cancel{8}^2}{9} = \frac{2}{9}$$

Example 2. Divide $\frac{3}{8}$ by 6.

$$\frac{3}{8} \div 6 \text{ means } \frac{1}{6} \text{ of } \frac{3}{8}; \text{ or, } \frac{1}{\cancel{6}_2} \times \frac{\cancel{3}^1}{8} = \frac{1}{16}$$

To divide a mixed number by a whole number, we proceed as shown above, except that we first change the mixed number to an improper fraction.

Find the quotients:

	A	B	C	D	E
1.	$\frac{5}{8} \div 2$	$\frac{3}{4} \div 3$	$\frac{1}{5} \div 2$	$\frac{5}{12} \div 10$	$\frac{9}{10} \div 3$
2.	$\frac{1}{4} \div 8$	$\frac{7}{8} \div 7$	$\frac{1}{8} \div 4$	$\frac{3}{8} \div 12$	$\frac{9}{16} \div 6$
3.	$2\frac{1}{4} \div 3$	$3\frac{1}{2} \div 7$	$10\frac{1}{2} \div 6$	$5\frac{1}{2} \div 11$	$6\frac{2}{3} \div 5$

Dividing a Whole Number by a Fraction

If each of 3 melons is cut into fourths, how many pieces will the 3 melons make? Here we are asking: how many $\frac{1}{4}$'s are there in 3 wholes? We see that there are 4 fourths in 1 whole; so there must be 3 times as many fourths in 3 wholes. Then the 3 melons will make 3×4 fourths, or 12 pieces; $3 \div \frac{1}{4} = 12$.

Whether we write $3 \div \frac{1}{4}$ or 3×4 or $3 \times \frac{4}{1}$, the answer is the same. This suggests a short way of dividing a whole number by a fraction. When we write $\frac{1}{4}$ (the fraction by which we are dividing) as $\frac{4}{1}$, we have **inverted** the fraction. We then multiply the inverted fraction:

$$3 \div \frac{1}{4} = 3 \times \frac{4}{1} = 12$$

Example 1. Divide 2 by $\frac{2}{3}$. Dividing 2 by $\frac{2}{3}$ means finding how many $\frac{2}{3}$'s there are in 2 wholes. Do you see from the diagram that there are *three* $\frac{2}{3}$'s in 2?

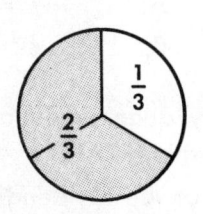

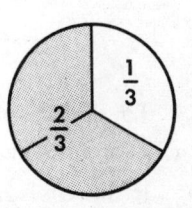

$$2 \div \frac{2}{3} = \overset{1}{\cancel{2}} \times \frac{3}{\cancel{2}} = 3$$

Example 2. Divide 28 by $\frac{7}{8}$. $28 \div \frac{7}{8} = \overset{4}{\cancel{28}} \times \frac{8}{\underset{1}{\cancel{7}}} = 32$

	A	B	C	D	E
1.	$6 \div \frac{2}{3}$	$8 \div \frac{1}{2}$	$10 \div \frac{3}{5}$	$5 \div \frac{3}{4}$	$1 \div \frac{2}{3}$
2.	$3 \div \frac{4}{5}$	$12 \div \frac{3}{4}$	$3 \div \frac{5}{6}$	$3 \div \frac{2}{3}$	$4 \div \frac{1}{4}$
3.	$9 \div \frac{1}{3}$	$6 \div \frac{3}{5}$	$24 \div \frac{3}{8}$	$6 \div \frac{5}{8}$	$10 \div \frac{3}{4}$

Dividing a Fraction by a Fraction

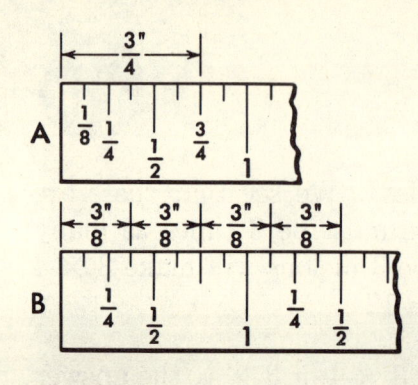

These diagrams show an inch divided into fourths and eighths.

A. How many $\frac{1}{8}$'s of an inch are there in $\frac{3}{4}$ inch? This is the same as asking, $\frac{3}{4} \div \frac{1}{8} = ?$ You can see that there are six $\frac{1}{8}$'s of an inch in $\frac{3}{4}$ inch; or, $\frac{3}{4} \div \frac{1}{8} = 6$.

B. How many $\frac{3}{8}$'s are there in $1\frac{1}{2}$ inches? This means: $1\frac{1}{2} \div \frac{3}{8} = ?$ You can see that there are four $\frac{3}{8}$'s of an inch in $1\frac{1}{2}$ inches; or, $1\frac{1}{2} \div \frac{3}{8} = 4$.

These two examples can also be worked without using the diagrams, as shown below; study them carefully.

A. $\frac{3}{4} \div \frac{1}{8} = \frac{3}{4} \times \frac{8}{1} = 6$
B. $1\frac{1}{2} \div \frac{3}{8} = \frac{3}{2} \times \frac{8}{3} = 4$

To divide any quantity by a fraction, we simply invert the divisor and multiply.

If the divisor or the dividend is a mixed number, we change the mixed number to an improper fraction before we divide.

Example. $\frac{9}{16} \div 4\frac{1}{2} = \frac{9}{16} \times \frac{2}{9} = \frac{1}{8}$

Find the quotients:

	A	B	C	D
1.	$\frac{9}{16} \div \frac{1}{4}$	$\frac{4}{5} \div \frac{2}{3}$	$\frac{1}{3} \div \frac{3}{4}$	$\frac{3}{8} \div \frac{2}{3}$
2.	$\frac{3}{8} \div \frac{1}{8}$	$\frac{1}{10} \div \frac{9}{10}$	$2\frac{1}{2} \div \frac{1}{2}$	$\frac{1}{10} \div \frac{2}{5}$
3.	$\frac{1}{2} \div \frac{1}{2}$	$\frac{4}{5} \div 1\frac{1}{2}$	$\frac{3}{4} \div \frac{4}{3}$	$\frac{3}{8} \div 1\frac{1}{4}$
4.	$6\frac{1}{4} \div 1\frac{1}{4}$	$1\frac{1}{2} \div \frac{2}{3}$	$4\frac{1}{2} \div 1\frac{1}{2}$	$\frac{1}{6} \div 1\frac{1}{3}$
5.	$5\frac{1}{2} \div 5\frac{1}{2}$	$1 \div 4\frac{1}{2}$	$\frac{4}{5} \div 1\frac{1}{3}$	$5\frac{1}{2} \div 2\frac{2}{5}$

Practice in Dividing with Fractions

Find the quotients:

	A	B	C	D
1.	$2\frac{1}{2} \div 2$	$4 \div \frac{1}{2}$	$8\frac{1}{4} \div 3$	$6 \div \frac{2}{3}$
2.	$12 \div 2\frac{1}{4}$	$10\frac{1}{2} \div 4$	$\frac{1}{4} \div 8$	$8 \div \frac{1}{4}$
3.	$4 \div \frac{1}{8}$	$\frac{1}{8} \div 4$	$1\frac{5}{8} \div 2$	$1\frac{1}{2} \div 3$
4.	$5 \div \frac{2}{3}$	$1 \div 1\frac{1}{2}$	$3\frac{1}{4} \div 2$	$1\frac{1}{2} \div \frac{3}{8}$
5.	$\frac{5}{6} \div 3$	$\frac{1}{4} \div \frac{1}{2}$	$1\frac{1}{2} \div 3\frac{1}{2}$	$3\frac{1}{2} \div 1\frac{1}{2}$
6.	$2\frac{1}{4} \div 4$	$1\frac{1}{2} \div 1\frac{1}{4}$	$2 \div \frac{5}{6}$	$\frac{2}{3} \div 2\frac{1}{3}$
7.	$\frac{1}{2} \div \frac{3}{5}$	$3 \div 2\frac{1}{2}$	$\frac{2}{3} \div \frac{3}{4}$	$\frac{4}{5} \div 2$

We usually have to divide only with simple fractions and mixed numbers such as those above. Sometimes we have to divide with more unusual numbers, such as those below.

Find the quotients:

	A	B	C	D
8.	$42\frac{1}{2} \div 4$	$68 \div 1\frac{1}{2}$	$4\frac{3}{16} \div 2$	$125 \div 3\frac{1}{4}$
9.	$62\frac{1}{2} \div \frac{1}{4}$	$133\frac{1}{3} \div 8$	$12\frac{3}{8} \div 6$	$500 \div 5\frac{1}{2}$
10.	$144 \div 4\frac{1}{2}$	$27\frac{1}{2} \div 3$	$18\frac{3}{4} \div 2\frac{1}{2}$	$1000 \div 16\frac{1}{2}$

If you need more practice, turn to page 366.

JUST FOR FUN

On one side of a scale is a whole apple. On the other side is a $\frac{3}{4}$-oz. weight and $\frac{3}{4}$ of an apple of the same weight as the other apple. The scale exactly balances. How much does the whole apple weigh?

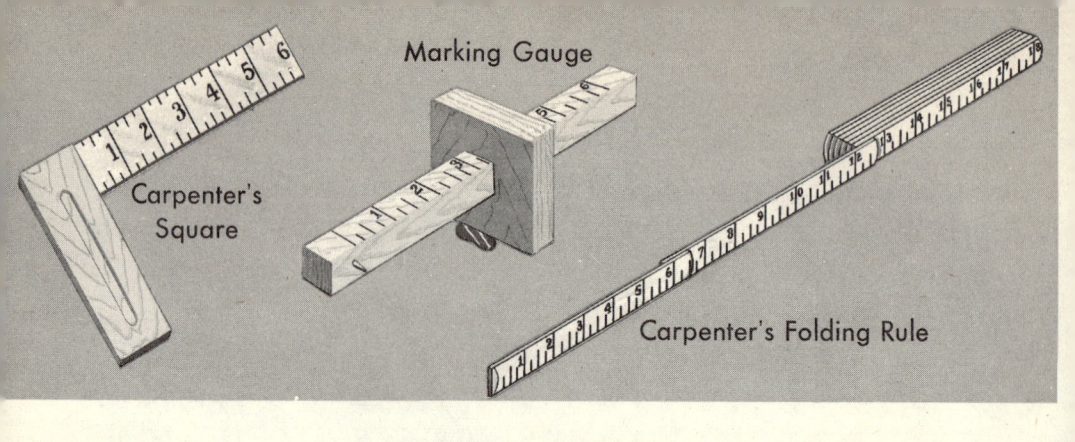

Using Fractions in Shop Work

When we make things, we often have to use measurements which are not always expressed as whole numbers. That is why measuring instruments, such as those shown above, are always marked in fractional parts of an inch.

1. A strip of wood $\frac{3}{8}$ of an inch thick is screwed to a board $\frac{3}{4}$ inch thick. What is their combined thickness?

2. A piece 5 ft. $6\frac{1}{4}$ in. long was cut from a board 14 ft. long. How long was the piece that remained?

3. A particular piece of plywood consists of 6 thin layers of wood carefully glued together. If each layer is $\frac{1}{16}$ of an inch thick, what is the total thickness of the plywood?

4. A board $7\frac{1}{2}$ feet long is cut into 6 equal pieces. How long is each piece?

5. If a strip of molding $17\frac{1}{2}$ inches long is cut into pieces each $3\frac{1}{2}$ inches long, how many such pieces will there be?

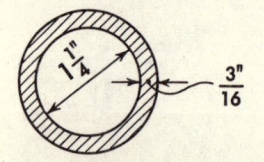

6. The opening in a pipe is $1\frac{1}{4}$ in. wide. The wall of the pipe is $\frac{3}{16}$ in. thick. Find the width of the entire pipe.

7. A strip of wood is $2\frac{3}{4}$ inches wide. If you want to plane it to a width of $2\frac{1}{8}$ inches, how much must be shaved off with the plane?

Reading a Blueprint

When a carpenter or a machinist makes something, he uses a working drawing, or a blueprint, as a guide. On such drawings, the dimensions of each part are clearly shown. A dimension tells the length, the width, the height, or the thickness of anything.

1. The drawing at the right shows the end of a bookrack that Tom made in school. Find the total height of the bookrack (the distance from C to E).

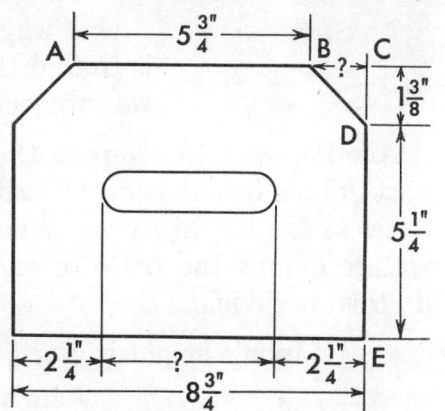

2. How long is the slot that is to be used as a handle?

3. How far from C is the corner B?

4. This drawing shows the front of a birdhouse that Tom and his friend were making. From the dimensions given, find the total height of the birdhouse from A to B.

5. How wide should the door be made? (CD = ?)

6. What is the diameter (distance across) of the circular hole above the door? What is its radius (half of the diameter)?

7. How far is it from E to F?

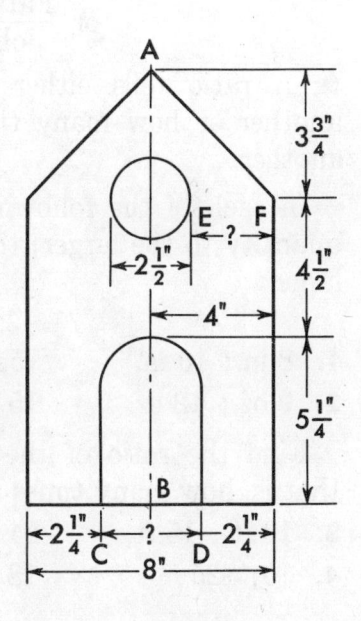

Comparing Quantities

John is 4 feet tall; his father is 6 feet tall. How do they compare in height?

One way to compare their heights is to find the *difference*. To do this we subtract.

Another way to compare their heights is to find what part John's height is of his father's height, or how many times as tall his father is. When we compare in this way, we are finding the **ratio** of one height to the other. To do this we divide.

A. John's height is $\frac{4}{6}$ or $\frac{2}{3}$ that of his father;

or, $\dfrac{\text{John's height}}{\text{Father's height}} = \dfrac{4}{6} = \dfrac{2}{3}$

B. Father is $\frac{3}{2}$ or $1\frac{1}{2}$ times as tall as John;

or, $\dfrac{\text{Father's height}}{\text{John's height}} = \dfrac{6}{4} = \dfrac{3}{2} = 1\frac{1}{2}$

▶ A ratio tells either what part one quantity is of another or how many times as large one quantity is as another.

In each of the following, find the ratio of the smaller quantity to the larger; that is, find what part it is of the larger.

	A	B	C
1.	8 in.; 10 in.	75¢; 15¢	10 qt.; 8 qt.
2.	9 oz.; 12 oz.	15 min.; 45 min.	$\frac{1}{2}$ in.; 4 in.

Find the ratio of the larger quantity to the smaller, that is, how many times as large it is:

3.	10 ft.; 15 ft.	24 oz.; 4 oz.	4 pt.; 6 pt.
4.	$5; $25	18 in.; 54 in.	30¢; 45¢

A ratio shows a relationship between two quantities. This relationship may be written in more than one way. For example, the ratio "3 to 4" may be written as the fraction $\frac{3}{4}$, or 3:4. The ratio sign (:) is simply an abbreviation for the division sign ($\div$).

If one number is 4 times another, we say that the ratio of the larger number to the smaller is 4 to 1, or 4:1. We can also say that the ratio of the smaller number to the larger is 1 to 4, or 1:4, or $\frac{1}{4}$.

In each of the following, find the ratio of the first quantity to the second quantity; in each case, write your answer as a fraction, and also with the ratio sign.

	A	B	C
5.	3 lb.; 4 lb.	12 yd.; 8 yd.	80 ft.; 100 ft.
6.	8 oz.; 2 oz.	40 min.; 30 min.	20 qt.; 16 qt.
7.	$24; $40	18 in.; 24 in.	15 mi.; 12 mi.

▶ If two quantities are to be compared, they must always be expressed in the same unit of measure.

Example. What is the ratio of 18 in. to 2 ft.?

$$2 \text{ ft.} = 24 \text{ in.} \quad \frac{18}{24} = \frac{3}{4}, \text{ or } 3:4$$

Or, 18 in. = $1\frac{1}{2}$ ft. $\quad \frac{1\frac{1}{2}}{2} = \frac{3}{2} \div 2 = \frac{3}{4}$, or 3:4

In each of the following, first write the ratio comparing the smaller quantity with the larger; then write the ratio comparing the larger with the smaller:

8.	3 ft.; 6 in.	6 hr.; $\frac{1}{2}$ hr.	2 yd.; 4 ft.
9.	25¢; $2	6 qt.; 2 gal.	2 mi.; $\frac{3}{4}$ mi.
10.	2 qt.; 3 pt.	8 oz.; 2 lb.	$\frac{1}{4}$ ton; 250 lb.
11.	66 in.; 6 ft.	60¢; $1.50	1 gal.; 6 pt.
12.	2 yd.; 30 in.	$1\frac{1}{2}$ yd.; 27 in.	$1\frac{1}{2}$ ft.; $2\frac{1}{2}$ yd.

Fractions and Decimals

When the denominator of a fraction is 10, 100, or 1000, we can write the fraction without its denominator; for example:

$\frac{3}{10} = .3 \qquad \frac{75}{100} = .75 \qquad \frac{245}{1000} = .245 \qquad \frac{18}{1000} = .018$

When a fraction is written in this way, it is called a **decimal fraction,** or simply a **decimal.** The decimal point shows that the number is a fraction. The number of places at the right of the point shows the value of the denominator. One decimal place means *tenths;* two places, *hundredths;* three places, *thousandths.*

Write these fractions as decimals:

1. A. $\frac{7}{10}$ B. $\frac{12}{100}$ C. $\frac{125}{1000}$ D. $\frac{25}{1000}$ E. $\frac{1}{100}$
2. A. $\frac{15}{100}$ B. $\frac{7}{100}$ C. $\frac{50}{100}$ D. $\frac{400}{1000}$ E. $\frac{7}{1000}$
3. A. $\frac{90}{100}$ B. $\frac{90}{1000}$ C. $\frac{2}{100}$ D. $\frac{100}{100}$ E. $\frac{1}{1000}$

Some fractions whose denominators are not 10, 100, or 1000 can easily be changed to decimal fractions.

Example 1. Change $\frac{3}{5}$ to a decimal. How can you change fifths to tenths?

$$\frac{3}{5} = \frac{2 \times 3}{2 \times 5} = \frac{6}{10} = .6$$

We multiply the 3 and the 5 by 2 because we are changing fifths to tenths, and there are two 5's in 10.

Example 2. Change $\frac{3}{4}$ to a decimal. How can you change fourths to hundredths? How many 4's in 100?

$$\frac{3}{4} = \frac{25 \times 3}{25 \times 4} = \frac{75}{100} = .75$$

Example 3. Change $\frac{3}{8}$ to a decimal. How can you change eighths to thousandths? How many 8's in 1000?

$$\frac{3}{8} = \frac{125 \times 3}{125 \times 8} = \frac{375}{1000} = .375$$

Write these fractions as decimals:

	A	B	C	D	E
4.	$\frac{1}{2}$	$\frac{1}{4}$	$\frac{2}{5}$	$\frac{3}{20}$	$\frac{1}{50}$
5.	$\frac{4}{5}$	$\frac{7}{8}$	$\frac{1}{25}$	$\frac{1}{5}$	$\frac{9}{25}$

A ratio may also be written as a decimal fraction, since ratios are fractions. For example: the ratio 2:5, or $\frac{2}{5}$, may be expressed as .4 or .40. Write these ratios as decimals:

6. 7:10 3:4 18:20 1:5 1:8
7. 4:5 50:100 6:8 1:10 1:100
8. 1:25 3:6 1:2 3:8 9:25

Bucher from Nesmith

This scientist is making careful measurements and is using decimal fractions when weighing.

You know that 1 decimal place means tenths; 2 decimal places, hundredths; 3 places, thousandths. Study the second column:

0.3	tenths	0.0003	ten-thousandths
0.03	hundredths	0.00003	hundred-thousandths
0.003	thousandths	0.000003	millionths

9. Read these decimals:
.0008 .0175 .0039 .0025 .00025 .00125 .000950

We round decimals as we round whole numbers:
.037 rounded to the nearest hundredth is .04
.092 rounded to the nearest hundredth is .09
.0236 rounded to the nearest thousandth is .024
.2973 rounded to the nearest thousandth is .297
.2973 rounded to the nearest hundredth is .30

Round, first to the nearest thousandth, then to the nearest hundredth:

	A	B	C	D
10.	.0291	.0271	.7575	.0092
11.	.0362	.0625	.7984	.2008

Changing Any Fraction to a Decimal

Any common fraction can be changed to a decimal fraction simply by dividing, as shown below.

Example 1. Change $\frac{1}{16}$ to a decimal. Place a decimal point after the 1; annex as many zeros as necessary. Do you see that 1.0000 is the same as 1? Divide by 16. Why was one annexed zero not enough? Would two zeros have been enough? Why did we use four zeros? $\frac{1}{16} = .0625$.

$$\begin{array}{r} .0625 \\ 16\overline{)1.0000} \end{array}$$

Example 2. Change $\frac{3}{7}$ to a decimal, to the nearest thousandth. To do this, we carry the quotient to 4 decimal places; therefore, we annex 4 zeros. The quotient, to four decimal places, is .4285; rounding to the nearest thousandth, $\frac{3}{7} = .429$.

$$\begin{array}{r} .4285+ \\ 7\overline{)3.0000} \end{array}$$

Example 3. Change $\frac{15}{13}$ to a decimal, to the nearest thousandth. Carrying the quotient to three decimal places, we see that the remainder, 11, is more than half the divisor, 13; so we see, without dividing further, that the quotient, to the nearest thousandth, is 1.154.

$$\begin{array}{r} 1.153 \\ 13\overline{)15.000} \\ 13 \\ \hline 20 \\ 13 \\ \hline 70 \\ 65 \\ \hline 50 \\ 39 \\ \hline 11 \end{array}$$

Change these common fractions to decimal fractions of not more than three places:

	A	B	C	D	E	F
1.	$\frac{3}{8}$	$\frac{7}{11}$	$\frac{2}{3}$	$\frac{2}{9}$	$\frac{4}{19}$	$\frac{7}{12}$
2.	$\frac{1}{3}$	$\frac{3}{16}$	$\frac{5}{32}$	$\frac{5}{6}$	$\frac{8}{9}$	$\frac{1}{6}$
3.	$\frac{12}{5}$	$\frac{3}{11}$	$\frac{21}{13}$	$\frac{5}{7}$	$\frac{18}{17}$	$\frac{15}{14}$

Adding and Subtracting Decimals

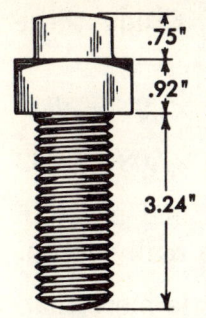

This picture represents a bolt. The dimensions are given at the side. What is the total length of the bolt? We add decimals just as we add whole numbers, but we write the decimal points directly under each other. The decimal point in the sum is placed directly under the other decimal points.

```
  .75
  .92
 3.24
 4.91
```

The picture below shows a metal sheet with some of its dimensions given. Find the difference between the widths of the two ends; find the distance from A to B.

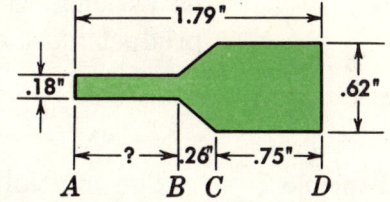

```
  .62        .26       1.79
 −.18       +.75      − 1.01
  .44       1.01        .78
```

When we add or subtract decimals, we keep the decimal points directly under each other, with the decimal point in the answer directly under the other decimal points.

Add:

1. A. 3.9   B. 6.29   C. 122.6   D. $ 25.98
        .8   2.82   390.8   3.06
       1.2   .17   46.5   15.21
       4.5   1.93   208.7   132.75

2. A. $64.2 + 3.9 + 28.4 = ?$
   B. $9.75 + 8.25 + 6.45 + 7.32 = ?$

3. A. $16.62 − 9.28 = ?$ C. $.843 − .293 = ?$
   B. $138.4 − 96.9 = ?$ D. $1.572 − .489 = ?$

If you need more practice, turn to page 367.

Multiplying with Decimals

Let us see how decimals are multiplied. Study these examples:

A. $.6 \times .9 = \frac{6}{10} \times \frac{9}{10} = \frac{54}{100}$; or, $.6 \times .9 = .54$

B. $.4 \times .08 = \frac{4}{10} \times \frac{8}{100} = \frac{32}{1000}$; or, $.4 \times .08 = .032$

We can often tell where to place the decimal point in the product by thinking what the numbers really mean.

Example 1

```
  3.5
  1.2
 ----
  7 0
3 5
 ----
4.2 0
```

Here when we multiply a little more than 3 by a little more than 1 we get a product a little greater than 4. The answer could not be as small as .42 or as large as 42. The product must be 4.20, or 4.2.

Example 2

```
  15.4
   .87
  ----
 1 078
12 32
 -----
13.398
```

The multiplier .87 is a little less than 1. Multiplying a little more than 15 by a little less than 1 gives a product of about 15, or a little less than 15. So the answer must be 13.398; it could not be 1.3398 or 133.98.

Example 3

```
  .32
   .9
 ----
 .288
```

When a number is multiplied by .9, the product is a little less than the multiplicand. Do you see that .288 is a little less than .32? (Is .32 the same as .320?)

The number of places in the product equals the number of places in the multiplicand plus the number of places in the multiplier.

If the product ends in one or more zeros, the zeros are counted as places when deciding where to put the point.

If the number of figures in the product is less than the number of places required, we must write enough zeros after the decimal point to give us the required number of places.

Example 4. $.03 \times .06 = .0018$

Example 5.
```
    .12
   .005
  ──────
  .00060, or .0006
```

Tell how many decimal places there will be in each of these products; then find the products.

	A	B	C	D
1.	$.2 \times .3$	$.2 \times .03$	$.02 \times .3$	$.02 \times .03$
2.	$.2 \times 3$	$.2 \times .003$	$.002 \times .3$	$.002 \times .03$
3.	$2 \times .003$	$.02 \times .003$	$.0002 \times 3$	$.002 \times .003$

In which of the following pairs of numbers are the two numbers almost the same?

4.	.5, .54	.8, .09	.4, .37	6.1, .62
5.	.12, .1	.019, .02	3.75, 3.8	1.9, 20

Find the products:

	A	B	C	D
6.	$2 \times .5$	$3 \times .09$	$4 \times .02$	$6 \times .03$
7.	$.04 \times .2$	$.4 \times .3$	$.8 \times .03$	$.7 \times .7$
8.	$.5 \times .8$	$.07 \times .1$	$.5 \times .2$	$4 \times .25$
9.	$.05 \times .3$	$.6 \times .05$	$4 \times .08$	$3 \times .01$
10.	$.8 \times .02$	$9 \times .10$	$.25 \times .2$	$.1 \times .02$

If you need more practice, turn to page 368.

Courtesy Radio Corporation of America

The scientist is using an electron microscope. This marvelous instrument can measure to .0000004 (4 ten-millionths) of an inch.

Multiplying by 10, by 100, and by 1000

In the examples below, what happens to the decimal point when you multiply by 10? by 100? by 1000?

$10 \times .507 = 5.07$ $10 \times 23.65 = 236.5$
$100 \times .507 = 50.7$ $100 \times 23.65 = 2365.$
$1000 \times .507 = 507.$ $1000 \times 23.65 = 23650.$

To multiply a decimal
  by 10, simply move the decimal point 1 place to the right;
  by 100, move the decimal point 2 places to the right;
  by 1000, move the decimal point 3 places to the right.

Find the products:

	A	B	C
1.	$100 \times .0069$	$100 \times .029$	$1000 \times .0625$
2.	$1000 \times .08$	1000×3.75	100×3.1416
3.	$1000 \times .0015$	$10 \times .50$	1000×96.875
4.	100×1.073	$100 \times .004$	1000×103.75

5. A certain sheet of paper is .003 inch thick. How thick will 500 of these sheets be?

JIFFY QUIZ

1. Dividing a number by 3 is the same as multiplying the number by __?__.
2. Which is the largest number: 33, .33, .333?
3. Ten billion is how many times as great as 100 million?
4. Does $5 \times 0 = 0 \times 5$?
5. How many years are "four score and seven years"?
6. Does $.01 \times 7 = .7 \times 100$?

Dividing with Decimals

A. Three books, all alike, cost $6.75. How much does each book cost? We divide $6.75 by 3; that is, we divide a decimal by a whole number. We know where to place the decimal point, because a little more than $6 divided by 3 must be a little more than $2.

$$\begin{array}{r} \$2.25 \\ 3\overline{)\$6.75} \end{array}$$

B. Evelyn's mother paid $6.60 for a turkey. The price was $.55 a pound. How much did the turkey weigh? We divide $6.60 by $.55. The quotient is 12. We know that this is a reasonable answer because .55 is about ½ and 6.60 is about 6; there are 12 halves in 6.

$$\begin{array}{r} 12 \\ .55\overline{)6.60} \\ \underline{5\ 5} \\ 1\ 10 \\ \underline{1\ 10} \end{array}$$

You know that the number of decimal places in the multiplicand *plus* the number in the multiplier equals the number in the product. Since 4.1 × 3.2 = 13.12, then 13.12 divided by 3.2 equals 4.1. This shows that the number of decimal places in the quotient is equal to the number in the dividend *minus* the number in the divisor.

$$\begin{array}{r} 3.2 \\ 4.1 \\ \hline 3\ 2 \\ 12\ 8 \\ \hline 13.1\ 2 \end{array} \qquad \begin{array}{r} 4.1 \\ 3.2\overline{)13.1\ 2} \\ \underline{12\ 8} \\ 3\ 2 \\ \underline{3\ 2} \end{array}$$

Common sense often helps us to decide where to place the decimal point in the quotient. In the above example, a little more than 13 is divided by a little more than 3. The quotient must be about 4. It could not be as large as 41 or as small as .41; it must be 4.1.

The number of decimal places in the quotient equals the number of places in the dividend minus the number of places in the divisor.

Annexing Zeros When Dividing by a Decimal

When there are more decimal places in the divisor than in the dividend, we annex zeros to the dividend. We make sure that there are at least as many decimal places in the dividend as there are in the divisor.

Example 1. Divide: .03)1.5. Here we must annex *one zero.* Why?

$$50 \\ .03)\overline{1.50}$$

Example 2. Divide: .004)9.6. Here we must annex *two zeros.* Why?

$$2\,400 \\ .004)\overline{9.600}$$

Example 3. Divide: 1.5)6. Here we annex a zero to a whole number; but we must first place a decimal point after the whole number. Do you see that 6.0 is the same as 6?

$$4 \\ 1.5)\overline{6.0}$$

▶ When we place a decimal point after a whole number, annexing zeros does not change the value of the number.

Divide; remember to annex zeros if necessary.

	A	B	C	D
1.	.2)̅.4	.2)̅.04	.02)̅.4	.02)̅.04
2.	.2)̅.004	.002)̅.4	.2)̅4	.002)̅.004

	A	B	C	D	E
3.	4)̅3.6	3)̅.27	6)̅.3	8)̅.96	.3)̅.69
4.	.5)̅.35	.4)̅1.28	.6)̅24	.7)̅.56	.9)̅63
5.	.2)̅.5	.8)̅40	2.5)̅.75	.12)̅1.44	1.1)̅7.7
6.	12.4 ÷ .4	2.6 ÷ .13	.04 ÷ .5	.06 ÷ 2	8 ÷ .2
7.	1.8 ÷ .6	20 ÷ .4	1.5 ÷ 3	3 ÷ 1.5	7 ÷ .05
8.	1.9)̅4.18	.13)̅5.2	1.8)̅324	2.3)̅1.38	3.8)̅45.6
9.	.004)̅1.44	.75)̅60	.41)̅.246	1.4)̅29.4	.17)̅.068

If you need more practice, turn to page 369.

We often carry division to two or three decimal places, and then round the quotient to the nearest tenth or the nearest hundredth.

Example 1

$.12 \overline{)\,.5320}$ 4.43, or 4.4 to the nearest tenth

Example 2

$2.6 \overline{)\,.4620}$ .177, or .18 to the nearest hundredth

Find the quotients to the nearest tenth:

	A	B	C	D
10.	$.63\overline{)5.098}$	$.034\overline{)\,.2723}$	$.24\overline{)\,.057}$	$.052\overline{)\,.0693}$
11.	$.012\overline{)\,.508}$	$.15\overline{)1.98}$	$.044\overline{)\,.2463}$	$.26\overline{)\,.72}$

Find the quotients to the nearest hundredth:

12.	$4.3\overline{)2.193}$	$1.9\overline{)\,.703}$	$.98\overline{)\,.1076}$	$.33\overline{)\,.0528}$
13.	$.92\overline{)1.0045}$	$5.7\overline{)13.462}$	$.61\overline{)5.0239}$	$.125\overline{)\,.0009}$

Dividing by 10, by 100, and by 1000

Study the examples below:

$10\overline{)3.90}$ = .39 $100\overline{)3.900}$ = .039 $100\overline{)39.00}$ = .39 $1000\overline{)39.000}$ = .039

To divide a decimal number
by 10, simply move the decimal point 1 place to the left;
by 100, move the decimal point 2 places to the left;
by 1000, move the decimal point 3 places to the left.

Find the quotients:

	A	B	C	D
1.	$10\overline{)\,.05}$	$100\overline{)\,.625}$	$1000\overline{)1.2}$	$100\overline{)\,.5}$
2.	$10\overline{)\,.75}$	$100\overline{)103.2}$	$1000\overline{)200}$	$100\overline{)39.37}$
3.	$2.2 \div 1000$	$454 \div 1000$	$2.54 \div 100$	$125.3 \div 1000$

Precision in Measuring

A modern airplane often has as many as 300,000 or more different parts. Each one of these parts must fit very closely, or the airplane will not operate as it should. Many of these parts are made in different factories, and to make sure that they will fit properly, they must be measured with great care. The same is true of a watch, a camera, an automobile engine, a radio, or, in fact, any machine.

No measurement is ever "perfectly exact." However, a thing may be measured more and more nearly correctly, as shown below.

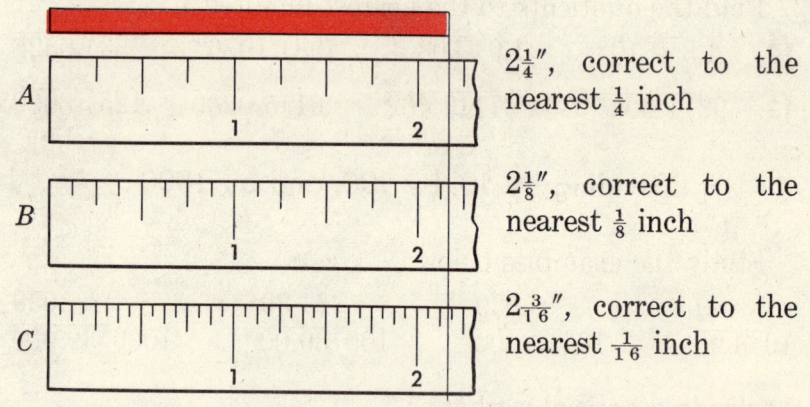

A $2\frac{1}{4}''$, correct to the nearest $\frac{1}{4}$ inch

B $2\frac{1}{8}''$, correct to the nearest $\frac{1}{8}$ inch

C $2\frac{3}{16}''$, correct to the nearest $\frac{1}{16}$ inch

All of these measurements are right. We say that B is *more precise* than A; also, that C is more precise than either B or A. The least precise of the three measurements is A; the most precise is C.

Every measurement is an approximation. By using smaller divisions on our scale, we make the measurement more precise. But it can never be "perfect", or complete, for that would require an endless number of divisions on the scale, which is impossible. A very precise measurement is a very close approximation.

Understanding Measurements

The divisions on a scale are also called **graduations.** This scale is graduated in halves, fourths, and eighths of an inch. How long is the bar *RS*? If we measure it to the nearest $\frac{1}{4}$ inch, it is $1\frac{2}{4}$ or $1\frac{1}{2}$ inches long. This measurement is correct *to the nearest $\frac{1}{4}$ of an inch;* the end *S* is nearer to the $1\frac{1}{2}$-inch mark on the scale than to the $1\frac{1}{4}$-inch mark.

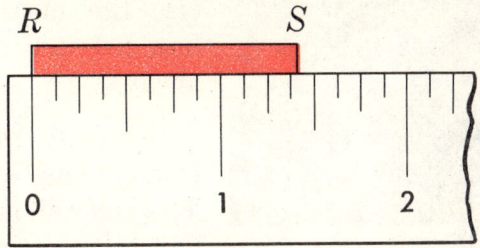

If we measure the bar to the nearest $\frac{1}{8}$ of an inch, it is $1\frac{3}{8}$ inches long; the end *S* is nearer to the $1\frac{3}{8}$-inch mark than to the $1\frac{4}{8}$-inch mark.

Measuring to the smallest division of the scale, then, the bar *RS* is $1\frac{3}{8}$ inches long. It does not differ from the actual length by more than half of the smallest division of the scale (half of $\frac{1}{8}$ inch). If we want to measure the length of *RS* more precisely, we would have to use a scale graduated in sixteenths of an inch.

1. Find the length of *AB* to the nearest $\frac{1}{8}$ of an inch; of *CD* as precisely as you can.

2. A. Read as precisely as you can the length of *EF*. Find its length to the nearest $\frac{1}{8}$ of an inch. **B.** Find the length of *GH* as precisely as you can.

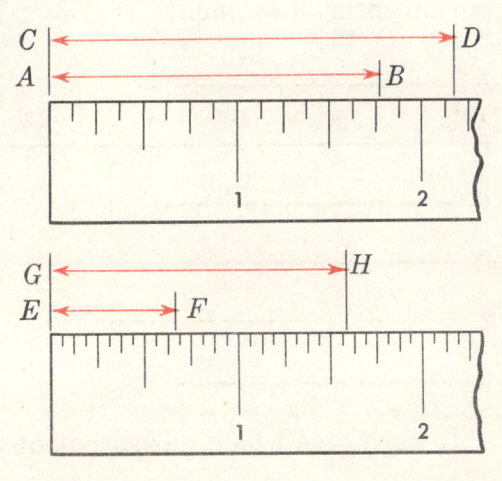

Error of a Measurement

The difference between the exact length and the measured length is called the **error** of the measurement. The smaller the error, the more precise the measurement. No matter how precisely we measure, there will always be an error.

By using more precise measuring instruments, the error will be smaller. The error should never be more than half the smallest division on the scale.

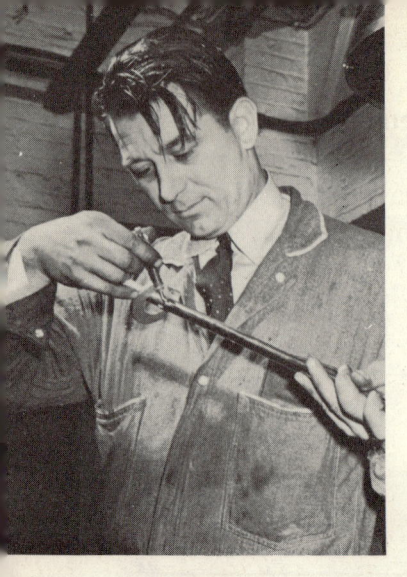

R. I. Nesmith

This mechanic is using an instrument called a micrometer to measure very accurately, but he knows that there will be a slight error even in this measurement.

1. If you use a scale graduated in sixteenths of an inch, what is the largest error you should make? What should it be if the scale is graduated in tenths of an inch?

2. Measure each of these lengths, first using a scale graduated in eighths of an inch, and then one graduated in sixteenths of an inch:

A ─────────────

B ──────────────────────

C ──────────

D ────────────────

E ────────

F ──────────

In each case which measurement is more precise?

Measuring Lengths and Distances

1. What unit of length would you use to measure:
   A. The dimensions of a living-room rug?
   B. The amount of material needed to cover a chair?
   C. The distance from your city to the next city?
   D. The size of your bicycle tire?

2. Complete these statements:
   A. One foot contains _?_ inches.
   B. One yard contains _?_ feet, or _?_ inches.
   C. There are $5\frac{1}{2}$ yards, or _?_ feet, in one rod.
   D. A mile is equivalent to _?_ feet, or _?_ yards.

3. Mary bought a roll of ribbon. It was marked "$8\frac{1}{2}$ yd." She needs 30 inches of ribbon for each package she wishes to wrap. How many packages will she be able to tie with the ribbon? How much will be left over?

4. At the athletic meet, Harry ran 440 yards in 1 minute and 28 seconds. What part of a mile did he run? How many feet per second did he run?

5. The city surveyor measured Mr. Tulley's property, and found that the dimensions were 140.6 ft. along one side, 48.8 ft. along the rear, 129.3 ft. along the other side, and 42.6 ft. along the front. What is the perimeter of his property, that is, the distance around it?

6. Mrs. Thomas needs new shelf paper for her pantry. There are five shelves, each 52 inches long. The paper that is the correct width for her shelves comes in rolls each $1\frac{1}{2}$ yards long. How many rolls must she buy?

7. Find the sums or differences:
   A. 6 ft. 2 in. + 4 ft. 9 in. + 3 ft. 5 in. = _?_ ft. _?_ in.
   B. $2\frac{1}{4}$ yd. + $3\frac{1}{2}$ yd. + 27 in. = _?_ yd.
   C. 8 ft. 3 in. − 5 ft. 8 in. = _?_ ft. _?_ in.
   D. $6\frac{3}{4}$ yd. − 54 in. = _?_ yd.

Measuring Surfaces

The measure of a surface, such as the top of your desk or the space enclosed by a rectangle, square, or circle, is called an *area*. For small surfaces, area is expressed in square inches, square feet, or square yards; for larger surfaces, such as land areas, the acre and the square mile are used.

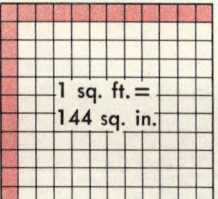

A *square inch* is the area enclosed by a square each side of which is 1 in. long. It is easy to see that there are 144 sq. in. in a *square foot*, or a square whose sides are each 1 ft. long.

1. A *square yard* is the area enclosed by a square each side of which is 1 yd. long. Make a rough sketch that shows how many square feet there are in a square yard.

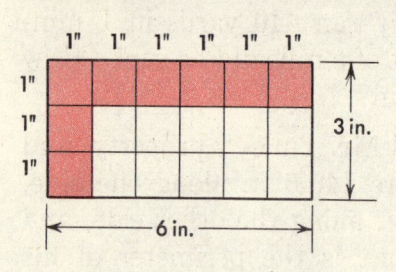

The area of a rectangle is equal to the product of its length and width, as seen from the figure at the left; the area is 3 × 6, or 6 × 3, or 18 sq. in. We may write:

Area = $l \times w$, or $A = lw$.

2. Find the area of a rectangle $4\frac{1}{2}$ ft. wide and $6\frac{1}{2}$ ft. long. How many square yards is this?

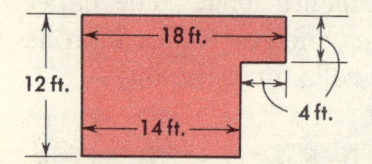

3. What is the area of the floor space shown on the drawing at the left?

4. Find the area of a square $2\frac{1}{2}$ in. on a side; $\frac{1}{2}$ in.

5. A square 20 in. by 20 in. is how many times as large as a square 10 in. by 10 in.? Explain.

Measuring Weight

1. What units of measure are used to tell the weight of:
   A. The amount of baggage a passenger is allowed to carry on an airplane?
   B. A small baby?
   C. A loaf of bread?
   D. A carload of coal?
   E. A tennis racket?

2. A. How many $\frac{1}{4}$-pound packages are equal to 5 pounds?
   B. Two hundred pounds is what fractional part of a ton?
   C. A parcel weighing 34 ounces weighs how many pounds?
   D. Three and a half tons of coal will fill how many bags each holding 100 lb.?

3. A bookseller sends a book by parcel post. The book weighs $1\frac{3}{4}$ lb., and the wrapping weighs 2 oz. What is the total weight of the package in ounces?

4. The parcel post rate to a certain zone is 13¢ for the first pound; 16¢ up to 2 lb.; 19¢ up to 3 lb.; and so on. What is the postage to this zone on a parcel weighing 6 lb.? a package weighing 8 lb. 9 oz.? 11 lb. 3 oz.?

5. Mrs. Pratt can buy her favorite brand of strawberry jam in 16-oz. jars at 36¢ each, or in the small size (10-oz.) at 27¢ each. How much more, or less, will she get if she buys two large jars instead of three small ones? How much less will she spend?

6. When Bob entered the eighth grade on September 2, he weighed 84 lb. The following June 2 he weighed $88\frac{1}{2}$ lb. On the average, by how many ounces a month did his weight increase?

How Much Do They Hold?

The capacity, or **volume**, of a container means how much it can hold. If a container, such as a bottle, a can, or a barrel, is used for liquids, its capacity is sometimes measured in pints, quarts, or gallons. This is called **liquid measure.** If the container is used for fruit, vegetables, or grains, its capacity is measured in quarts, pecks, or bushels. This is called **dry measure.**

Liquid Measure	Dry Measure
2 cups = 1 pint	2 pints (dry) = 1 quart (dry)
2 pints = 1 quart	8 quarts = 1 peck
4 quarts = 1 gallon	4 pecks = 1 bushel

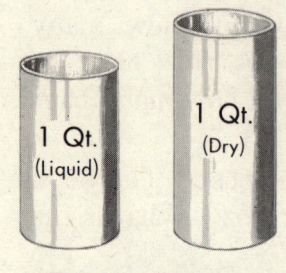

The dry quart is about 16% larger than the liquid quart; or, 7 liquid quarts very nearly equal 6 dry quarts.

Many things are sold by *weight* instead of by *bulk.* This is done partly because liquid pints and quarts are often mistaken for dry pints and quarts. Also, the dry pints and quarts are convenient measures for small amounts of dry commodities.

1. How many half-pint jars of honey are equivalent to one quart jar? How many quart jars are equivalent to two 1-gallon jars?

2. A boy picked 20 qt. of beans. How many pecks is this?

3. An ordinary apple barrel holds 3.28 bushels. To the nearest peck, how many pecks is this?

4. A bushel of apples weighs 50 lb. What is the weight of a barrel of apples? (See Problem **3.**)

5. Fred picked a 14-quart pail (liquid) of blackberries. How many quart baskets would this fill? (Remember the difference between a dry quart and a liquid quart.)

Liquid Ounces

When measuring small amounts of liquids by volume (not by weight), we often use the **fluid ounce** as a unit of measure. Fluid means "liquid." A fluid ounce is not the same as an ounce of weight; it is a measure of capacity, or volume, not a measure of weight.

There are 16 fluid ounces in a pint. This is easy to remember, as there are 16 ounces in a pound. Since a pint of water weighs approximately one pound, a fluid ounce of liquid (volume) weighs approximately one ounce (weight). But this is only approximate, for some liquids are heavier than water, and some are lighter.

1. How many fluid ounces are there in 1½ pints of orange juice?

2. How many fluid ounces are there in ½ gal. of maple syrup?

3. The directions for making a photographic solution say that 12 fluid ounces of water are to be used. What fractional part of a pint is this?

4. A druggist has 1½ qt. of liquid which he wants to pour into bottles, each having a capacity of 6 fluid ounces. How many such bottles will he need?

5. An 8-ounce bottle of witch hazel sells for 33¢, and a pint bottle sells for 49¢. How much is saved by purchasing a pint bottle instead of two 8-oz. bottles? What is the cost of one ounce when buying the small size?

6. When preparing the formula for the baby, a mother wishes to fill six 8-ounce bottles with the prepared mixture. How many pints must she prepare?

7. If 16 tablespoons make one cup and 2 cups make 1 pint, how many tablespoons are there in a pint?

Capacity in Cubic Feet

When measuring storage space, such as the capacity of a coal bin, a silo, or a freight car, we generally use the cubic foot as the unit of measure.

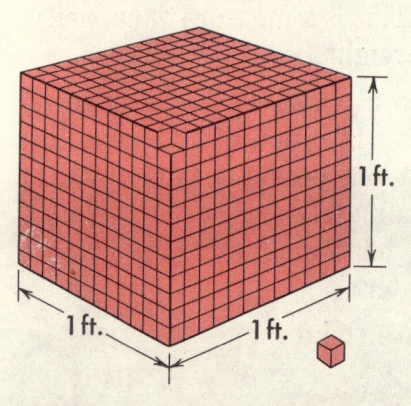

If the length, width, and height of a block, such as a toy block, are equal, the block is a *cube*. A block 1 inch long, 1 inch wide, and 1 inch high occupies one **cubic inch**.

If each edge of the block is 1 foot long, the block occupies one **cubic foot**.

The picture above represents a cube, each edge of which is 12 inches long. How many cubic inches are there in a single row of small cubes? How many rows of these cubes are there in each layer? How many layers are there? How many cubic inches are there in one cubic foot?

1. One cubic yard is 3 ft. long, 3 ft. wide, and 3 ft. high. How many cubic feet are there in a cubic yard?

2. A coal bin has a capacity of 300 cu. ft. If 1 cu. ft. of coal weighs 50 lb., how many tons can the bin hold?

3. How many cubic feet of storage space are required to store 12 tons of coal? (Problem **2**.)

4. A freight car has a capacity of 3440 cu. ft. Each cubic foot of space will hold 0.8 bushel. How many bushels will the car hold?

42

Learning to Solve Problems

Estimating the Result

When people use arithmetic to solve problems they frequently estimate the answers; sometimes an approximate answer is all that is needed. Estimating the result also helps us to avoid careless mistakes.

1. A floorwax is sold in ½-gallon cans at $1.89 each, and in 1-gallon cans at $3.25 each. Mr. George can save about ($1.25, 75¢, 55¢) if he buys a gallon can; what is the exact amount saved?

2. Mrs. George read a poster which said you could get a round-trip ticket from New York to Chicago for $46.75 and save $14.67 on two one-way tickets. Then, a one-way ticket would cost about ($54, $30, $42); what is the exact cost of a one-way ticket?

3. Teacups and saucers are priced at $18.75 a dozen. If Mrs. Lee buys 8 cups and saucers, she will have to pay about ($10, $16, $12); what is the exact amount?

4. A gross is 12 dozen. At $15 a gross, the cost of one article is about ($.10, $1.00, $.15); to the nearest tenth of a cent, what is the actual cost?

5. A train covers a distance of 961 miles at an average speed of 60 miles an hour. The trip takes about (14 hr., 16 hr., 18 hr.); what is the actual time?

6. Tell in each case which answer is the best estimate; then find the exact amount.
  A. $47 \times \$1.24 = $ ($60, $100, $50)
  B. $16.4 \div 0.4 = $ (4, 40, 400)
  C. $.018 \times \$4.50 = $ ($1, $.01, $.10)
  D. $\frac{7}{16}$ of $260 = $ (300, 120, 200)

Metric Units of Measure

To measure length and distance for everyday purposes, we use the inch, the foot, the yard, and the mile. This is known as the English system. But for scientific purposes, and in most European and South American countries, a different system is used—the **metric system.**

The units of measure in the metric system are based on decimals.

The standard unit of length in the metric system is called the **meter.** A meter is slightly longer than a yard.

1 yard = 36 inches

1 meter = 39.37 inches

The meter is divided into smaller units by taking tenths, hundredths, and thousandths of a meter.

.1 meter   = 1 decimeter, or 10 decimeters   = 1 meter
.01 meter   = 1 centimeter, or 100 centimeters   = 1 meter
.001 meter = 1 millimeter, or 1000 millimeters = 1 meter

We see that **deci-** means .1, or $\frac{1}{10}$; **centi-** means .01, or $\frac{1}{100}$; and **milli-** means .001, or $\frac{1}{1000}$.

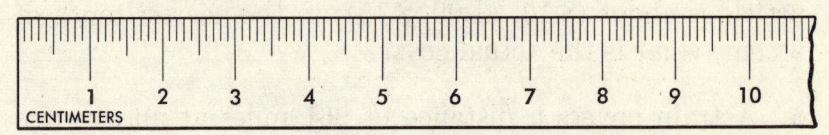

Study the centimeter (cm.) ruler shown above.

1. Lay your inch ruler against the diagram. Is an inch very nearly equal to 2.5 centimeters?

2. One meter is exactly 39.37 inches. **A.** What part of a meter is 1 centimeter? **B.** A centimeter is what part of an inch (nearest hundredth)? **C.** Is .39 almost the same as .4? **D.** What part of an inch is a centimeter (nearest tenth)?

3. How many centimeters (cm.) are there in a meter (m.)?

4. How many millimeters (mm.) are there in a centimeter?

5. How many times as long as a centimeter is a meter?

6. How many times as long as a millimeter is a centimeter?

7. The standard size motion picture film is 35 mm. wide. How many centimeters is this? How many inches is this? (1 cm. = 0.4 in.)

8. Some motion picture films are 16 mm. wide. How many centimeters is this? What part of an inch is this?

9. Amateur photographers sometimes use 8 mm. motion picture film. About what fraction of an inch is this?

10. A meter is about 1.1 yd. About how many yards are there in 2 meters? in 10 meters? in 200 meters?

11. A yard is about 0.9 of a meter. About how many meters are there in 3 yd.? in 10 yd.? in 300 ft.?

12. A meter is 39.37 inches. **A.** How many inches are there in 1000 meters? **B.** How many feet are there in 1000 meters? Round your answer to the nearest ten feet.

13. A thousand meters (1000 m.) is called a **kilometer** (**km.**). If a kilometer is about 3280 ft., about what fraction of a mile is 1 km. (nearest tenth)?

14. Using 1 kilometer as 0.6 mile, find the number of miles in 2 km.; in 140 km.; in 500 km.

15. The air-line distance between Panama City and Rio de Janeiro is given as 5330 km. About how many miles is this?

16. Find, to the nearest tenth of a kilometer, how many kilometers there are in one mile.

17. The speed limit on certain parts of the Pan American Highway is 100 km. per hour. About how much is this in miles per hour?

18. The railroad distance from New York to Albany is about 142 miles. About how many kilometers is this?

The World of Sports

The meter is used in connection with athletic games and other sports, especially the international Olympic Games.

In American track and field events, the distances run are usually 50 yards, 100 yards, 220, 440, 600, 880, and 1000 yards; 1 mile, 2 miles, etc. Similar events in the Olympic Games are for 100 meters, 200, 400, 800, 1500, 5,000, and 10,000 meters.

In the first three problems, take 1 yard as 0.9 meter, and 1 meter as 1.1 yards.

1. A 440-yard dash is equivalent to about how many meters?

2. About how many yards is a 400-meter race? a 1600-meter relay race? a 10,000-meter walk?

3. In the Olympic Games held in London in 1948, the men's swimming team of the United States won the 800-meter relay in 8 minutes and 46 seconds. How many yards are 800 meters?

4. The international women's running high jump record, made in 1948 by Alice Coachman of the United States, was 1.68 meters. Taking 1 meter as 39.37 inches, how many inches is this? Express this in feet and inches.

5. The 110-meter hurdle race in the 1948 Olympics was won by William Porter, of the United States, who finished in 13.9 seconds. What was the distance run in yards? (Take 1 meter as 1.09 yards.)

6. In a recent year, a world air record was made when a plane was flown over a 3-kilometer course at a maximum speed of 1,079.841 kilometers per hour. Taking a kilometer as .621 mile, express this record speed in miles per hour, correct to two decimal places.

7. Olie Andersson, of Sweden, holds a world walking record. He walked 25,531 meters in 2 hours. How many kilometers is this? Taking a kilometer as .621 mile, find his rate in miles per hour to two decimal places.

Keeping in Practice

	1.	2.	3.	4.	5.	6.
	$8\frac{1}{2}$	$4\frac{1}{6}$	$7\frac{1}{8}$	$10\frac{3}{4}$	16	$12\frac{1}{3}$
	3	$6\frac{2}{3}$	$6\frac{1}{4}$	$-9\frac{7}{8}$	$-8\frac{3}{4}$	$-8\frac{2}{3}$
	$2\frac{1}{4}$	$3\frac{5}{6}$	$5\frac{5}{8}$			

A **B** **C**

7. $\frac{1}{8} \times 6\frac{2}{5} = ?$ $24 \div \frac{2}{3} = ?$ $4\frac{1}{2} \div 3 = ?$

8. $3\frac{1}{2} \times 4 = ?$ $10 \div 2\frac{1}{2} = ?$ $\frac{1}{4} \div 1\frac{1}{2} = ?$

9. $.24 \times 1.5 = ?$ $.08 \times 1.25 = ?$ $6.2 \times 1.09 = ?$

10. $3.6\overline{)72}$ $.5\overline{).0075}$ $.004\overline{)17.2}$

Pounds and Kilograms

In the metric system, the standard unit of weight is the **kilogram**. One kilogram is a little more than 2 pounds.

For smaller weights, the **gram** is used; for larger weights, the **metric ton** is used.

Metric Weights	Approximate Equivalents
1000 grams (gm.) = 1 kilogram (kg.)	1 kilogram = 2.2 pounds
1000 kilograms = 1 metric ton	1 pound = .45 kilogram

Complete the following:

1. A. One gram = _?_ pound. B. One kilogram = _?_ ounces.
2. A. One pound = _?_ grams. B. One gram = _?_ ounce.
3. One ounce = _?_ kilogram, or _?_ grams.
4. Ten pounds of apples weigh how many kilograms?
5. One-quarter of a pound of butter weighs how many grams?
6. A silver dollar, when new, weighs approximately 25 grams. What part of an ounce is this?
7. A bushel of oats weighs 32 pounds. How many kilograms is this?
8. When Betty was in Mexico, she weighed herself. The scale read 41.5 kilograms. How many pounds did she weigh?
9. According to postal regulations, 30 grams is the equivalent of 1 ounce. At 3¢ an ounce or fraction of an ounce, what is the postage on a letter weighing 74 grams?
10. An importer purchased 5000 kilograms of olive oil. How many pounds did he buy?
11. About how many pounds are there in a metric ton? This is how many more pounds than our ton?

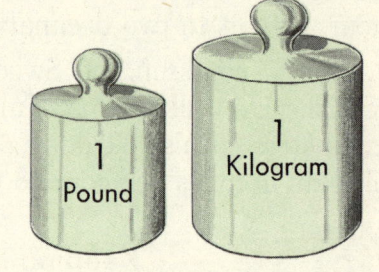

Liters and Quarts

In the metric system, the standard unit of volume is the **liter**. A liter is a little more than a liquid quart, but a little less than a dry quart. The liter is used both for liquid and for dry measure.

For most purposes, we may use these approximations:

  1 liter = 1.06 liquid qt.   1 liquid qt. = 0.95 liter
  1 liter = 0.91 dry qt.   1 dry qt. = 1.1 liters

1. One hundred liquid quarts equal how many liters?

2. A liquid quart is what decimal part of a liter?

3. One hundred liters equal how many liquid quarts?

4. A liter is how many times as great as a liquid quart?

5. One gallon equals how many liters?

6. One liquid pint equals what part of a liter?

7. One-half liter is what part of a liquid quart?

8. Two and a half liters equal how many liquid quarts?

9. A bottle has a capacity of 8 quarts. How many liters does it contain?

10. The gas tank of a certain car holds 16 gallons. What is the capacity of the tank in liters?

11. If a container has a capacity of 2 liters, how many dry quarts of berries can it hold?

12. A liter is divided into 1000 units called **milliliters** (**ml.**). A patient in a hospital received a transfusion of 500 milliliters of blood. Is this about equal to a pint?

Learning to Solve Problems

Deciding What to Do

Complete the following statements; the first has been done for you.

1. To change quarts to pints, (multiply) by (2).
2. To change gallons to quarts, _?_ by _?_.
3. To change pints to gallons, _?_ by _?_.
4. To change ounces to pounds, _?_ by _?_.
5. To change tons to pounds, _?_ by _?_.
6. To change inches to feet, _?_ by _?_.
7. To change yards to feet, _?_ by _?_.
8. To find the total cost of a number of like items, we multiply _?_ by _?_.
9. To find the distance traveled, we find the product of the _?_ and the _?_.
10. To find the cost of one item when we know the total cost of several like items, we _?_ the total cost by _?_.
11. To find the time required for a trip, we _?_ the _?_ by the speed.
12. To find the speed, we divide the _?_ by the _?_.
13. To find the side of a square, we _?_ the perimeter by _?_.
14. To find the annual cost, we _?_ the monthly cost by _?_.

JIFFY QUIZ

1. Without copying, add: $4.25; $2.50; $3.75.
2. Which is larger, .080 or .075? How much larger?
3. What is the difference between .100 and .001?
4. How many times as large as .001 is 0.1?
5. Does 1.0 have the same value as 1?

Air Transportation

1. Besides pilots and co-pilots, commercial airliners must employ other people, such as office workers, mechanics, and ticket agents. Recently, the domestic airlines had a total of about 60,000 employees. Of this number, about 5000 were pilots and co-pilots. What is the ratio of total employees to pilots and co-pilots?

2. Domestic airlines carried an average of 1,241,400 passengers per month during a recent year. About how many passengers were carried in the year? (Round to the nearest hundred thousand.)

3. International air travel has grown rapidly. In 1940, about 160,000 people traveled from one country to another by air. In 1950, the total was about 1,600,000. This was how many times the number in 1940?

4. There is tremendous power in airplane engines. Automobiles sometimes have engines of about 100 horsepower. A *Stratocruiser* has 4 engines, each with 2200 horsepower. How many times as great as a 100 horsepower automobile engine is the total horsepower of the *Stratocruiser?*

5. In one hour a *Stratocruiser* may go about 320 miles and use about 400 gallons of gasoline. How far does the plane fly on one gallon? An automobile may go 16 miles on one gallon. This is how many times as far as the distance a *Stratocruiser* travels on one gallon?

Atmospheric Pressure

Vacuum

29.9 inches

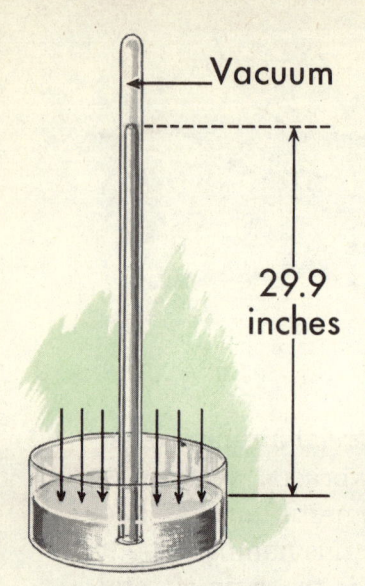

Air pressure is measured by an instrument called a **barometer**.

If this long tube is filled with mercury, then turned upside down and dipped below the surface of the mercury in the dish, the mercury in the tube will drop until it is about 29.9 inches high, leaving a vacuum in the top of the tube.

The air pressure on the mercury in the dish "holds up" a column of mercury 29.9 inches high, at sea level.

The air pressure changes slightly from place to place, and at various altitudes above sea level, and under different weather conditions.

1. In an observation station of the Weather Bureau, the barometer reading at 2 P.M. was 29.31 inches. By 8 P.M. the reading was 28.66 inches. Find the amount of decrease.

2. At sea level, 1 cubic foot of air weighs about $\frac{1}{12}$ of a pound. How many ounces is this?

As we go above sea level, the air becomes "thinner" and the pressure decreases. At 90 ft. above sea level, the pressure decreases enough for the mercury in the barometer to drop 0.1 inch. At 180 ft. above sea level, the pressure is 2 × 0.1, or 0.2 inch less. At very high altitudes, the decrease in pressure is not so great.

3. At 1080 ft. above sea level, how much lower will the barometer reading be than at sea level?

4. Allowing $\frac{1}{10}$-inch drop for every 90 ft. increase in altitude, what height has a mountain climber reached if the barometer reads 25.1 inches? (Barometer reading at sea level = 29.9 in.)

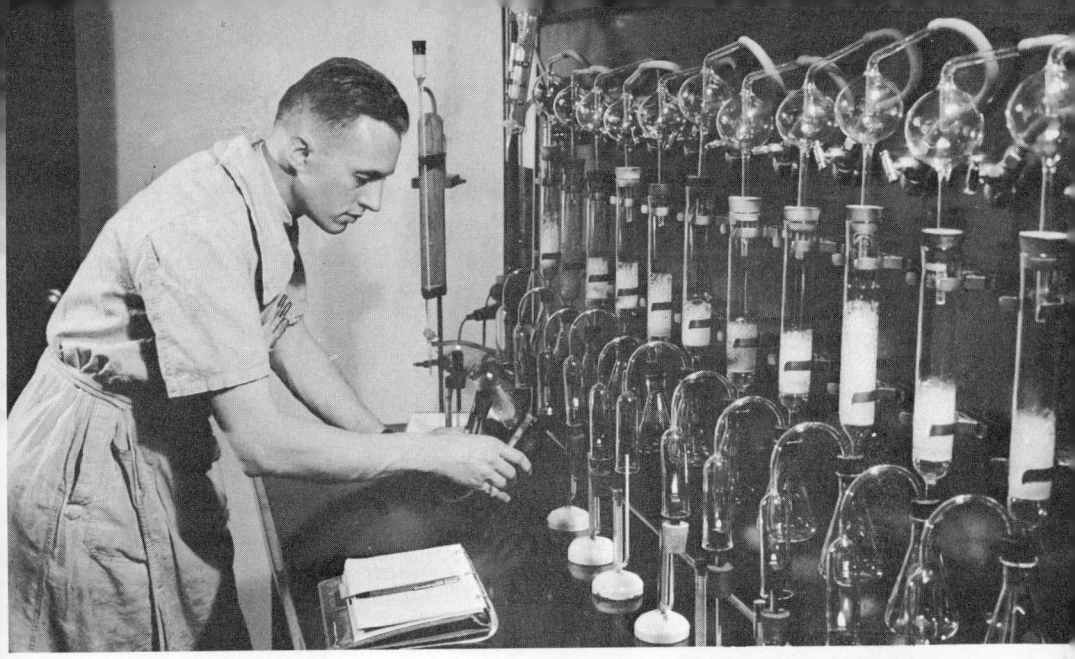

Courtesy Ethyl Corporation

Using Decimals in Science

1. One fluid ounce of water weighs 28.4 grams. Glycerine is 1.26 times as heavy as water. What is the weight of one fluid ounce of glycerine expressed to the nearest tenth of a gram?

2. During a certain chemical process the temperature rises from 118.9 degrees to 134.2 degrees. How many degrees is the increase?

3. A certain sample of mineral contains 2.4 ounces of impurities. The entire sample weighs 200 ounces. How many ounces of the pure material does the sample contain? How many ounces of impurities are there in every 100 ounces of the sample?

4. A steel cable 1000 feet long expands .02 foot for each degree of temperature increase. How much longer is the cable when the temperature has risen from 70 degrees to 95 degrees?

Estimating the Answer

It is helpful to estimate when we wish to check our answers. In estimating, we often use rounded numbers. For example, 2867 rounded to the nearest ten is 2870; to the nearest hundred, 2867 is 2900; to the nearest thousand, 2867 is 3000.

Round these numbers, first to the nearest ten; then to the nearest hundred:

	A	B	C	D
1.	312	203	419	926
2.	91	786	467	497

Round these numbers, first to the nearest hundred; then to the nearest thousand:

3.	8085	974	2060	10,780
4.	29,639	19,094	7869	3087

Round these numbers to the nearest thousand:

5.	51,678	1795	23,452	67,810
6.	156,127	89,360	704,807	512,600

Round these numbers, first to the nearest 10,000; then to the nearest 100,000:

7.	293,420	516,025	210,890	300,860
8.	486,240	790,673	807,120	192,493

Example 1. Estimate, by rounding, the product of 19 and 29. Think: 19 is about 20, and 29 is about 30. $20 \times 30 = 600$. Then 19×29 is about 600. The exact product is 551.

Example 2. Estimate the product of 47 and 62. Think: 47 is about 50, and 62 is about 60. $50 \times 60 = 3000$. Then 47×62 is about 3000. The exact product is 2914.

Example 3. Estimate: 13.9 × 0.46. We think: 13.9, about 14; 0.46, about $\frac{1}{2}$. Then 13.9 × 0.46 is about 14 × $\frac{1}{2}$, or about 7. Exact answer: 6.394.

Example 4. Estimate: 44 × .32. We think: 44, about 45; .32, about .33$\frac{1}{3}$, or $\frac{1}{3}$. Then 44 × .32 is about 45 × $\frac{1}{3}$, or about 15. Exact answer: 14.08.

Example 5. Estimate: $\frac{7}{24}$ × 176. We think: $\frac{7}{24}$, about $\frac{6}{24}$, or $\frac{1}{4}$; 176, about 180. Then $\frac{7}{24}$ × 176 is about $\frac{1}{4}$ × 180, or about 45. Exact answer: 51$\frac{1}{3}$.

Estimate the answers; then work the examples and compare your answers with your estimates:

	A	B	C
1.	53 × 29	137 × 11	144 × 62
2.	48 × 23	72 × 38	28 × 207
3.	21.2 × .34	6.2 × 4.2	.76 × 80.5
4.	.39 × 56	1.92 × 30	21 × 1$\frac{3}{8}$
5.	.24 × 157	.88 × 23.9	.55 × 104
6.	$\frac{5}{12}$ × 152	$\frac{17}{32}$ × 400	$\frac{5}{16}$ × 368

Estimate the answers before finding the exact answers:

7. At $1.48 an hour, the wages for 40 hr. are __?__.

8. At 29¢ a dozen, the cost of 4$\frac{1}{2}$ doz. is __?__.

9. A railroad coach fare from one city to another, within a state, is $10.13, without tax. If the rate is 3.375 cents per mile, how many miles apart are the two cities?

10. To prevent destruction by an insect pest, 413,469 acres of Douglas-fir forests in the Northwest were sprayed. The total cost was $649,146. Find the cost of spraying per acre (nearest cent).

Practice with Measures

1. A label on a can of paint read: "$\frac{1}{12}$ U.S. Gal.; 10.66 Liq. Oz." Is this correct? Explain.

2. The wrapper on a package of gelatine dessert read: "Net weight, 3 ounces; metric equivalent, 85.05 grams." Is this correct, if we take the approximate value of 1 lb. as 454 gm.? Is it correct, if we use the more precise value of 1 lb. as 453.592 gm.?

3. The maximum weight of baggage per passenger that may be carried, without charge, on transatlantic flights is 66 lb. How many kilograms is this, if the airlines use the metric equivalent, 2.2 lb. = 1 kg.?

4. One pound of shelled pecans is approximately equivalent to 2.5 lb. of unshelled pecans. How many pounds of unshelled pecans must be used to obtain 100 lb. of shelled pecans?

5. One pound of shelled peanuts is obtained from $1\frac{1}{2}$ lb. of unshelled peanuts. How many pounds of shelled peanuts can be obtained from 300 lb. of unshelled peanuts?

6. On a can of evaporated milk the label read: "Net weight, 6 oz.; liquid measure, $5\frac{1}{3}$ oz." **A.** Find the weight in ounces of 1 fluid ounce of this milk. **B.** Find the weight, in pounds and ounces, of 1 pint.

7. The label on a can of motor oil read: "$2\frac{1}{2}$ gal., or 9.463 liters." Taking the more precise value of 1 liquid quart as .94633 liter, is this statement correct to the nearest thousandth?

8. The standard U.S. gallon contains 231 cu. in.; the standard gallon used in Canada (the imperial gallon) contains 277.42 cu. in. Compare the number of cubic inches in 6 U.S. gallons with the number of cubic inches in 5 imperial gallons.

Using Roman Numbers

Roman numerals are used occasionally in dates on public buildings and monuments, for chapter and volume numbers in magazines and books, and in some other places. The seven numerals used are I (1), V (5), X (10), L (50), C (100), D (500), M (1000).

Today we do not always write them as the Romans did; we write IV for 4 and IX for 9, while the Romans usually wrote IIII and VIIII instead. We still see IIII on some clocks and watches. Years ago, 1905 was written MDCCCCV; today we are more likely to write it MCMV.

When a smaller numeral stands before a larger one, its value is subtracted from the larger numeral; for example:

XXXIX = 39   XCII = 92   MCMXXX = 1930
XLIV = 44   CDXX = 420   MCMXL = 1940

We may write: I before V and X only;
X before L and C only;
C before D and M only.

But we never subtract V, L, and D from another numeral.

1. Write these Arabic numbers in Roman numerals:
   A. 45   B. 512   C. 1300   D. 1912   E. 1895

Tell which of the Roman numbers is correct:
2. 495 = (CDXCV, VD, CDVC)
3. 999 = (DID, IM, CMXCIX)
4. 1945 = (MCMVL, MCMXLV, MDCCCCVL)

Write these Roman numbers in Arabic numerals:

	A	B	C	D
5.	CXIX	MDCCCXL	MDCCXC	CXLIX
6.	MCMXXI	MCMIX	MCMX	MCMLV
7.	MCMLX	MCMI	MMXL	MDCCXLIV

JUST FOR FUN

How many of these can you answer?

1. Peter said he had 11 fingers. Beginning with his left thumb, he counted: "10-9-8-7-6; five more fingers on the right hand; 6 and 5 are 11." What is wrong with this?

2. How many quarter-inch marks are there in the space of one inch on an ordinary ruler?

3. Are there 6 rows of 8 stars or 8 rows of 6 stars in the American flag when held so that the stripes are horizontal?

4. Which is heavier, a pound of feathers or a pound of coal?

5. Which is more, six dozen dozen or half a dozen dozen?

6. A bottle and a cork cost $1.10. The bottle costs one dollar more than the cork. What is the cost of each?

7. We can abbreviate such a date as March 10, 1952 by writing 3/10/52. Find out what 3/10/52 means when used on official letters of the United States Army or Navy.

Keeping in Practice

	A	B	C
1.	$\frac{2}{3} \times 7\frac{1}{2} = ?$	$0.012 \times 17 = ?$	$2\frac{1}{12} + 2\frac{3}{8} = ?$
2.	$308 \times 206 = ?$	$3\frac{1}{3} \div \frac{5}{6} = ?$	$17\overline{)300}$
3.	$37{,}908 - 469 = ?$	$\frac{3}{4} \div 8 = ?$	$.004\overline{).8}$
4.	$18 \div 1\frac{1}{2} = ?$	$101\frac{1}{2} - 69\frac{3}{4} = ?$	$6\frac{1}{4} \div 2\frac{1}{2} = ?$

Making Sure

If you miss any of these examples, turn to the pages listed at the ends of the rows and study these pages again.

1. Without copying, add or subtract: 5
   A. $.85 + $2.50 + $1.10   B. $20 − $9.89
2. A. 715 × 3200 = ?   C. 5600 × 180 = ?   6, 28-30
   B. 100 × 9.78 = ?   D. 3.14 × 0.16 = ?
3. A. Round to the nearest hundred: 54-55
   $3,168.22; 887; $87.98.
   B. Round to the nearest thousand:
   11,115; 52,650; 10,075.
4. In each example, write the ratio of the smaller quantity to the larger:
   A. 4 yd.; $2\frac{1}{4}$ ft.   B. 12 oz.; $1\frac{3}{4}$ lb.   C. $6; $60   22-23
5. Which is more nearly equal to $\frac{3}{4}$, .72 or .8?   24
6. Express as decimals to 3 places: $\frac{3}{7}$; $\frac{7}{12}$; $\frac{5}{8}$.   26
7. A. $2\frac{3}{4} + 9\frac{5}{6} = ?$ B. $3\frac{1}{4} + 4\frac{5}{16} = ?$ 9-12
8. A. $12\frac{2}{3} - 8\frac{7}{8} = ?$ B. $16 - 4\frac{3}{8} = ?$ 9-12
9. A. $\frac{2}{3} \times 3\frac{1}{2} \times \frac{7}{8}$ C. $8\frac{1}{3} \div 2\frac{1}{2}$ 13-19
   B. $4\frac{1}{2} \times 6\frac{2}{3}$ D. $\frac{1}{2} \div \frac{1}{2}$
10. Find the quotients to the nearest hundredth: 31-33
    A. $.062 \overline{)9.76}$ B. $1000 \overline{)67.3}$ C. $1.07 \overline{)5.2}$
11. 8 ft. 3 in. + 5 ft. 10 in. = _?_ ft. _?_ in.   37
12. A. 10 qt. = _?_ gal. _?_ qt.   40-41
    B. $\frac{1}{4}$ gal = _?_ fluid ounces.
13. A. $3\frac{1}{2}$ kilograms = _?_ lb.   B. 200 meters = _?_ yd.   C. 350 kilometers = _?_ miles.   45, 48
    D. 24 lb. = _?_ kilograms.
14. A. Write in Roman numerals: 34, 96, 111.   57
    B. Write in Arabic numerals: XLI, LXIX, MCMIV.

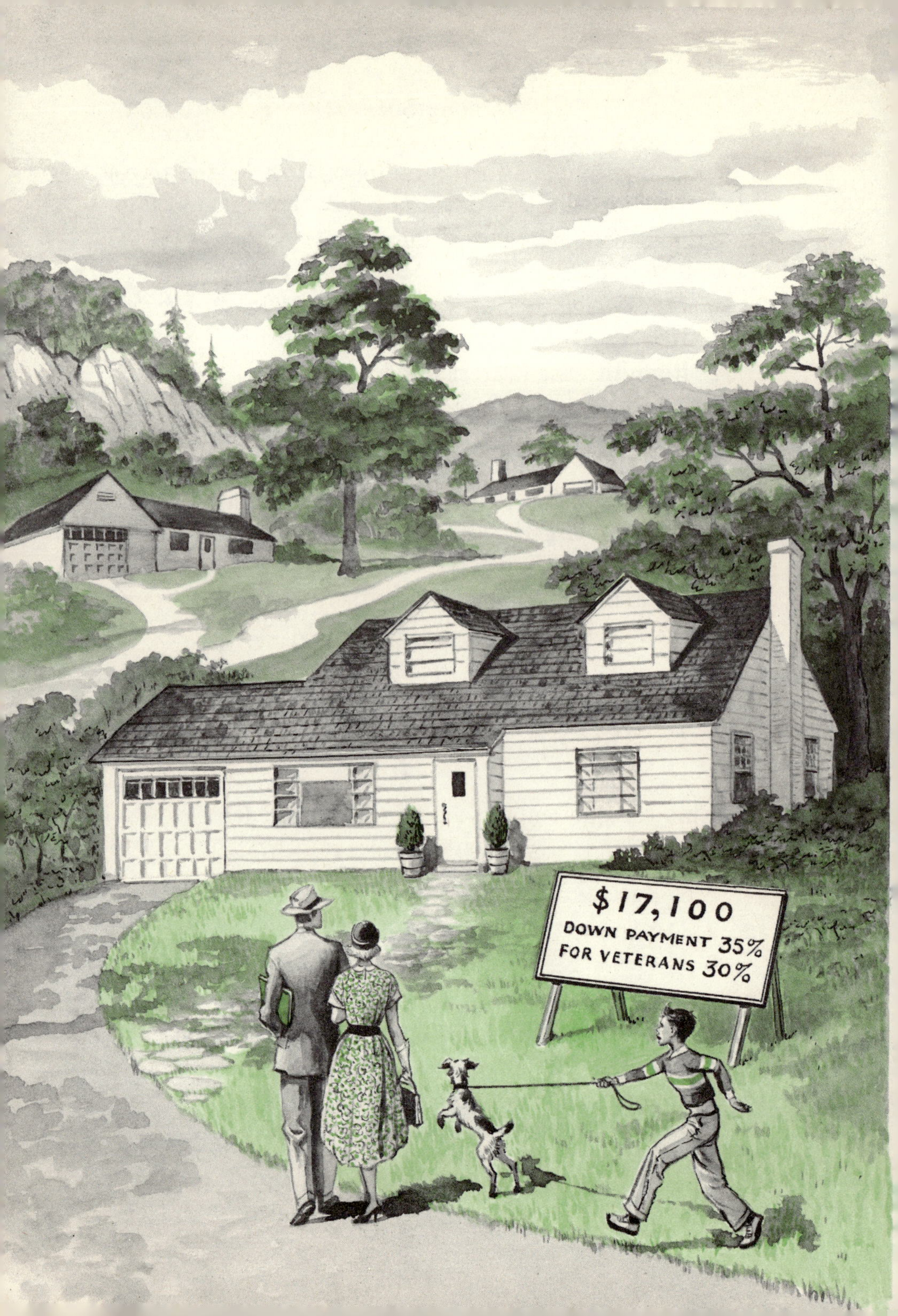
$17,100
DOWN PAYMENT 35%
FOR VETERANS 30%

2

PERCENTAGE

Per Cents Have Many Uses

1. A camera selling regularly at $65 is on sale at 50% off. What is the sale price?

2. The school paper announced that the baseball team had won 75% of all games played. If they played 12 games in all, how many did they lose?

3. A World War II veteran bought a house priced at $17,100. He was required to pay 30% of this amount in cash. How much did he pay? How much did he still owe?

4. Mrs. Frost bought a floor lamp on sale at a reduction of 40% of the original price. The original price was $24.95. How much did she save?

5. A saleswoman told Mrs. Condon that the fabric she bought was 30% wool. If the rest was cotton, what per cent of the material was cotton?

6. According to a farm bulletin, 42% of all eligible boys and girls in a certain county were members of the 4-H Club. There were 2150 boys and girls in the county who were eligible. How many members were there?

7. The Hendersons have just bought a refrigerator. The price was $219.50. They paid 40% of the purchase price in cash. What was the cash payment?

8. A newspaper reported that in a certain year the wheat crop was 16% greater than the crop of the previous year. For every 100 bushels produced in the first of the two years, how many were grown in the second year?

Changing Fractions and Decimals to Per Cents

A common fraction or a decimal fraction is a way of expressing a part of something. A **per cent** is another way of expressing a part of something. But per cents always mean hundredths. 1% means $\frac{1}{100}$; 60% means $\frac{60}{100}$.

A common or decimal fraction must be expressed as hundredths before it can be expressed as a per cent.

A. $\frac{3}{4} = \frac{75}{100} = .75 = 75\%$ B. $\frac{1}{10} = \frac{10}{100} = .10 = 10\%$

To change any common fraction to hundredths, annex two zeros to the numerator and divide by the denominator.

$\frac{7}{20} = 20\overline{)7.00}^{.35} = 35\%$ $\frac{5}{8} = 8\overline{)5.00}^{.62\frac{1}{2}} = 62\frac{1}{2}\%$

1. Change these fractions to hundredths, or per cents:

$\frac{1}{4}$ $\frac{1}{5}$ $\frac{3}{10}$ $\frac{3}{8}$ $\frac{2}{3}$ $\frac{3}{7}$ $\frac{5}{12}$

Hundredths may be expressed as per cents. We write the per cent sign (%), which stands for hundredths; then we may drop the decimal point. For example:

.15 = 15% .2 = .20 = 20% .08 = 8% .1 = .10 = 10%

Actually we move the decimal point two places to the right; but we do not write it except when we are expressing as a per cent a decimal number which is, or contains, a part of a per cent. For example:

.152 = 15.2%   .005 = .5%   .0625 = 6.25%
.045 = 4.5% = 4$\frac{1}{2}$%   .165 = 16.5% = 16$\frac{1}{2}$%

Here the point was moved two places to the right, but had to be written to express a part of a per cent.

Write these decimals as per cents:

	A	B	C	D	E	F
2.	.45	.016	.625	.9	.123	.16$\frac{2}{3}$
3.	.5	.025	.09	.099	.0325	.06$\frac{1}{4}$

Changing Per Cents to Decimals

We can also express a per cent as a decimal. We know that a per cent is simply another way of expressing hundredths. For example:

25% = .25   3% = .03   80% = .80

When we change a per cent to a decimal, we drop the per cent sign (%), which stands for hundredths, and write the decimal point.

Write each of these per cents as a decimal:

	A	B	C	D	E
1.	18%	5%	50%	98%	70%
2.	20%	10%	6%	30%	100%
3.	36%	75%	11%	90%	8%
4.	2%	1%	40%	24%	60%

Sometimes a per cent contains a fraction. Such per cents can usually be written as decimals. We express the fraction as a decimal, then move the decimal point two places to the left. For example:

$12\frac{1}{2}\% = 12.5\% = .125$
$3\frac{1}{2}\% = 3.5\% = .035$
$2\frac{1}{4}\% = 2.25\% = .0225$

Write each of these per cents as a decimal. What do you do with the decimal point? What takes the place of the per cent sign?

	A	B	C	D	E
5.	$2\frac{1}{2}\%$	$5\frac{1}{4}\%$	4.5%	2.1%	$1\frac{1}{2}\%$
6.	4.3%	14.8%	8.9%	$10\frac{1}{2}\%$	$37\frac{1}{2}\%$
7.	1.1%	$3\frac{3}{4}\%$	3.25%	$6\frac{1}{4}\%$	62.5%
8.	2.34%	3.75%	4.95%	12.3%	99.44%

9. Which is more: 10% or $\frac{1}{10}$? 5% or $\frac{1}{5}$?

Per Cents and Fractions

Since a per cent shows a fractional part of something, we can express a per cent as a common fraction. For example:

$$30\% = \tfrac{30}{100} = \tfrac{3}{10} \qquad 75\% = \tfrac{75}{100} = \tfrac{3}{4} \qquad 4\% = \tfrac{4}{100} = \tfrac{1}{25}$$

To change a number which is written as a per cent to a common fraction, drop the % sign and write the number as the numerator of a fraction whose denominator is 100; then reduce this fraction to lowest terms.

Write each of these per cents as a common fraction in lowest terms:

1. 55%   4. 90%   7. 12%   10. 8%   13. 10%
2. 70%   5. 66%   8. 18%   11. 1%   14. 98%
3. 35%   6. 4%   9. 2%   12. 5%   15. 15%

Some per cents are used so often that it is very useful to learn and remember the equivalent fractions.

$25\% = \tfrac{1}{4} \qquad 50\% = \tfrac{1}{2} \qquad 75\% = \tfrac{3}{4}$
$20\% = \tfrac{1}{5} \qquad 40\% = \tfrac{2}{5} \qquad 60\% = \tfrac{3}{5} \qquad 80\% = \tfrac{4}{5}$

Per cents with fractions can also be changed to fractions and reduced to lowest terms. For example:

$$37\tfrac{1}{2}\% = .37\tfrac{1}{2} = .375 = \tfrac{375}{1000} = \tfrac{3}{8}$$

$$4\tfrac{1}{4}\% = .04\tfrac{1}{4} = .0425 = \tfrac{425}{10000} = \tfrac{17}{400}$$

Using the method in the examples above, express each of these per cents as a common fraction in lowest terms:

16. $3\tfrac{1}{2}\%$ 18. $87\tfrac{1}{2}\%$ 20. $62\tfrac{1}{2}\%$ 22. $5\tfrac{1}{2}\%$ 24. $2\tfrac{1}{4}\%$
17. $12\tfrac{1}{2}\%$ 19. $1\tfrac{1}{4}\%$ 21. $3\tfrac{1}{4}\%$ 23. $2\tfrac{1}{2}\%$ 25. $10\tfrac{1}{2}\%$

Practice in Changing Fractions to Per Cents

Express each of these fractions as a per cent:

	A	B	C	D	E
1.	$\frac{1}{3}$	$\frac{7}{8}$	$\frac{1}{7}$	$\frac{2}{9}$	$\frac{1}{6}$
2.	$\frac{5}{16}$	$\frac{5}{9}$	$\frac{15}{16}$	$\frac{1}{12}$	$\frac{1}{8}$
3.	$\frac{7}{12}$	$\frac{1}{16}$	$\frac{5}{6}$	$\frac{1}{15}$	$\frac{11}{16}$

Some fractions are used so often that you should memorize their per cent values and be able to recognize them.

$\frac{1}{4} = 25\%$	$\frac{1}{5} = 20\%$	$\frac{1}{8} = 12\frac{1}{2}\%$	$\frac{1}{3} = 33\frac{1}{3}\%$
$\frac{1}{2} = 50\%$	$\frac{2}{5} = 40\%$	$\frac{3}{8} = 37\frac{1}{2}\%$	$\frac{2}{3} = 66\frac{2}{3}\%$
$\frac{3}{4} = 75\%$	$\frac{3}{5} = 60\%$	$\frac{5}{8} = 62\frac{1}{2}\%$	$\frac{1}{6} = 16\frac{2}{3}\%$
	$\frac{4}{5} = 80\%$	$\frac{7}{8} = 87\frac{1}{2}\%$	$\frac{5}{6} = 83\frac{1}{3}\%$

4. Tell what per cent of each figure below is colored. What per cent is not colored?

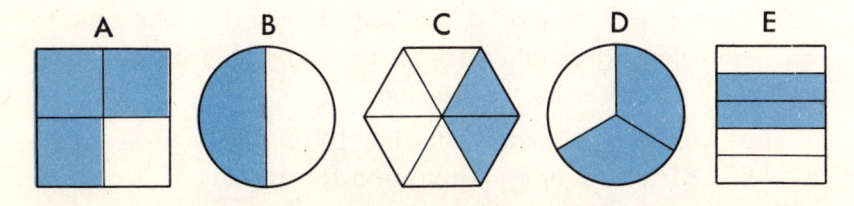

A B C D E

5. On a history test, Grace answered $\frac{2}{3}$ of the questions correctly. What per cent did she have correct?

6. If $\frac{7}{20}$ of a mixture is water, what per cent is water?

7. A gram is about $\frac{1}{25}$ of an ounce; about what per cent of an ounce is it?

8. The dry quart is about $\frac{4}{25}$ larger than the liquid quart; about what per cent larger is it?

9. If $\frac{1}{50}$ of the price of an article is added as a sales tax, then the tax is what per cent of the price?

Finding a Per Cent of a Number

A. A special kind of fuel is made up of a mixture of gasoline, alcohol, and other material. If 35% of this mixture is gasoline, how many gallons of gasoline are there in 220 gallons of the fuel mixture?

Here we change the per cent to a decimal fraction before multiplying.

$$35\% = .35$$

```
   220 gal.
      .35
   ------
    11 00
    66 0
   ------
    77.00 gal.
```

B. A nurse uses a solution that contains 25% of a certain medicine. How many ounces of this medicine are there in 48 ounces of the solution?

Here we change the per cent to a common fraction before multiplying. Why?

$$25\% = \tfrac{1}{4}$$
$$\tfrac{1}{4} \text{ of } 48 \text{ oz.} = 12 \text{ oz.}$$

To find a per cent of a number, change the per cent to an equivalent decimal fraction or common fraction; then multiply the number by the fraction.

How would you decide whether to change a per cent to a decimal fraction or to a common fraction?

Decide whether you should change the per cent to a decimal or to a common fraction; then do the examples.

1. 25% of 36 = ?
2. 15% of 340 = ?
3. 10% of 150 = ?
4. $33\tfrac{1}{3}$% of 450 = ?
5. 42% of $120 = ?
6. 75% of $200 = ?
7. 40% of $50 = ?
8. 5% of $80 = ?
9. 50% of 320 = ?
10. $12\tfrac{1}{2}$% of 480 = ?
11. 20% of 60 = ?
12. $16\tfrac{2}{3}$% of 240 = ?
13. $3\tfrac{1}{2}$% of $160 = ?
14. 88% of $45 = ?
15. 2.5% of $600 = ?
16. 80% of $350 = ?

JUNE 1951						
Sun	Mon	Tue	Wed	Thu	Fri	Sat
					1	2
3	4	5	6	7	8	9
10	11	12	13	14	15	16
17	18	19	20	21	22	23
24	25	26	27	28	29	30

JULY 1951						
Sun	Mon	Tue	Wed	Thu	Fri	Sat
1	2	3	4	5	6	7
8	9	10	11	12	13	14
15	16	17	18	19	20	21
22	23	24	25	26	27	28
29	30	31				

make this YOUR ½ FARE CALENDAR

Yes, the big SAVING days in this calendar are shaded... that's the time to take the family with you at just *half* the cost. For on those days, a full fare ticket for yourself entitles you to ½ fare tickets for your wife and all children under 22. Plan to travel the first of the week and SAVE.

Courtesy American Airlines

Using Per Cents in Everyday Activities

1. An airline folder says that the one-way fare between two cities is $19. On a round-trip ticket a discount of 5% on two one-way fares is allowed. What is the round-trip fare?

2. To all fares there must be added a 15% federal tax. **A.** What is the cost, including tax, of a one-way ticket between the cities in Problem **1**? **B.** What is the cost, including tax, of a round-trip ticket?

3. Mr. Burton took his wife and two children on a plane trip, leaving on a Tuesday to take advantage of the ½-fare plan described above. The regular one-way fare was $38.50; under this plan there is no 5% reduction for round trips, but the federal tax must be paid. How much did it cost the Burtons to make the round trip?

4. For two hotel rooms Mr. Burton paid $4.75 per day, each, plus 5% city tax. How much did they cost per day?

5. The Burtons plan to use 25% of their income for rent, 32% for food, 16% for clothing, 12% for other expenses, and 8% for savings. The rest they spend for recreation and vacations. If the family income is $4600, how much do they allow for each item?

Using Per Cents in Business

1. Rogers' Store advertised a 40% reduction on all summer sportswear. Betty wants to buy a bathing suit which was marked $3.50 before the sale. How much will she have to pay for it? How much will she save?

2. What would you pay for an electric refrigerator marked $194.50 and sold at a reduction of 10%?

3. During Christmas season, the Crown Store hired extra help to take care of the holiday rush. They increased their regular staff of 36 employees by 25%. How many additional persons were employed?

4. In November, the Crown Store's sales were $64,500. The December sales were 35% greater than the November sales. What were the December sales?

5. A merchant is allowed to deduct 2% of the amount of his bill for goods purchased if he pays the bill on or before the 10th of the month. He paid a bill of $364.50 on May 6. How much did he deduct? How much did he pay?

6. A merchant's records showed that during one month his sales amounted to $2860, and his expenses were 22% of the amount of the sales. What were his expenses?

7. A manufacturer plans to spend $7\frac{1}{2}\%$ of the amount of his previous year's sales for advertising. Last year his sales were $480,000. How much does he plan to spend for advertising this year?

Finding What Per Cent One Number Is of Another

The directions on a can of paint state that 4 pints of water should be mixed with each gallon of the prepared paste. The water added is what per cent of the mixture?

$$1 \text{ gal.} = 4 \text{ qt.} = 8 \text{ pt.}$$
The mixture = 8 pt. (paste) + 4 pt. (water) = 12 pt.
The water = $\frac{4}{12}$, or $\frac{1}{3}$ of the mixture. $\frac{1}{3} = 33\frac{1}{3}\%$

Check: $33\frac{1}{3}\%$ of 12 pt. = 4 pt.

To find what per cent one number is of another, first find what part it is; then change the part (fraction) to a per cent.

Complete, without doing the work on paper:

1. A. 2 is _?_% of 8
   B. 3 is _?_% of 10
   C. 1 is _?_% of 20
   D. 6 is _?_% of 100
   E. _?_% of 5 is 3
   F. _?_% of 15 is 15
   G. _?_% of 60 is 20
   H. _?_% of 200 is 100

2. A. 16 is _?_% of 64
   B. 12 is _?_% of 32
   C. 30 is _?_% of 150
   D. 80 is _?_% of 1000
   E. _?_% of 1000 is 350
   F. _?_% of 450 is 300
   G. _?_% of 1200 is 300
   H. _?_% of 175 is 140

3. In a class of 27 pupils, 18 are girls. What per cent are girls?

4. A club has 52 members. Only 39 have paid their dues. What per cent have paid?

5. Out of 25 games played, a chess team won 21 games. What per cent did the team win?

6. Jane had $.96, and spent $.24. What per cent of her money did she spend?

7. Herbert's older brother has performed 27 experiments in science out of a list of 45 experiments. What per cent of the entire list has he completed?

Base, Rate, and Percentage

When we say 20% of 75 is 15, the number 75 is called the **base** (whole = 100%); the number 15 is called the **percentage**; the 20 is called the **per cent**, or the **rate**.

You have just learned how to find what per cent one number is of another. This is the same as finding the rate. For example:

A. Last fall Mr. Boyle planted 40 rose bushes. Over the winter, 6 of them died. What per cent died?

$$\left. \begin{array}{l} \text{Base} = 40 \\ \text{Percentage} = 6 \end{array} \right\} \frac{6}{40} = \frac{3}{20} = 15\%, \text{ the rate}$$

B. At the same rate, how many bushes would have died if he had planted 80 bushes? 100 bushes? Do you see that 6 out of 40, or 12 out of 80, is the *same rate* as 15 out of 100, or 15%?

Solve these problems; then tell, in each case, which is the base, which is the rate, and which is the percentage.

1. On a certain stormy day, 30 pupils out of a class of 36 came to school. What per cent were present that day?

2. Mr. Packer has a farm of 150 acres, of which 105 acres can be cultivated. What per cent can be cultivated?

3. A bank loaned $500 for one year. At the end of the year, the bank received $25 interest on the $500. The interest received was what per cent of the loan?

4. In a certain town the fire department consists of both paid firemen and volunteers. If 15 out of the 75 firemen are paid, what per cent are volunteers?

5. Mrs. Moore bought a dress at a reduction of $6.25. The regular price was $18.75. Find the rate of reduction.

6. Mr. Blake raises turkeys. He started with 160 turkey chicks, but 32 died. What per cent of his chicks died?

Uneven Per Cents

In a certain city 31 out of 48 fatal automobile accidents were due to collision with pedestrians. What per cent of the fatalities were due to this cause?

$$\text{Percentage} = 31$$
$$\text{Base} = 48$$
$$\text{Rate} = \tfrac{31}{48}$$

```
        .6458+
    48)31.0000
       28 8
        2 20
        1 92
          280
          240
          400
          384
           16
```

The rate expressed as a decimal equals .6458+. Written as a per cent, this is 64.58+%. Since the remainder (16) is less than half the divisor (48), the per cent, to the nearest hundredth, is 64.58%; to the nearest tenth, the rate is 64.6%; to the nearest whole per cent, it is 65%.

1. Express each of the following as a per cent to the nearest tenth of a per cent:
 A. $\tfrac{4}{13}$ B. $\tfrac{6}{11}$ C. $\tfrac{12}{17}$ D. $\tfrac{20}{21}$ E. $\tfrac{5}{9}$ F. $\tfrac{7}{18}$

2. Express each of the following as a per cent to the nearest hundredth of a per cent:
 A. $\tfrac{7}{15}$ B. $\tfrac{2}{19}$ C. $\tfrac{4}{7}$ D. $\tfrac{2}{3}$ E. $\tfrac{9}{14}$ F. $\tfrac{3}{35}$

3. Express each of the following as a per cent. Round each to the nearest whole per cent:
 A. $\tfrac{3}{16}$ B. $\tfrac{11}{15}$ C. $\tfrac{1}{45}$ D. $\tfrac{7}{12}$ E. $\tfrac{5}{32}$ F. $\tfrac{5}{6}$

4. Fred has gained 7 pounds in weight. A year ago he weighed 85 pounds. To the nearest tenth of a per cent, his gain is what per cent of his weight a year ago?

5. A class pledged $75 for a library fund. So far they have raised $67. To the nearest tenth of a per cent, this is what per cent of the amount pledged?

Baseball Pitching Records

Per cents and averages are often used in baseball and other sports records. Here is part of a baseball pitching record for a recent season.

PLAYER	G.	W.	L.	PC.
HUTCHINSON (Detroit)	33	15	7	.682
LEMON (Cleveland)	37	22	10	.688
SPAHN (Boston)	38	21	14	.600
SCHMITZ (Chicago)	36	11	13	.458

1. Hutchinson, a Detroit pitcher, pitched in 33 games. He received credit for winning 15 games, and was charged with losing 7 games. In how many other games did Hutchinson pitch?

2. A pitcher's per cent, or "PC.," means the per cent which the number of games won is of the number of games won and lost. What is Hutchinson's PC. as given in the table? How many decimal places does this "per cent" have? Is it really a *per cent?*

3. Check the per cent in Problem **2**; that is, find it to the nearest thousandth:

$$\frac{W}{W+L} = \frac{15}{15+7} = \frac{15}{22} = ?$$

4. Check the per cent for Lemon of the Cleveland team.

5. Check the per cent for Spahn of the Boston team.

6. Check the per cent for Schmitz of the Chicago team.

Figuring Discount

To have a clearance sale, or for other reasons, a merchant often allows a **discount** on the regular price of an article.

Jean Parker bought a blouse at a discount of 40%. The original price was $6.50. How much did she pay for the blouse? How much did she save?

FIRST METHOD	SECOND METHOD
Regular price = $6.50	Original price = 100%
Per cent of discount = 40%	Per cent saved = 40%
	Per cent paid = 60%
.40 × $6.50 = $2.60, amount saved	.60 × $6.50 = $3.90, amount paid
$6.50 − $2.60 = $3.90, amount paid	$6.50 − $3.90 = $2.60, amount saved

The amount saved equals the **amount of the discount.**

The amount actually paid, called the **net price**, equals the original price less the amount of the discount.

1. At a sale of shoes the discount allowed was 25%. What was the net price of a pair of shoes regularly priced at $9? How much was saved?

2. Handkerchiefs of a certain grade regularly sell for $5 a dozen. On sale, they are advertised at $33\frac{1}{3}$% off. How much is saved when buying a dozen handkerchiefs at the sale price? In figuring discounts, one-half cent or more in the discount is counted as a whole cent.

3. Find the discount and the net price:
    A. $36; 40% discount   D. $24; 15% discount
    B. $44.50; 25% discount   E. $68.75; 20% discount
    C. $49.50; $33\frac{1}{3}$% discount   F. $132; 10% discount

Finding the Discount Rate

A. Mrs. Gordon paid $6.60 for a blanket originally priced at $8.80. What per cent of discount was she allowed?

$8.80 = Original price
6.60 = Net price
─────
$2.20 = Amount of discount

$2.20 ÷ $8.80 = .25 = 25%, the rate of discount

Check: 25% of $8.80 = $2.20, amount of discount.

B. In another shop Mrs. Gordon bought a sewing table. The regular price of the table was $35, but she saved $7 by buying it at a spring furniture sale. What was the discount rate? How much did she pay for the table?

Discount = $7
Original price = $35

$\frac{\$7}{\$35} = \frac{1}{5} = 20\%$, discount rate

$35 − $7 = $28, net price

Check: 20% of $35 = $7, amount of discount.

1. Because it was slightly damaged, a $20 camera was sold for $16. What was the rate of discount?

2. When closing out his stock of lamps and shades, a dealer sold a floor lamp for $14.40. If the regular price of the lamp was $24, what was the discount rate?

3. Mr. James saved $12 when he bought a winter coat at a spring sale. The regular price of the coat was $60. What was the discount rate?

4. The difference between the sale price and the regular price of a vacuum cleaner is $9. If the sale price is $66, what discount rate is allowed?

5. A shopkeeper offers slightly imperfect neckties at $1.50 each. If the regular price is $2.50, what is the discount rate?

Per Cent of Increase or Decrease

A. Marjorie is a salesgirl in a dress shop. Her salary now is $60 a week. When she took the position, her salary was $48 a week. What is the per cent of increase?

$$\text{Increase in salary} = \$12$$
$$\text{Original salary} = \$48$$

$$\text{Per cent of increase} = \frac{\$12}{\$48} = \frac{1}{4} = 25\%$$

B. At a sale, a $42 bicycle was sold for $37. Find, to the nearest tenth of a per cent, the decrease in price.

$$\text{Decrease in price} = \$5$$
$$\text{Original price} = \$42$$

$$\text{Per cent of decrease} = \frac{\$5}{\$42} = 11.9\%$$

To find the per cent of increase or decrease, we find what per cent of the original quantity the amount of increase or decrease is.

1. Last summer Ted worked on a farm, earning $12 a week. This summer he will be paid $15 a week. What is the per cent of increase?

2. As a holiday season approached, the sales of a gift shop rose from $1800 a month to $2400 a month. What is the per cent of increase?

3. The price of oranges increased from 49¢ to 69¢ a dozen. What was the per cent of increase, to the nearest tenth of a per cent?

4. If the price of a loaf of bread is increased from 15¢ to 17¢, what is the per cent of increase (nearest tenth)?

If any number is to be increased (or decreased) by a certain per cent, we find that per cent of the number and add it to (or subtract it from) the number.

Example: A community wishes to increase its last year's contribution to the American Red Cross by 20%. Last year its contribution was $4400; how much should be raised this year?

This year's total should equal $4400 + 20% of $4400
20% of $4400 = .20 × $4400 = $880
The required total = $4400 + $880 = $5280

5. On a certain date, a shopkeeper had 150 pairs of tennis shoes on hand. At the end of the month, his stock had decreased by 50%. How many pairs were left? Later, his original stock decreased 100%; how many were left then?

6. An advertisement stated that, because of an improvement, the sales of a certain product had increased 100%. If the sales before the improvement were $24,000, what were the sales after the improvement?

7. In one city, coal costs $15 a ton; in another city, $18 a ton. Do people in the second city pay 20% or $16\frac{2}{3}$% more than people in the first city?

8. A farmer raised 1600 bushels of corn one year and 1800 bushels the next year. Find the per cent of increase.

9. Can a per cent of decrease ever be greater than 100%?

10. The original price of a baseball suit was $13.95. If all athletic goods are raised 20% in price, what will be the new price of this suit?

Learning to Solve Problems

Understanding Per Cents in Problems

1. The price of an article has increased from $4 to $5. What is the per cent of increase?

2. A pocketknife bought for $.50 originally cost $.75. What was the per cent saved?

3. An error of one inch in a measurement of 50 inches is an error of what per cent?

4. An error of 1 centimeter in a measurement of 20 cm. is an error of what per cent?

5. The price of an article was lowered 25%. The new price is what per cent of the old price?

6. The admission price to a motion picture theatre is 60¢. The tax is 20% of the admission price. What is the amount of the tax? How much will the ticket actually cost?

7. When making a certain motion picture, 250,000 feet of film were used. In the finished picture, only 10,000 feet of this film were used. What per cent of the original film was used? What per cent was not used?

8. Last month a merchant's sales were $5000; this month they were 25% greater. What were the sales this month?

9. The total cost of a gallon of gasoline is 30¢, including a federal tax of $1\frac{1}{2}$¢, a state tax of 5¢, and a city sales tax of 2¢. **A.** Find the price of a gallon, exclusive of taxes. **B.** What per cent of the price of the gasoline alone are the combined taxes? **C.** What per cent of the total cost are the combined taxes?

10. A silver-plated candy dish originally priced at $13.50 is sold at a discount of 10%. The purchaser must pay a 20% luxury tax on the actual selling price. How much will the dish cost the purchaser?

More Than 100 Per Cent

The whole of anything is 100% of it. More than the whole is more than 100% of it.

1. Find: A. 50% of $40 B. 100% of $40 C. 150% of $40

   Do you see that:
   $$\begin{aligned} 100\% \text{ of } \$40 &= \$40 \\ 50\% \text{ of } \$40 &= 20 \\ \hline 150\% \text{ of } \$40 &= \$60 \end{aligned}$$

2. 150% of 600 = 1.50 × 600 = 1½ × 600 = ?
3. 175% of 500 = 1.75 × _?_ = ?
4. 200% of $700 = _?_ × $700 = ?
5. 250% of $200 = ?
6. A. What part of 40 is 20? What per cent of 40 is 20?
   B. What part of 40 is 40? What per cent of 40 is 40?
   C. How many times 40 is 60? What per cent of 40 is 60?
7. A. How many times 20 is 30? What per cent of 20 is 30?
   B. How many times 40 is 50? What per cent of 40 is 50?
   C. How many times 30 is 60? What per cent of 30 is 60?
   D. How many times 60 is 90? What per cent of 60 is 90?
   E. How many times 60 is 150? What per cent of 60 is 150?

   Find:
8. A. 150% of 60   C. 125% of 60   E. 133⅓% of 60
   B. 200% of 60   D. 300% of 60   F. 225% of 60
9. A. 160% of 25   C. 210% of 100 E. 250% of $200
   B. 175% of 40   D. 125% of 800 F. 320% of $400
10. Change to common fractions, whole numbers, or mixed numbers:
    A. 150%   C. 200%   E. 300%   G. 120%   I. 180%
    B. 125%   D. 250%   F. 133⅓%   H. 225%   J. 175%
11. Write as decimal mixed numbers:
    A. 120%   C. 150%   E. 275%   G. 110%   I. 165%
    B. 250%   D. 350%   F. 225%   H. 140%   J. 189%

12. Express each multiplier as a per cent:
   A. $2\frac{1}{2} \times 50$
   B. 3×72
   C. $1\frac{1}{3} \times 96$
   D. 4.5×320
   E. $2\frac{1}{4} \times 480$
   F. 1×900

13. In each of the following, the selling price is what per cent of the cost?
   A. a dress costing $7 which sells for $14
   B. a hat costing $6 which sells for $15
   C. a lamp costing $16 which sells for $24
   D. a handbag costing $10 which sells for $16
   E. a sweater costing $12 which sells for $18

14. If an article costing $8 is sold for $12, what is the amount of increase of the selling price over the cost? What is the per cent of increase? Is 50% more than $8 equal to 150% of $8?

15. If the price of a football is increased from $7.50 to $10, what is the per cent of increase? What per cent of the original price is the new price? Does this mean that the new price is $33\frac{1}{3}\%$ more than the original price?

Does $33\frac{1}{3}\%$ more than an amount mean the same as $133\frac{1}{3}\%$ of that amount? Does $\frac{1}{3}$ more mean the same as $1\frac{1}{3}$ times as much?

16. A town's population increased from 10,000 to 15,000.
   A. Is this an increase of $33\frac{1}{3}\%$, 50%, or 150%?
   B. Is the population now 50% or 150% of what it was?

17. If the cost of living is 160% of what it was at one time, it is _?_ per cent more than it was; we can also say it is now _?_ times as much as it was.

18. Rewrite each of these statements, using per cents:
   A. In the 50 years from 1900 to 1950, the population of the United States doubled.
   B. In 1900 there were one and a half times as many people living in rural areas as in urban areas.

Working for a Commission

In his spare time, Jane's uncle makes toys which Jane sells. She is allowed to keep 25% of the money she gets. One day Jane sold 8 toys at 75¢ each. What was Jane's share of the money? her uncle's share?

Total sales = 8 × $.75 = $6.00
25% of $6.00 = $\frac{1}{4}$ of $6.00 = $1.50, Jane's share
$6.00 − $1.50 = $4.50, her uncle's share

The money Jane received is called the **commission** on her sales. The amount of Jane's commission was $1.50. Her **rate of commission** was 25%. The $4.50 which was left for her uncle after the commission was deducted is called the **net proceeds**.

1. Helen sells greeting cards. She receives a commission of 25% on all sales. One holiday season her sales amounted to $38. What was her commission?

2. Last week John Henley sold $36 worth of subscriptions to magazines. His commission rate is 15%. How much was his commission?

3. The week before last, John's sales amounted to $44. How much commission did he receive? (Problem **2.**) How much did the magazine company receive?

4. A real estate agent sold Mr. White's house for $12,600. If the rate of commission for selling it was 5%, how much did the agent receive in commission?

A salesman sold $470 worth of paint in one week. His commission was $70.50. Find his rate of commission.

Here we find what per cent one number is of another. We find what per cent $70.50 is of $470.

Rate of commission = $70.50 ÷ $470 = .15 = 15%

Rate of commission = amount of commission ÷ amount of sales

5. A salesman earned $60 one week from sales amounting to $400. What rate of commission was he paid?

6. A book agent sold 20 sets of books at $13.95 a set, and received a commission of $83.70. Find his rate of commission.

7. A collection agency makes it a business to collect bills that have not been paid. For such services the agency receives a commission on the amount collected. The agency collected a bill of $640, and received $32 commission. What rate was charged?

8. The plans for a new town library called for a building costing $140,000. The architect's commission was $7000. What rate of commission did he charge?

9. Mr. Dolan works in a hardware store at a salary of $42 a week and a commission of 6% of the amount of his sales. Last week he sold $288 worth of merchandise. How much did he earn that week in all?

Keeping in Practice

1. Which is greater, $\frac{1}{9}$ or $\frac{1}{19}$? $\frac{2}{9}$ or $\frac{2}{19}$?

2. A. $1\frac{1}{2} \times 1\frac{1}{2} \times 4 = ?$ B. $4\frac{1}{2} \times 5 \div 9 = ?$

3. A. $.08\overline{)4.8}$ B. $2.1\overline{).189}$ C. $.025\overline{).75}$ D. $1.75\overline{)140}$

4. A. $.015 \times 33$ B. 2.08×25 C. $.0375 \times 800$

5. Write in Arabic numerals: CDL; MDCCCLXV.

What Is Your Reaction Time?

Here is an interesting experiment. Place your feet together. Have another person hold a pencil about 31 inches above a mark on the floor which you can reach with your foot. Without warning you, the other person drops the pencil. If you can move your foot under the pencil before it strikes the floor, your "reaction time" is about $\frac{2}{5}$ of a second.

Our minds and bodies do not respond instantly. A fraction of a second passes before we can act. This fraction of a second is called the **reaction time**. It is slightly different for different people, and it varies somewhat under different conditions. The average reaction time of motorists is about 0.75 of a second.

When a motorist tries to stop his car suddenly to avoid an accident, he thinks he applies the brakes "instantly." But during the reaction time of about $\frac{3}{4}$ of a second the car continues to move at the same speed. The diagram below shows the distance the car will travel, at different speeds, before the brakes can be applied.

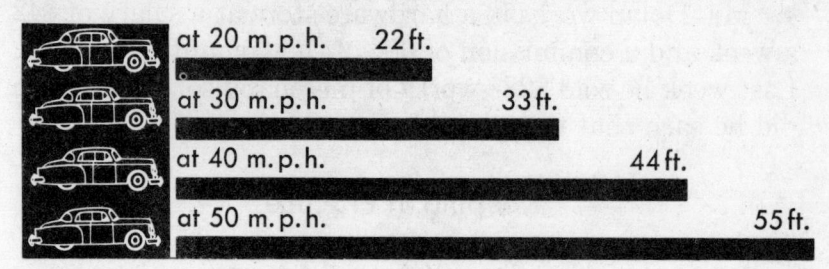

at 20 m.p.h.	22 ft.
at 30 m.p.h.	33 ft.
at 40 m.p.h.	44 ft.
at 50 m.p.h.	55 ft.

1. From the chart, tell how far a car will travel before the driver applies the brakes when traveling 20 miles per hour; 40 miles per hour; 50 miles per hour.

2. Can you tell how far a car will go before the brakes are applied when traveling 35 m.p.h.? 60 m.p.h.?

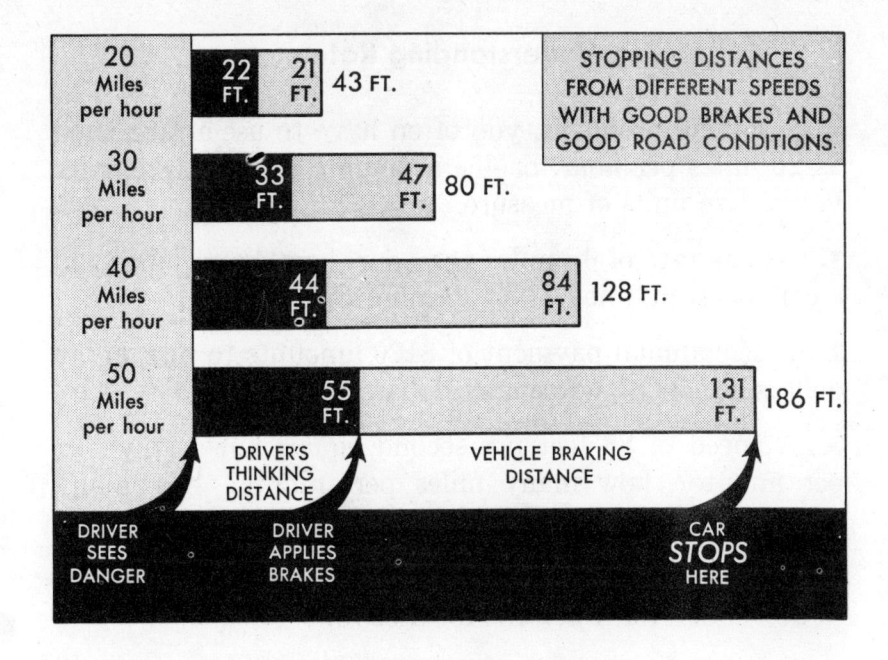

Speed	Driver's Thinking Distance	Vehicle Braking Distance	Total
20 Miles per hour	22 FT.	21 FT.	43 FT.
30 Miles per hour	33 FT.	47 FT.	80 FT.
40 Miles per hour	44 FT.	84 FT.	128 FT.
50 Miles per hour	55 FT.	131 FT.	186 FT.

STOPPING DISTANCES FROM DIFFERENT SPEEDS WITH GOOD BRAKES AND GOOD ROAD CONDITIONS

DRIVER SEES DANGER — DRIVER APPLIES BRAKES — CAR STOPS HERE

3. Study the chart above. What is the per cent of increase in the "driver's thinking distance" when the speed is increased from 20 to 30 miles per hour? when increased from 30 to 40 miles per hour? 40 to 50 miles per hour? if increased from 50 to 60 miles per hour?

4. What is the "vehicle braking distance" when the car is traveling 20 miles per hour? 40 miles per hour? If the speed is doubled, the braking distance becomes how many times as great?

5. What is the stopping distance (braking + thinking distance) at 40 miles per hour? At this speed about what part of a city block 440 feet long would a car travel before it could stop to avoid danger?

6. The braking distance becomes 9 times as great when the speed is tripled. Find the braking distance at 60 miles per hour. Find the stopping distance. How does this distance compare with the length of a football field?

Learning to Solve Problems

Understanding Rates

In solving problems, you often have to use a rate, such as 20 miles per hour, or 45¢ a pound. A rate always involves two units of measure.

1. At the rate of 45 miles per hour, how many miles will a car travel in 3 hours? in 20 minutes?

2. A semiannual payment of $120 amounts to how many dollars a month? how many dollars a year?

3. A speed of 88 feet per second equals how many feet per minute? how many miles per minute? how many miles per hour?

4. A hotel rate of $4.50 per person per day, would amount to how much for 3 persons for 2 days?

5. A quarterly payment of $35 on a loan amounts to how many dollars a year? how many dollars per week?

6. Regular weekly payments of $1.50 each will amount to how many dollars per year? how many dollars quarterly?

7. At the rate of 13¢ a quarter of a pound, how much will half a pound cost? one pound? $1\frac{1}{2}$ pounds?

8. At the rate of 48¢ a pound, how much will 8 ounces cost? 6 ounces? What is the rate per ounce?

9. Which of the following are *rates*, and which are not?
   A. 2 ft. per second
   B. 4 lb. of sugar
   C. 10 mi. per hour
   D. $3.50 a day
   E. semiannually
   F. 5 ft. wide
   G. 3% a year
   H. 95¢ a dozen
   I. 3 lb. for a quarter
   J. 16 gallons of gasoline
   K. 16 miles per gallon
   L. 4 times a year
   M. monthly payments
   N. 1 teaspoonful 3 times a day

Using Per Cents to Show Ratios

Terry's puppy weighs 24 oz., and Jim's puppy weighs 30 oz. How do the two puppies compare in weight?

Terry's puppy is $\frac{24}{30}$, or $\frac{4}{5}$ as heavy as Jim's puppy. We can also say the weight of Terry's puppy is 80% of the weight of Jim's puppy. Notice that the fraction $\frac{4}{5}$, the ratio 4:5, the decimal .8, and 80% all express the same relationship—the comparison of 24 oz. with 30 oz.

If we compare Jim's puppy with Terry's, we see that it is $\frac{5}{4}$, or $1\frac{1}{4}$ times as heavy. We can also say that the weight of Jim's puppy is 125% that of Terry's puppy; or, it is 25% heavier. The fraction $\frac{5}{4}$, the ratio 5:4, the decimal 1.25, and the 125% are simply different ways of expressing the same relationship—the comparison of 30 oz. with 24 oz.

When comparing two quantities by division, how do you know which quantity is the divisor?

1. A. 8 is __?__% of 20;   B. $\frac{1}{2}$ is __?__% of 4.
2. A. 60 is __?__% of 40;   B. A quarter is __?__% of $1.
3. A. 100 is __?__% of 50;   B. $1 is __?__% of a quarter.
4. A. 18 in. is __?__% of 2 ft.;   B. A foot is __?__% of a yard.
5. A. 20 oz. is __?__% of 2 lb.;   B. $2\frac{1}{2}$ pt. is __?__% of 1 gal.
6. A. A nickel is __?__% of a quarter;   B. of a half-dollar.
7. A. $5 is how many times $1?   B. What is the ratio of $5 to $1?   C. $5 is what per cent of $1?
8. A. What is the ratio of 500 to 200?
   B. 500 is what per cent of 200?
9. A. 200 lb. is what per cent of 160 lb.?
   B. 160 lb. is what per cent of 200 lb.?
10. What per cent of 2 lb. is 32 oz.?

Fractions of a Per Cent

You have learned that 1 per cent of something is $\frac{1}{100}$ of it.

We can also think of a part of a per cent. Just as we can think of one-half an inch or one-fourth of a yard, we can think of one-half of a per cent, or $\frac{3}{4}$ of 1%, or .25 of 1%.

We can easily picture a fraction of a per cent. The large square contains 100 small squares. Each small square is 1% of the large square.

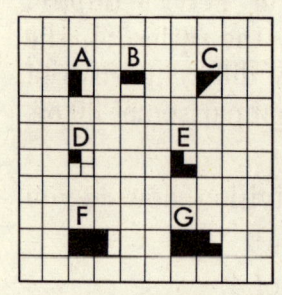

Each of the black parts A, B, and C, is $\frac{1}{2}$ of 1%; this may be written $\frac{1}{2}$%, or .5%. The black part D is $\frac{1}{4}$ of 1%; we can write this $\frac{1}{4}$%, or .25%. The black part E is $\frac{3}{4}$ of 1%, or $\frac{3}{4}$%, or .75%. The black part F is $1\frac{1}{2}$%, or 1.5%; G is $1\frac{3}{4}$%, or 1.75%.

Fractions of a per cent are frequently used in business and banking, as well as in science and engineering.

A. Every 6 months, a certain savings bank pays a depositor $1\frac{1}{4}$% of the smallest amount he has on deposit during that period. How much will the bank pay on $2000 at the end of 6 months?

$$1\% \text{ of } \$2000 = \$20$$
$$\tfrac{1}{4}\% \text{ of } \$2000 = \tfrac{1}{4} \text{ of } \$20, \text{ or } \$5$$
$$1\tfrac{1}{4}\% \text{ of } \$2000 = \$20 + \$5 = \$25$$

As you have already learned, there is another way to find the answer:

$$1\tfrac{1}{4}\% = 1.25\% = .0125$$
$$\text{Then, } 1\tfrac{1}{4}\% \text{ of } \$2000 = .0125 \times \$2000 = \$25$$

B. A chemist finds that the per cent of impurities in a substance is .12%. What is the weight of the impurities in a sample of this material which weighs 260 grams?

$$.12\% = .12 \text{ of } 1\% = .0012$$
$$.0012 \times 260 = .312 \text{ gram of impurities}$$

Find the following, using either of the methods explained in Example A on page 86.

1. .5% of 4000
2. .1% of 2500
3. $\frac{3}{10}$% of 10,000
4. $\frac{7}{8}$% of 16,000
5. .2% of $6000
6. $\frac{1}{8}$% of $12,000
7. $1\frac{1}{2}$% of $6000
8. $\frac{3}{4}$% of $20,000
9. $1\frac{3}{4}$% of $4000
10. .15% of 6000
11. $1\frac{1}{4}$% of $8000
12. .25% of 800

13. A sample of coal contains .68% sulfur. How much sulfur would there probably be in 100 pounds of this coal?

14. A surveyor measured a certain distance and found it to be 184.6 feet. If the error is .3% of the measurement, what is the error to the nearest tenth of a foot?

15. An agent receives a commission of $\frac{5}{8}$% for selling a shipment of wheat for $12,000. How much is his commission?

16. A certain kind of stainless steel contains .08% carbon. How many pounds of carbon are there in one ton of such steel?

Keeping in Practice

1. A. $26\overline{)793}$ B. $63\overline{)4138}$ C. $97\overline{)64527}$ D. $44\overline{)8608}$
2. A. $\frac{2}{3} + \frac{3}{8}$ B. $4\frac{1}{5} + 6\frac{3}{10}$ C. $\frac{3}{4} + \frac{5}{6} + \frac{1}{3}$
3. A. $.04 \times 1.05$ B. $5200 \times .006$ C. $1200 \times .08$
4. A. $.64 \div .004$ B. $0.8 \div .05$ C. $.6 \div 1.2$

Learning to Solve Problems

Checking Your Work

Checking your work is an essential part of problem solving. By now you probably realize that in solving a problem there is the "thinking" part and the "doing" part.

In the "thinking" part you try to understand what the problem tells you and what you are asked to find, and you decide what operations should be performed.

In the "doing" part you actually do the work of computing—adding, subtracting, multiplying, or dividing.

It is important to know how to check your computation. To check means to discover whether or not you have made a mistake. The examples on these pages show some of the ways to find out whether or not your work is correct.

1. Tell the most convenient way to check addition.

2. What is the simplest way to check subtraction?

One way to check multiplication is to interchange the numbers and multiply. Another way is to divide the result by either of the given numbers. For example:

	Check 1	Check 2	Check 3
49	36	49)1764	36
× 36	× 49	144	49)1764
294	324	324	147
147	144	324	294
1764	1764		294

3. Multiply 359 by 674 and check in three ways.

4. Multiply 821 by 509 and check in three ways.

5. Which of the three methods of checking multiplication do you think is the best? Why?

Division may be checked by multiplying the quotient by the divisor or by multiplying the divisor by the quotient; in either case, remember to add the remainder to the product. For example:

```
    43 R14        Check 1:   43         Check 2:   26
26)1132                      26                    43
   104                      258                    78
    92                       86                   104
    78                     1118                  1118
    14                       14                    14
                           1132                  1132
```

6. Divide 8495 by 28 and check in two ways.

7. Divide 2316 by 195 and check in two ways.

In some of the examples below, the answers are incorrect; check to find the mistakes:

	A	B	C	D
8.	28	3004	$17.50	$216.55
	305	269	4.29	44.10
	692	1828	2.98	100.00
	84	750	2.75	83.72
	580	144	18.95	9.85
	1725	3090	47.50	216.75
	633	516	3.19	11.21
	4027	9601	$87.16	$682.18
9.	39,640	417,500	$28,750	$806,491
	− 29,828	− 206,932	− 19,810	− 94,327
	9,812	211,668	$ 8,940	$812,174
10.	62	405	625	382
	× 54	× 27	× 109	× 650
	3248	8415	68,125	248,300
11.	21R27	41	10R10	31R40
	33)720	16)701	49)600	81)2515

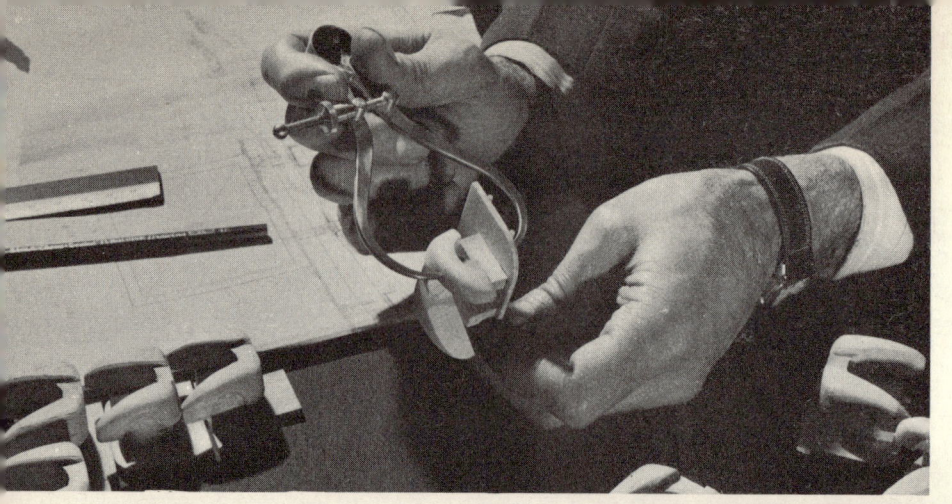

Courtesy Ford News Bureau

In a machine shop, scale models must be carefully measured for per cent of error

Using Per Cents in Industry

1. In a machine part 2.500 inches long, a tolerance of 1% is allowed in the length. This means that the length of an acceptable piece cannot differ from 2.500 inches by more than 1% of 2.500 inches either way. What is the longest acceptable piece? the shortest acceptable piece?

2. Vanadium steel, used in making tools, is a very strong steel; it contains 0.3% vanadium. How many pounds of vanadium are there in one ton of this steel?

3. Cement used for concrete contains 64% lime, 22% silica, 7% alumina, and 5% magnesia. What per cent of other materials does it contain? How many pounds of lime are there in 500 lb. of cement?

4. Type metal used in printing sometimes consists of 10% tin, 30% antimony, and 60% lead. How many pounds of each are needed to make 480 pounds of type metal?

5. An electric motor has an efficiency of 86%. This means that only 86% of the power that it receives can do useful work. If the motor receives 150 horsepower, how many horsepower will it furnish?

Per Cents in the News

1. A news article stated that the urban population of the United States had increased about 39% in the twenty years from 1930 to 1950. If the urban population was about 69,000,000 in 1930, about what was it in 1950?

2. Newspaper headlines told of a 20% increase in the number of crimes of a certain kind in one of the larger cities. In the previous year there had been 170 such crimes. What was the increase?

3. The total value of exports from the United States in a recent year was $12,613,000,000. The exports to Europe were 34% of this total. What was the value of European exports?

4. A trade journal reported an increase of $12\frac{1}{2}$% in the wage rate of all workers in a certain industry. What is the daily increase in the wages of a worker who had been getting $12 a day? What is the new hourly wage rate of a worker who had been getting $1.80 an hour?

Finding the Whole When Only a Part of It Is Known

A. John and his friends were playing a number game. John said, "One-third of a number is 28; what is the number?"

$\frac{1}{3}$ of the number = 28
All of the number = $\frac{3}{3}$ of it
But $\frac{3}{3}$ = 3 × $\frac{1}{3}$
Then $\frac{3}{3}$ of the number = 3 × 28 = 84

B. Helen said, "Three-fourths of all my books equals 36. How many books do I have?"

$\frac{3}{4}$ of Helen's books = 36
But $\frac{1}{4}$ = $\frac{1}{3}$ of $\frac{3}{4}$ (Explain.)
So $\frac{1}{4}$ of Helen's books = $\frac{1}{3}$ of 36 = 12
And, since $\frac{4}{4}$ = 4 × $\frac{1}{4}$,
$\frac{4}{4}$ of Helen's books = 4 × 12 = 48

C. Jane said, "Three small pies cost 36¢; how much will 4 pies cost?"

Problem **C** is very much like Problem **B**. Here are both problems worked out side by side:

cost of 3 pies = 36¢	$\frac{3}{4}$ of the books = 36
cost of 1 pie = $\frac{1}{3}$ of 36¢ = 12¢	$\frac{1}{4}$ of the books = $\frac{1}{3}$ of 36 = 12
cost of 4 pies = 4 × 12¢ = 48¢	$\frac{4}{4}$ of the books = 4 × 12 = 48

Find the total number in each case:

1. $\frac{2}{3}$ of my money = $12; all of it = __?__.
2. $\frac{3}{4}$ of my pictures = 27; all of them = __?__.
3. $\frac{3}{8}$ of my fishing hooks = 15; all of them = __?__.
4. $\frac{4}{5}$ of my stamps = 112; all of them = __?__.
5. $\frac{5}{6}$ of a number = 35; the whole number = __?__.
6. $\frac{5}{8}$ of a number = 75; the whole number = __?__.

Finding the Base, or 100%

When we know a part of something, we can express that part as a per cent.

Henry's share of the cost of an outing is 40%; if his share is $3.20, what is the entire cost of the outing?

$$40\% = \tfrac{2}{5}$$
$\tfrac{2}{5}$ of the entire cost = $3.20
$\tfrac{1}{5}$ of the entire cost = $\tfrac{1}{2}$ of $3.20 = $1.60
$\tfrac{5}{5}$ of the entire cost = 5 × $1.60 = $8

1. Complete the following:
    A. 30 is 60% of ?
    B. 15 is $37\tfrac{1}{2}$% of ?
    C. 100 is 80% of ?
    D. $700 = $87\tfrac{1}{2}$% of ?
    E. $140 = $66\tfrac{2}{3}$% of ?
    F. $54 = 75% of ?

Here is another way to find the base, or 100%.

Doris read this sign in a shop window: "Belts on sale at 15% less than regular prices." She paid $1.70 for the belt she bought. What was the regular price?

15% of the regular price = the amount deducted
85% of the regular price = $1.70
1% of the regular price = $1.70 ÷ 85 = $.02
100% of the regular price = 100 × $.02 = $2

Check: 85% of $2 = $1.70, price paid
15% of $2 = $ .30, reduction
$2.00, regular price

2. Complete the following:
    A. 24 is 8% of ?
    B. 12 is 40% of ?
    C. 2% of ? = 20
    D. 15% of ? = 90
    E. 12% of ? = $360
    F. 5% of ? = $20
    G. $18 = 30% of ?
    H. $720 = 90% of ?

Finding the Whole Amount

Problems in finding the whole amount, or the base, do not occur very often. It is easy to see why. In order to know how much a certain part of the whole is, we must first know what the whole amount is. But if we already know the whole amount, we do not have to find it.

However, in business, it is sometimes necessary to find the whole, or 100%. The problems on this page are similar to those that may arise in business.

1. On a certain article a merchant's profit was $1.80, or 15% of the selling price. What was the selling price?

2. The Star Sports Shop is selling all its stock at a reduction of 40%. What was the regular price of a tennis racket now selling for $3.60?

3. Two businessmen are partners. One receives 35% of the profit. In one year, his share of the profit was $7000. What was the entire profit that year?

4. A scatter rug, on sale for 60% of its original price, was sold for $15. Find the original price.

5. In a sportswear shop the goods are priced so that the profit is 16% of the amount of the sales. What must be the amount of the sales if a profit of $80,000 is expected?

6. A woman bought a dress at "$33\frac{1}{3}$% off," which means that she paid only $66\frac{2}{3}$% of the regular price. If she paid $13.30 for the dress, what was the original price?

7. A manufacturer of art supplies spent $3000 for advertising during a certain period. If this was 25% of his expenses, what was the total of his expenses?

8. Mr. Brooks owns 30% of a business. If his share amounts to $9600, what is the total value of the business?

Practical Problems in Per Cents

1. A salesman received a commission of $600 for selling $4800 worth of goods. What was his rate of commission?

2. A restaurant increased the price of its regular $1.50 dinner to $1.75. What was the rate of increase?

3. A round-trip plane fare is $172.30, plus tax. If the tax is 15%, what is the total cost?

4. Within a few years, the price of a magazine increased from 5¢ to 15¢ per copy. What was the per cent of increase?

5. The cost of the yearly subscription to this magazine rose from $1.50 to $6; find the per cent of increase.

6. A clerk's salary was increased from $2000 to $2800 during a period in which the cost of living increased 65%. By what amount should his salary have increased for the per cent increase in salary to be the same as the per cent increase in the cost of living?

7. In buying a certain house, the purchaser was required to pay 25% of the purchase price in cash. The amount of cash paid was $3975. What was the purchase price of the house?

8. At the end of the first year, an automobile has depreciated $33\tfrac{1}{3}\%$ in value. If it cost $2295 when new, what is it worth when it is one year old?

JIFFY QUIZ

1. Round to the nearest dollar: $189.49.
2. How much is 200% of $100?
3. Add horizontally: $4.95 + $10.04 + $5.98.
4. How many pints are there in half of half a gallon?
5. Which is greater: 0.3 or .28? $\tfrac{5}{8}$ or .6?

Learning from Graphs

You know that graphs are a useful way of showing numerical facts. Sometimes it is possible to use different kinds of graphs to show the same facts. For example, the three graphs on this page show the same facts. They all tell what happens to the wood that is cut each year from our forests. Can you tell why the first graph is called a divided bar graph?

| 43% Made into Useful Products | 35% Waste | 22% Used for Fuel |

←————————— 100% —————————→

1. What facts does this divided bar graph tell you?

Sometimes a picture graph, or **pictograph,** helps us to see numerical facts easily and quickly. Notice that the picture graph below shows the same facts as the bar graph above, but in a different way. Read the pictograph and compare it with the bar graph.

Made into Useful Products	🌲🌲🌲🌲🌲🌲🌲🌲🌲🌲🌲🌲🌲🌲🌲🌲🌲🌲🌲🌲½
Waste	🌲🌲🌲🌲🌲🌲🌲🌲🌲🌲🌲🌲🌲🌲🌲🌲½
Used for Fuel	🌲🌲🌲🌲🌲🌲🌲🌲🌲🌲🌲

EACH TREE REPRESENTS 2% OF ALL WOOD CUT

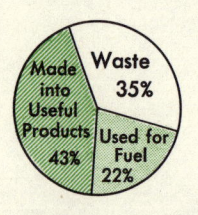

Another kind of graph which is used to show comparisons of numerical facts is the **circle graph.** Notice that again the same facts are shown, but in still a different way.

2. Which of these three graphs do you think show the facts most readily? The total of all per cents shown in a circle graph or a divided bar graph must equal what per cent?

3. The graph below shows the per cent of land area used for growing crops in each of seven countries. Can you tell why this graph is called a **horizontal bar graph?**

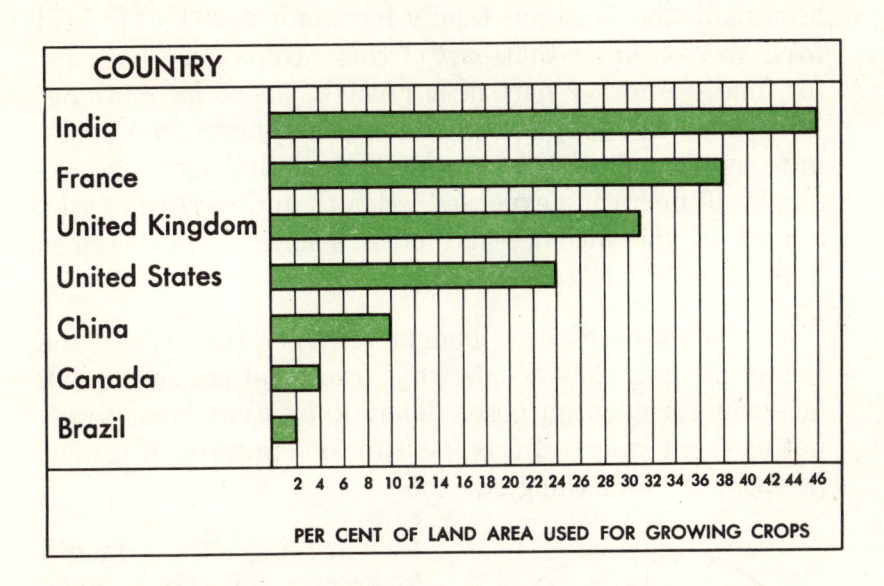

COUNTRY	
India	
France	
United Kingdom	
United States	
China	
Canada	
Brazil	

2 4 6 8 10 12 14 16 18 20 22 24 26 28 30 32 34 36 38 40 42 44 46

PER CENT OF LAND AREA USED FOR GROWING CROPS

4. What does the horizontal scale show? What does each division on the horizontal scale represent?

5. Does the graph show the number of acres used for growing crops in each of the countries?

6. Tell what per cent of land area in each of the countries is used for growing crops.

7. Notice that the United Kingdom, a very small country, has a higher per cent than the United States, a large country. Does this mean that the United Kingdom has more cultivated land than the United States? Explain your answer.

8. Could a circle graph or a divided bar graph be used to show the information given in the horizontal bar graph above? Why or why not?

Budgets and Per Cents

After federal income and social security taxes have been paid, the Weston's family income is $4200. Mr. and Mrs. Weston know that part of this income must be spent for food. Another part of it must be spent for clothing. They must live somewhere, so rent, or charges on a home, must come out of this income. Heat and light are examples of operating expenses. Health and recreation take a part of the income, and both insurance and savings must come out of their income.

The Westons make a budget. Before they spend the family income, they decide what fractional part of it shall be spent for each purpose. They know that money cannot be spent twice—if it is spent for one purpose, it cannot be spent for something else too.

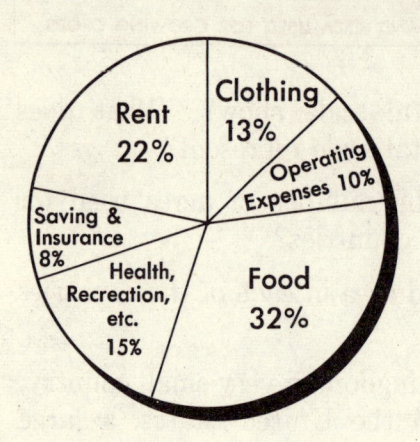

1. They pay $77 a month for rent. This is a *fixed charge,* which means that they must allow $77 every month for this purpose, no matter how they divide the rest of their income. How much rent do they pay in one year? What per cent of their yearly income is spent for rent?

2. When they divide the rest of their income in planning the budget, they use per cents instead of fractions. What per cent is their entire income? If 22% of their income is required for rent, what per cent can they allow for all other purposes? What amount can they spend each year for all other purposes?

3. They divide their total income as shown by the circle graph on page 98, allowing 32% of their yearly income for food. How much can they spend for food each month?

4. If in one year the Westons spend $595 for clothing, by how much do they go beyond their allowance for clothing?

5. The item called "health and recreation" includes education, vacation, camp, Scouts, movies, doctor, and dentist. How much have the Westons allowed for all these items for the entire year? If they expect to pay $78 for hospitalization and dental care, how much remains?

6. How much do they plan to allow for savings and insurance? If they pay $94.50 a year for life insurance, how much is left in this item of the budget?

7. Mr. Weston estimates that coal, gas, and electricity will cost $265. How much is left for other operating expenses?

8. Name some other items that might be included under the heading "Operating Expenses." When people operate their homes on budgets, they are not likely to spend too much for luxuries or to neglect necessities. They are not tempted to spend too much today while not planning enough for tomorrow.

Keeping in Practice

1. A. 105% of $1000 = ?   B. 200% of $75 = ?

2. A. $\frac{1}{2}$% of $500 = ?   B. $\frac{1}{10}$ of 1% of $2450 = ?

3. What per cent of 20 is 8? What per cent of 8 is 20?

4. When the rate of interest on savings bank deposits is increased from $1\frac{1}{2}$% to 2%, what is the per cent of increase?

5. If 75% of a number is 72, what is the whole number?

Learning to Solve Problems

Understanding Terms

In solving problems, it is important to know what certain words and special terms mean. These exercises will check your understanding of some of these terms.

1. The *discount* means: A. the original amount; B. the reduced amount; C. the amount of the reduction; D. any amount.

2. *Rate of commission* refers to: A. the discount at which goods are sold; B. the per cent of the amount of the sales which is paid to the salesman; C. the total amount of goods sold; D. the net proceeds from sales.

3. The *regular price* refers to: A. the price before reduction; B. the price after reduction; C. the rate of reduction; D. the amount of the reduction.

4. The *base* refers to: A. the whole amount; B. the larger part; C. the smaller part; D. the per cent.

5. The terms, *net proceeds*, refers to: A. the amount of the commission; B. the rate of commission; C. the amount before the commission is deducted; D. the amount after the commission and other expenses have been deducted.

Complete the following:

6. A dress that has been reduced 40% is bought for $12.
   A. original price = ?   C. net price = ?
   B. amount saved = ?   D. amount of reduction = ?

7. Smith's share of a trip costing $400 is 25%.
   A. the rate = ?   C. the base = ?
   B. the per cent = ?   D. the percentage = ?

8. Hobson received a commission of 15% for selling $2000 worth of goods.
   A. amount of commission = ?   C. the rate = ?
   B. the net proceeds = ?   D. the base = ?

Understanding Per Cents

1. Write these per cents as decimals:
   35%   4%   2½%   92.8%   .5%   10%

2. Write these decimals as per cents:
   .68   .02   .20   .8   1.5   .015   .15

3. Write these fractions as per cents:
   $\frac{95}{100}$ $\frac{30}{100}$ $\frac{4\frac{1}{2}}{100}$ $\frac{1}{100}$ $\frac{37\frac{1}{2}}{100}$ $\frac{1\frac{1}{4}}{100}$

4. Write these fractions as per cents:
   $\frac{3}{4}$ $\frac{7}{8}$ $\frac{2}{10}$ $\frac{4}{5}$ $\frac{5}{20}$ $\frac{2}{3}$ $\frac{1}{8}$ $\frac{9}{20}$

5. Write these per cents as decimals:
   7.5%   .75%   75%   175%   1.75%   17.5%

6. Write these decimals as per cents:
   .045   .0625   .125   .01   .0015   .005

7. Find what per cent the first number is of the second:
   A. 14, 28   C. 30, 45   E. 12, 18   G. $48, $60
   B. 16, 4   D. 70, 100   F. 18, 12   H. $3.20, $8

8. A cent is _?_% of a nickel. A nickel is _?_% of a dime. A nickel is _?_% of a cent.

9. Which is the higher per cent of games won: 16 out of 20, or 18 out of 25?

10. A. 1 qt. is _?_% of 1 gal.   C. 1½ ft. are _?_% of 1 yd.
    B. 4 oz. are _?_% of 1½ lb.   D. 1 pt. is _?_% of 1 gal.

11. An increase from $4 to $6 is an increase of _?_%.

12. A decrease from $6 to $4 is a decrease of _?_%.

13. Which is larger, 30% or $\frac{1}{3}$? 0.33 or 0.3?

14. An increase of 50 to 150 is an increase of (100%, 200%, 300%).

15. A. 225 is how many times 75?
    B. 225 is what per cent of 75?

Using Per Cents

Complete the following:

1. To find a certain per cent of a quantity, we change the per cent to a __?__ or a __?__ and then multiply.

2. To find what per cent one number is of another, we __?__ the first number by the second, round the quotient to the nearest hundredth, and then use the __?__ sign instead of the decimal point.

3. The sum of all the parts of a whole equals __?__ per cent.

4. John has $30 and Henry has $40. To compare the amount John has with the amount Henry has, we can ask:
  A. John has how much less money than Henry?
  B. John's money is what part of Henry's money?
  C. What is the ratio of John's money to Henry's money?
  D. John's money is what per cent of Henry's money?
  E. John has what per cent less money than Henry?

5. In Problem **4**, we can compare the amount Henry has with the amount John has by asking:
  A. Henry has how much more money than John?
  B. Henry has how many times as much as John?
  C. What is the ratio of Henry's money to John's money?
  D. Henry's money is what per cent of John's money?
  E. Henry has what per cent more money than John?

6. The price of a bag of candy is raised from 15¢ to 20¢:
  A. This is an increase of what per cent?
  B. The old price is what per cent of the new price?
  C. The new price is what per cent of the old price?

7. An interest rate is reduced from 6% to 3%:
  A. This is a reduction of what per cent?
  B. The old rate is what per cent of the new rate?
  C. The new rate is what per cent of the old rate?

Learning to Solve Problems

Thinking in Per Cents

1. One tenth of one per cent is equal to: $\frac{1}{100}$, 0.1, .001, .9.

2. If there is a sales tax of 2%, how many cents must be paid as tax on every dollar purchase?

3. One "part" may mean one cup, or one ounce, or one pound. If one part means one cup, then "2 parts" means 2 cups. A recipe calls for 1 part sugar and 3 parts flour. What per cent of this mixture is flour?

4. Three parts of every 25 parts equal what per cent?

5. If 50% of a certain amount is $40, what is the entire amount?

6. Which is greater: $\frac{1}{8}$ of a quantity or 10% of it?

7. A mixture contains 20% lemon juice; the rest of the mixture is water. How many pints of water will there be in 10 pints of this mixture?

8. Does 25% of a quantity mean the same as 25% less than that quantity?

9. If a person saves $2 out of every $20 he earns, what per cent of his income does he save?

10. An error of one foot in a measurement of 200 feet is an error of what per cent?

11. If a quantity is decreased by 50%, it becomes what part of the original amount: $\frac{1}{5}$, $\frac{1}{50}$, .05, .5?

12. If a quantity is decreased by 25%, it becomes what part of the original amount: $\frac{1}{25}$, $\frac{24}{25}$, $\frac{3}{4}$, $\frac{1}{4}$?

13. A family spends $40 a month for rent. This is 20% of its monthly income. Find the monthly income.

14. Which is the higher score: 6 out of 20 or 9 out of 27?

15. If one quantity is 200% of another, the first quantity is how many times as great as the second: 100, 200, 2, 1?

~ 103 ~

JUST FOR FUN

1. A gardener has a circular flower bed. The distance around the bed is 100 ft. If he puts stakes around the edge every 5 feet, how many stakes will he need?

2. If it takes a minute to make each cut, how long will it take to cut a 12-foot board into 12 equal pieces?

3. How much is $9 \times 8 \times 7 \times 6 \times 5 \times 4 \times 3 \times 2 \times 1 \times 0$?

4. How many $\frac{1}{2}$-inch cubes will fit into a hollow cube one inch on an edge?

5. John has $50 in the bank. He withdraws it as shown at the right. Can you explain where the extra dollar comes from?

$20, leaving	$30
15, leaving	15
9, leaving	6
6, leaving	0
$50	$51

Keeping in Practice

	A	B	C
1.	$4.6 \times 28.5 = ?$	$8\frac{3}{4} - 5\frac{7}{8} = ?$	$7.2 \div .08 = ?$
2.	$3\frac{1}{7} \times 6\frac{1}{2} = ?$	$\$4200 - \$38.85 = ?$	$5\frac{2}{3} + 8\frac{5}{6} = ?$
3.	$\$236.40 \div 12 = ?$	$63\overline{)4000}$	$8.00 - .29 = ?$
4.	$\frac{5}{8} = \underline{\ ?\ }\%$	$150 = 200\%$ of ?	$\frac{3}{10}\%$ of $\$50,000 = ?$
5.	$25 = \underline{\ ?\ }\%$ of 125	$3.2 = 10\%$ of ?	50 is $\underline{\ ?\ }\%$ of 40
6.	$1 = \underline{\ ?\ }\%$ of 200	1% of $200 = ?$	$.02 = \underline{\ ?\ }\%$
7.	$300 \times 1.5 = ?$	$.004\overline{).128}$	$.061 \times .4 = ?$
8.	50% of $\$160 = ?$	5% of $\$160 = ?$	$\frac{1}{2}\%$ of $\$160 = ?$

Making Sure of Per Cents

Turn to the pages indicated if you need any help.

1. Express as per cents:
   A. .015   B. .003   C. .0225   D. .001   E. .0075   62

2. A. 28% of $2 = ?   D. 60% of $30 = ?   63, 64, 65, 66
   B. 75% of $10 = ?   E. $3\frac{1}{2}$% of $3000 = ?
   C. $1\frac{1}{2}$% of $10,000 = ?   F. 15% of $2000 = ?

3. A. 8 is _?_ % of 20   C. 50 is _?_ % of 50   69
   B. 50 is _?_ % of 1   D. 9 is _?_ % of 200

4. Find 20% of: $50, $200, 25 in., 35 min., 36 oz.   66

5. Express to the nearest whole per cent: 71
   A. $\frac{5}{18}$ B. $\frac{20}{41}$ C. $\frac{7}{32}$ D. $\frac{5}{14}$ E. $\frac{5}{7}$

6. A. 125% of 80 = ?   C. 120% of $250 = ?   78
   B. 300% of 15 = ?   D. 250% of $200 = ?

7. A. An increase from 21¢ to 24¢ is what per cent increase?   75
   B. A decrease from $250 to $235 is what per cent decrease?

8. Complete the following: 75, 76
   A. Regular price, $5; per cent of increase, 20%; new price, _?_.
   B. Regular price, $75; per cent of decrease, 15%; new price, _?_.

9. A. $\frac{1}{2}$% of $5000 = ?   C. .25% of $160 = ?   86, 87
   B. $\frac{3}{4}$% of $12,000 = ?   D. $1\frac{1}{4}$% of $2750 = ?

10. A. 20% of _?_ = 12   C. 75% of _?_ = 48   93
    B. 25% of _?_ = 13   D. 80% of _?_ = 44

11. A. 120% of $50 is _?_ per cent more than $50.   78, 79
       120% of $50 is _?_ times as much as $50.
    B. 200% of $8 is _?_ per cent more than $8.
       200% of $8 is _?_ times as much as $8.

3

MONEY AND INTEREST

Where Does the Money Go?

This graph shows the way in which many American families spend their money, that is, their net incomes after federal income taxes have been paid.

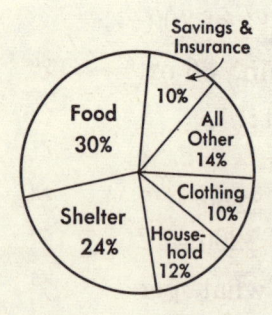

1. The Hendersons spend 30% of their net annual income of $3900 for food, including meals eaten out. How much do they spend a year for food? how much per month?

2. "All other" on the graph includes recreation, car, medical costs, and taxes other than federal income tax. The Hendersons spend $260 a year to run their car. What per cent of their income is this?

3. The Hendersons spend 5% of their net income for recreation. How much is this a year? What per cent of their income is left for medical expenses, recreation, and taxes other than federal income tax?

4. According to the graph, how much do the Hendersons spend a year for rent (shelter)? how much per month?

Using a Family Budget

To spend wisely, which is the secret of thrift, many families budget their incomes. A budget is usually planned for a year and, of course, budgets vary according to the income and family needs.

The per cents given below are based on net income after federal income tax and social security tax have been paid. In solving the problems use this table.

TYPICAL BUDGETS FOR SMALL FAMILIES

ANNUAL INCOME AFTER TAXES	RENT	FOOD	CLOTHING	HOUSEHOLD EXPENSES	SAVINGS	OTHER EXPENSES
$2000-$2999	25%	33%	10%	10%	10%	12%
$3000-$3999	24%	30%	10%	12%	10%	14%
$4000-$4999	22%	28%	12%	12%	12%	14%
$5000-$5999	20%	25%	12%	15%	12%	16%

1. A family's net annual income is $3500. On the basis of the above table, how much rent would they pay per month?

2. A mechanic receives $80 a week take-home pay. Allowing 52 weeks to the year, how much would he spend in a year on clothing for his family? on household expenses?

3. Mr. Tracy's net salary is $350 a month. What would he be able to save in a year?

4. Mr. Foster's net annual income is $3500, and his wife's net salary is $2400 a year. How much a month can they pay for rent? How much would they save in a year?

5. In a family of three, if the net yearly income is $4400, what amount would be allowed for food per month? what amount per month per person for food? What would they plan to save in a year?

6. Make a budget for the Billings family, whose net annual income is $2496, showing the monthly allowance for each of the items in the table.

7. A popular "rule of thumb" says that about one week's salary or income may be allowed for one month's rent. The Thompson family, whose net annual income is $3600, pays $75 a month for rent. Considering a month as $4\frac{1}{3}$ weeks, do the Thompsons follow this rule of thumb?

8. The Hale family has an annual income of $4500 after income tax and social security tax have been paid. What amount would they allow per month for each of the items in the table?

9. Household furnishings must be replaced from time to time. A budget should set aside definite amounts towards replacements and new purchases. Linens, for example, generally last about $4\frac{1}{2}$ years. If a family requires an average of $180 worth of linen every $4\frac{1}{2}$ years, how much should be allowed each year for replacements?

10. The budget item "savings" usually includes savings bank deposits, bond purchases, part of the cost of insurance, and part of the cost of payments on a house. Mr. Fay earns $325 a month, net; each month he buys a savings bond for $18.75. How much does he save in a year in bonds? If he budgets 10% of his income for savings, how much can he set aside for other savings in a year?

11. If a man's net weekly pay is increased from $66 to $72, and he continues to allow 10% for savings, how much more will he save in a year?

12. Last year the Hanson family's net income was $3480. They spent $1043 for food during that year and $462 for clothing. **A.** To the nearest whole per cent, what per cent of their net income was spent for each of the two items? **B.** Do these per cents agree with the allowances for these items in the table?

The Meaning of Thrift

1. Small day-by-day savings amount to considerable sums over a period of time. If a housewife saves an average of 30¢ a day on food by careful marketing, how much will be saved in this way in a year?

Dividing the pie (family income)

2. Thrifty people often save money by taking advantage of sales. If linens are offered on sale at 30% off, how much can Mrs. Daly save on linens originally priced at $60?

3. Mrs. Henley's day-by-day savings made it possible for her to take advantage of a sale on housewares. She bought an electric toaster at $\frac{1}{3}$ off; the regular price was $18.95. What did she save, to the nearest cent?

4. A person who owns an automobile frequently provides only for the cost of operating the car, and neglects to set aside enough money to buy a new car when the old one wears out. If the car is kept for 6 years, how much, on the average, must be set aside yearly to replace a car costing $2150 when new, allowing a "trade in" value of $350?

5. It costs Mr. Spencer $265 to operate his car in a certain year. He sets aside $325 toward replacement of the car. If his income is $4800, what per cent of his income is required to own and operate the car? How much does he have left for "other expenses" if he follows the budget shown on page 107? Do you think he spends more money on his car than he can afford to spend?

What Money Is

The business life of the modern world could not exist if money had not been invented. Money is used to pay for goods and services, as well as to express the value of these things.

Money was not used in very early times, and even today, in certain underdeveloped areas of the world, money is not used. The people of these areas seldom, or never, see money. Instead, commodities (goods) are exchanged for other commodities. This kind of trading is known as barter.

When people learned how to make coins, they were ready to develop a money system. You can easily see that buying and selling with money is much more convenient than barter.

Modern money includes bank notes, or paper money, as well as coins. Money in these forms is known as **cash**; or, because it circulates—is passed from hand to hand to pay for goods and services—it is often called **currency**.

In place of actual currency, in transacting business and even in settling small accounts, bank checks and drafts are used; these are called **credit instruments**. About 90% of all business carried on in the United States today is transacted with credit instruments instead of actual cash.

What Banks Do

Modern business and many everyday activities could not be carried on without banks.

1. Banks pay interest on savings accounts.
2. Banks hold money until wanted.
3. Banks provide checking account service.
4. Banks lend money.
5. Banks rent safe deposit boxes for storing valuables.

Banks also sell travelers checks, conduct Christmas Clubs, and issue credit instruments.

When money is deposited in a bank, a deposit slip such as the one shown here must be filled out.

ACCT. NO. 47,430 DEPOSITED BY		
NAME *William Kingston*		
ADDRESS 235 East 22 St.		
IN **Union Savings Bank** NEW YORK 3, N.Y.		
DATE *January 3, 1952*		
PLEASE LIST CHECKS SEPARATELY	DOLLARS	CENTS
BILLS	145	—
COIN	13	—
CHECKS	8	90
	20	—
	4	25
TOTAL	191	15

Fill out deposit slips for the following, using today's date; find the total in each case:

1. Mr. A. B. Klein; checks, $2.50, $4.75, $12.65, $7.90.

2. Dover Meat Market, Inc.; bills, $120; coin, $32; checks, $10.52, $8.77, $12.38.

3. Jane Harper; checks, $275.49, $25, $4.98, $12.90.

4. Donahue Brothers; bills, $65; coin, $15; checks, $5, $4.50, $10, $6.75.

Using Bank Checks

Businessmen, as well as others, pay most of their bills with checks. Usually salaries are paid with checks instead of coins and bills. Checks are useful when it is necessary to send money by mail; instead of sending cash, the money may be transferred safely by using checks.

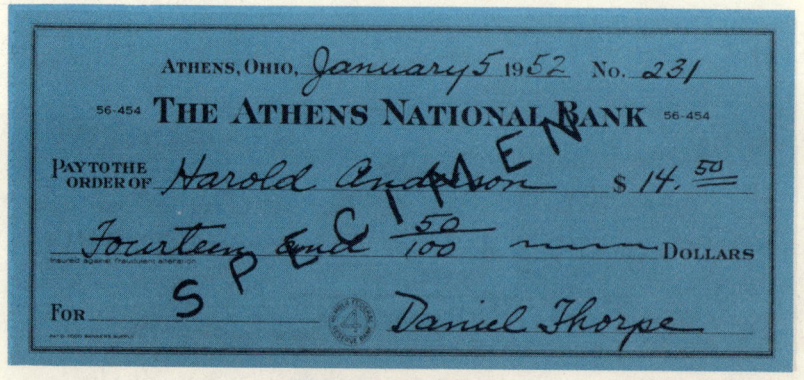

Courtesy Athens National Bank, © Ewing Galloway

Examine this check. You see that:

1. The person to whom the money is to be paid is Harold Anderson; he is called the **payee**.

2. The person who is paying the money is Daniel Thorpe; he is the **maker,** and signs the check.

3. The **amount** to be paid is $14.50.

4. The check is "drawn on" the Athens National Bank, which acts as agent in transmitting the money.

Athens National Bank, © Ewing Galloway

5. The **date** on which the check was written is January 5.

6. Before Mr. Anderson can cash the check, he must write his name on the reverse side of the check. This is called **endorsing** the check. A check is worthless until it has been endorsed.

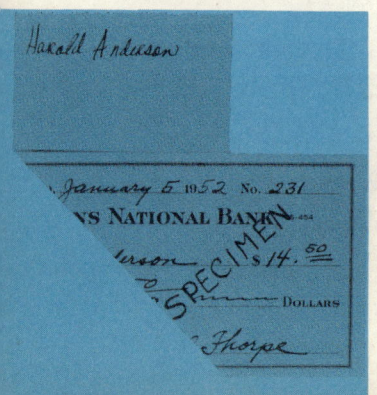

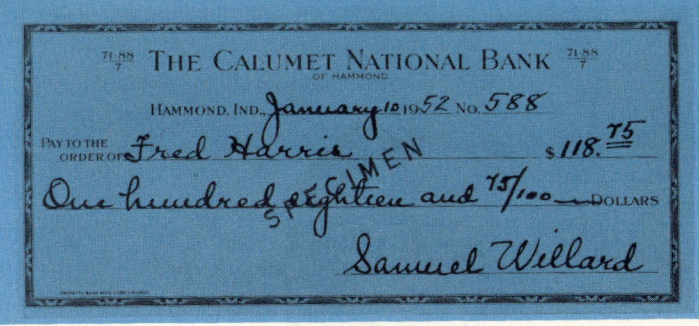

Courtesy Calumet National Bank, © *Ewing Galloway*

1. Who is the maker of this check?
2. On what bank is the check drawn?
3. When was the check drawn?
4. To whom is the money to be paid?
5. What is the amount of money to be paid?
6. Who is the payee?
7. Who must endorse the check?

THINGS TO REMEMBER WHEN WRITING A CHECK

1. Always write a check in ink.
2. Always write the figures close to the dollar sign.
3. Always write the number of dollars in words beginning at the extreme left.
4. Be sure that the amount stated in words agrees with the amount shown in figures.
5. Always date a check properly.
6. Never erase or scratch out anything.

Keeping in Practice

1. 600 increased by 25% is (625, 600.25, 750).
2. 20% less than 50 is (30, 40, 45, 10).
3. 120 is 75% of (90, 160, 360).
4. 150% of 400 equals (60, 6000, 550, 600).
5. Write in Arabic numerals: MMLII; MCMXIV.

Postal Money Orders

Miss Baldwin wishes to pay for some shrubs she bought from a nursery in Painesville, Ohio. She lives in Chicago, and must send the money by mail. Since she does not have a checking account, and it is not safe to send coins or bills in the mails, she decides to send a **postal money order.**

To purchase the money order from the post office, she fills out an application like the one at the right.

1. What amount would she have to give the clerk as a fee? Use the table below.

For orders from	Fee
$0.01 to $5.00	10¢
$5.01 to $10.00	15¢
$10.01 to $50.00	25¢
$50.01 to $100.00	35¢

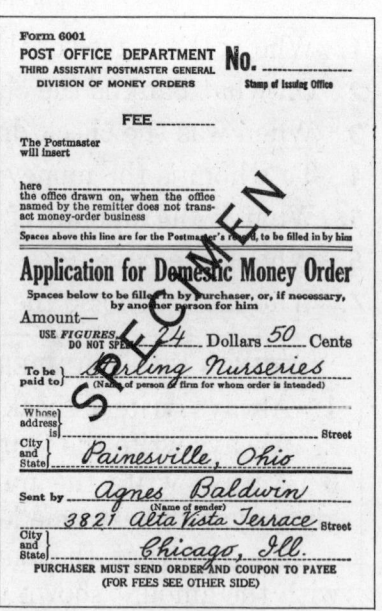

If more than $100 is to be sent by postal money order, two or more separate money orders must be sent, since the maximum amount of one money order is $100.

Using the table shown above, find the cost of sending each of the following amounts by postal money order:

2. $5, $9.89, $75, $42   **5.** $3.42, $56, $11.25

3. $18.95, $96, $34.20   **6.** $1.98, $12.50, $29.95

4. $2, $7.98, $10.95   **7.** $109.95, $144.95

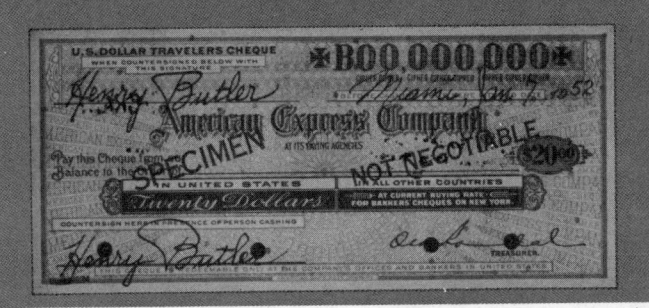

Courtesy American Express Company

Travelers Checks

One winter the Butlers took a trip to Florida. Since Mr. Butler did not want to carry a large amount of cash with him, he bought $400 worth of **travelers checks**.

Travelers checks are issued in denominations of $10, $20, $50, and $100. Although issued by a private company, they may be purchased at most banks, and will be accepted instead of cash almost anywhere. The charge is $\frac{3}{4}$ of 1% of the total amount of the checks, except that, for an amount of $50 or less, there is a minimum charge of $.40.

Study the picture above.

1. What is the amount of the check?
2. Who was the purchaser?
3. What company issued the check?
4. When and where did Mr. Butler cash the check?
5. How much money did he receive?
6. To get the money, Mr. Butler had to sign the check in the lower left-hand corner. He wrote his name exactly as he had written it in the upper corner when he bought the check. Did it matter whether the person who cashed it for him knew Mr. Butler personally? Why or why not?
7. Find the charge for issuing the following amounts in travelers checks:

    A. $200   C. $250   E. $1000   G. $800
    B. $80   D. $750   F. $40   H. $2500

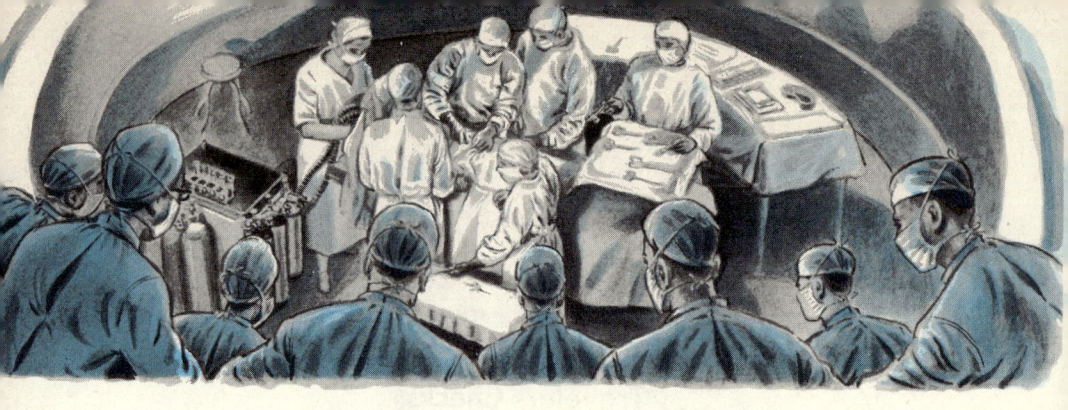

Paying for the Use of Money

To finish his training at medical school, Paul Hansen needs $500. He can borrow from the student loan fund at the rate of 4% a year. This means that he must pay 4% of $500 yearly for the use of the $500. At the end of a year, or two years, or at some other specified date, he must also return the $500.

A charge for the use of somebody else's money is called **interest**. The amount of money borrowed is called the **principal**. The yearly charge, expressed as a per cent of the principal, is called the **annual interest rate**.

1. How much interest will Paul Hansen have to pay on his loan at the end of the first year?

2. What is the total amount of interest he must pay during a period of 2 years? 3 years?

3. If he does not repay any part of the loan until 5 years have gone by, how much interest will he have to pay in all?

4. Suppose that at the end of two years, Paul repays $200 of the original loan. What is the amount of principal on which he must continue to pay interest? How much would this interest amount to during the third year?

5. If a sum of money is borrowed at a certain annual rate of interest, upon what does the amount of interest to be paid depend?

Simple Interest

1. When Mr. Rogers built his house, he paid a part of the cost in cash. He borrowed $2000 from a bank to pay the rest of the cost. The bank charged interest at the rate of 5% a year. How much interest did Mr. Rogers have to pay each year for his bank loan?

2. If he had borrowed $4000 instead of $2000, how much interest would he have had to pay annually?

3. At the same rate, how much would it cost Mr. Rogers to borrow $3000 for one year? How much interest would he have to pay each year on a loan of $5000?

4. If a certain amount of money is borrowed, upon what else does the amount of interest depend besides the length of time for which it is borrowed?

5. Instead of going to the bank, Mr. Rogers could have borrowed the $2000 from Mr. Welles, at an interest rate of $4\frac{1}{2}$% a year. How much interest would he then have had to pay each year? How much interest would he be saving each year?

6. If he borrowed $2000 for 5 years, what total interest would the bank charge at 5%? For the same length of time, how much would Mr. Welles charge at $4\frac{1}{2}$%?

117

Finding the Interest

The amount of interest that must be paid for the use of money depends upon:

1. The amount of money borrowed (the *principal*).
2. The annual rate of interest (the *rate*).
3. The length of time it is borrowed (the *time*).

1. Mr. Hughes wanted to make improvements on his house at a cost of $750. To do so, he had to borrow $450 from the bank for 1 year. The interest rate was 4% a year. What interest did Mr. Hughes have to pay?

2. If Mr. Hughes had borrowed the same amount for 2 years at the same annual interest rate, what would the interest have been?

3. If the annual interest rate had been $4\frac{1}{2}\%$ and Mr. Hughes borrowed the same amount for 1 year, what interest would he have paid?

The amount of interest is found by multiplying the principal by the annual rate, and then multiplying the product by the time in years.

4. What is the interest on $100 for 2 years at 4% per year?

5. What is the interest on $2500 for 1 year at an annual rate of 3%?

6. At 2% per year, find the interest on $5000 for 1 year.

7. On a $1000 bond, what is the interest received in one year at the rate of $4\frac{1}{2}\%$ per year?

8. Find the interest on $3600 for 3 years at 5% per year.

9. What is the interest on $1200 for 1 year at $2\frac{1}{2}\%$?

10. At $3\frac{1}{4}\%$ a year, find the interest on $2000 for 2 years.

Interest for Less Than One Year

Many business loans are made for less than a year—3 months, 60 days, or 30 days. When computing interest for a short period of time, we usually consider 30 days as a month, or $\frac{1}{12}$ of a year.

To find the interest for a certain number of months, we find the interest for one year, and then multiply by the fractional part of a year.

For 6 mo., multiply the interest for 1 yr. by $\frac{6}{12}$, or $\frac{1}{2}$.
For 3 mo., multiply the interest for 1 yr. by $\frac{3}{12}$, or $\frac{1}{4}$.
For 2 mo., multiply the interest for 1 yr. by $\frac{2}{12}$, or $\frac{1}{6}$.

Example 1. Find the interest on $600 for 3 months at 5% a year.

$$\begin{array}{r}\$600 \\ \times .05 \\ \hline \$30.00 \end{array} = \text{interest for 1 yr.} \qquad 3 \text{ mo.} = \tfrac{3}{12}, \text{ or } \tfrac{1}{4} \text{ yr.}$$

$$\begin{array}{r}\$ 7.50 \\ 4\overline{)\$30.00} \end{array} = \text{interest for 3 mo.}$$

Example 2. What is the interest on $900 for 30 days at 3% a year?

$$\begin{array}{r}\$900 \\ \times .03 \\ \hline \$27.00 \end{array} = \text{interest for 1 yr.} \qquad 30 \text{ da.} = 1 \text{ mo.} = \tfrac{1}{12} \text{ yr.}$$

$$\begin{array}{r}\$ 2.25 \\ 12\overline{)\$27.00} \end{array} = \text{interest for 30 da.}$$

1. What is the interest on $100 for 3 months at 6% a year?

2. On a loan of $1500, what is the interest for 4 months at the rate of 5% a year?

3. A bank loaned $480 for 90 days at 4%; what was the amount of interest charged?

4. On a 60-day loan, the interest rate was $5\tfrac{1}{2}\%$. What was the amount of interest due if the loan amounted to $1200?

Example 3. Find the interest on $500 for 8 months at $3\frac{1}{2}\%$ a year.

$500
× .035
─────
$17.50, interest for 1 yr.

8 mo. = $\frac{8}{12}$, or $\frac{2}{3}$ yr.

$\frac{2}{3}$ of $17.50 = $11.67, interest for 8 mo.

5. Find the interest on $750 for 9 months at 4% a year.

6. At 3% a year, what is the interest on $1000 for 8 months?

7. What is the interest for 120 days on $300 at 5% a year?

8. Find the interest on $2000 for 10 months at 2% annually.

9. What is the interest for 5 months, at 3% a year, on $2400?

10. Semiannual interest is paid every 6 months. Find the semiannual interest on $800 at $2\frac{1}{2}\%$ a year.

11. Quarterly interest is paid every 3 months. Find the quarterly interest on $4000 at $4\frac{1}{2}\%$ a year.

12. What is the amount of monthly interest on $6000 at an annual rate of $3\frac{1}{2}\%$?

13. Which is greater: the interest on $2000 for 6 months at 4% a year, or for 1 year at 2% a year?

14. Which is greater: the quarterly interest on $1000 at 5% a year, or the semiannual interest on $1000 at $2\frac{1}{4}\%$ a year?

Keeping in Practice

1. Reduce to lowest terms:

$\frac{75}{360}$ $\frac{24}{360}$ $\frac{45}{360}$ $\frac{92}{360}$ $\frac{15}{360}$ $\frac{84}{360}$ $\frac{18}{360}$

2. Express as common fractions:

$5\frac{1}{2}\%$ $1\frac{1}{2}\%$ $3\frac{1}{2}\%$ $2\frac{1}{4}\%$ $4\frac{1}{2}\%$ $3\frac{3}{4}\%$

3. A. $200 \times \frac{3}{100} \times \frac{1}{12} = ?$ D. $450 \times \frac{9}{200} \times \frac{24}{360} = ?$
B. $1200 \times \frac{4}{100} \times \frac{5}{12} = ?$ E. $750 \times \frac{11}{200} \times \frac{144}{360} = ?$
C. $800 \times \frac{3}{200} \times \frac{7}{12} = ?$ F. $1000 \times \frac{7}{200} \times \frac{45}{360} = ?$

Using an Interest Formula

You have learned that the amount of interest paid for a loan depends upon the amount of the principal, the length of time of the loan, and the interest rate.

The interest rate is usually a yearly rate. When the yearly rate is used, the time must be expressed in years or fractional parts of a year.

To find the interest, we multiply the principal by the yearly rate, and then multiply the product by the time in years. This may be written as a formula, usually as follows:
$$I = P \times r \times t, \quad \text{or} \quad I = Prt$$

Example 1. Find the interest on $250 for 2 yr. at 3%.
$$\$250 \times \frac{3}{100} \times 2 = \$15$$

Example 2. Find the interest on $1800 for 10 mo. at 4%.
$$\$1800 \times \frac{4}{100} \times \frac{10}{12} = \$60$$

Example 3. Find the interest on $4000 for 5 mo. at $3\frac{1}{2}$%.
$$3\frac{1}{2}\% = 3\frac{1}{2} \div 100 = \frac{7}{2} \times \frac{1}{100} = \frac{7}{200}$$
$$\$4000 \times \frac{7}{200} \times \frac{5}{12} = \$58.33$$

Using whichever method you prefer, find the interest on:

1. $500 for $1\frac{1}{2}$ yr. at 2%.
2. $900 for 8 mo. at 5%.
3. $750 for 6 mo. at 3%.
4. $1250 for 3 mo. at 4%.
5. $2500 for 1 yr. at $1\frac{1}{2}$%.
6. $5000 for 2 mo. at 3%.
7. $800 for 4 mo. at $2\frac{1}{2}$%.
8. $10,000 for 90 da. at $4\frac{1}{2}$%.

Interest for Any Number of Days

Interest is frequently computed for some particular number of days, as 75 days, 10 days, or 144 days. In such cases we usually consider a year as having 360 days.

To find the interest for any number of days, we multiply the interest for 1 year by the fractional part of 360 days.

Example. A businessman borrowed $600 for 20 days at the rate of $3\frac{1}{2}\%$ a year. Find the interest.

$600
.035
―――
$21.00, interest for 1 yr.

20 da. = $\frac{20}{360}$ yr. = $\frac{1}{18}$ yr.

$1.17 = interest for 20 da.
18)$21.00

Find the interest on:

1. $400 for 15 da. at 4%.
2. $250 for 72 da. at 3%.
3. $960 for 40 da. at 2%.
4. $800 for 10 da. at 5%.
5. $1200 for 105 da. at $2\frac{1}{2}\%$.
6. $2000 for 96 da. at 1%.
7. $600 for 150 da. at $3\frac{1}{2}\%$.
8. $1000 for $2\frac{1}{2}$ mo. at 6%.
9. $200 for 45 da. at 3%.
10. $1600 for 63 da. at $4\frac{1}{2}\%$.
11. $2400 for 24 da. at $1\frac{1}{2}\%$.
12. $2200 for 56 da. at $4\frac{1}{2}\%$.

JIFFY QUIZ

1. How many yards are there in 42 inches?
2. One pint is what per cent of half a gallon?
3. How much is 2% of 50? How much is 50% of 2?
4. What per cent of 60 is 9?
5. Is .03 more or less than .035? how much more or less?
6. What part of a pound are 10 ounces? what per cent?

Courtesy Manufacturers Trust Company

Interest in Everyday Affairs

1. A businessman borrowed $2000 for 90 days in order to purchase some merchandise. If the interest rate was 5%, how much interest did he have to pay on the loan?

2. If a savings bank pays interest at the rate of $2\frac{1}{2}\%$ a year, how much interest is earned during a quarterly period (3 months) on a deposit of $800?

3. A savings and loan association's rate of interest on loans is 4% a year. At this rate, what is the interest on a loan of $750, if the money is used for 8 months?

4. Find the interest for 6 months on a government bond of $10,000 at the rate of $1\frac{1}{2}\%$ a year.

5. The debt of the town of Hillsdale amounts to $750,000. What is the interest for a year on this sum at $3\frac{1}{2}\%$?

6. A tax bill is paid 27 days after it is due. The penalty for late payment is an interest charge at the rate of 6% a year for the time the bill is overdue. If the bill amounted to $84, what is the amount of the penalty?

7. If our national debt amounted to 257 billion dollars, what would be the interest on this amount for 1 day at the rate of 1% a year? (360 da. = 1 yr.)

Savings Accounts

Peggy has an account in a savings bank. A record of the amounts she puts in (deposits) and takes out (withdraws) is kept in a **passbook**. Part of a page of Peggy's passbook is shown below:

DATE	WITHDRAWAL	DEPOSIT	INTEREST	BALANCE
Dec. 29				192|39
Jan. 2		7|00	1|92	201|31
Feb. 18		5|00		206|31
Mar. 10	23|50			182|81
May 3		20|80		203|61
July 1			1|82	205|43

1. What was Peggy's balance before she made her deposit on January 2? What was it after she made the deposit?

2. On Feb. 18 how much did Peggy deposit? Then what was her balance?

3. On Mar. 10 she withdrew $23.50. How much was left in her account? What was her balance on May 3?

4. The interest dates of her bank are Jan. 2 and July 1. Interest is credited on the **smallest balance** between those dates. No interest is allowed on fractional parts of a dollar. What was the smallest balance between Jan. 2 and July 1?

5. The bank allows interest at 2% annually on the smallest balance within the six-month interest period. What is the interest on $182 for 6 mo. at 2%?

6. The clerk added the interest to her account as he would a deposit. Why? What was her balance on July 1?

7. If Peggy does not deposit or withdraw any money from July 1 to January 2 of the next year, how much interest will be credited to her account on Jan. 2?

Making Bank Deposits Safer

Because of business conditions beyond their control, especially in times of depression, banks sometimes fail. If a bank fails, its depositors may lose some of the money they have deposited.

To prevent such losses, Congress in 1933 organized the **Federal Deposit Insurance Corporation (F.D.I.C.)**. Each year the member banks pay a certain amount of money into a central fund managed by the F.D.I.C., which, through this reserve fund, guarantees to pay depositors any losses up to $10,000. In a recent year the F.D.I.C. held $1,207,000,000 in reserve.

Courtesy the First National Bank of Boston

1. If Mr. White has $12,400 on deposit in a bank that is a member of the F.D.I.C., how much of his deposit is not protected by insurance?

2. Any bank that belongs to the F.D.I.C. pays $\frac{1}{12}$ of 1% of its total deposits for this insurance. If a bank's deposits amount to $7,500,000, what must the bank pay to the F.D.I.C.?

3. If a non-insured bank closes, or fails, but is able to pay its depositors 70¢ for every dollar they have on deposit, how much would a man receive who had $1240 on deposit? How much would he lose?

4. If the bank in Problem **3** had been a member of the F.D.I.C., would the man have lost any of the money he had on deposit?

Postal Savings

Money can be deposited for safekeeping with the United States Post Office. These deposits are known as **postal savings** and must be made in dollar amounts. For example, $16 may be deposited but not $16.50. The Post Office gives the depositor certificates in denominations of $1, $2, $5, $10, $20, $50, $100, $200, and $500. No one may deposit more than $2500.

1. If Mr. Daly wishes to deposit $18 in postal savings, what certificates would the clerk probably give him?

2. If a person makes a deposit of $440, what is the smallest number of certificates he could receive? What denominations would they be?

Postal savings earn interest at the rate of 2% a year. A deposit made on *any day* of the month begins to earn interest on the first day of the following month. For each complete quarter-year after that date, a fourth of a year's interest can be collected.

3. Miss Hunter has $265 deposited in postal savings. How much interest do her savings earn in one year?

4. On May 20, John Coe bought a postal savings certificate for $500. When does it begin to draw interest? How much interest will he have to his credit Sept. 1? Dec. 1?

Some depositors turn their certificates in for new ones each year in order to collect the one year's interest the certificates have earned. If they choose to keep the same certificates for several years, the interest will amount to the interest for the first year times the number of years.

5. Mr. Gay has $2350 deposited in postal savings. How much interest do his savings earn in one year?

Understanding Money and Interest

1. Name three important services provided by banks.
2. What is the Federal Deposit Insurance Corporation?
3. Bills and coins are called _?_; checks and drafts are called _?_.
4. Upon what three quantities does the amount of interest depend?
5. Semiannually means _?_ times a year; quarterly means _?_ times a year.
6. At an annual rate of 5%, how much interest must be paid every six months on a loan of $100?
7. At an annual rate of $4\frac{1}{2}$%, how much interest is due every six months on a principal of $1000?
8. At an annual rate of 6%, how much interest is payable quarterly on a principal of $10,000?
9. The person who signs a check is called the _?_ of the check; the person to whom a check is made out is called the _?_.
10. What is meant by endorsing a check? Who endorses a check: the maker, the bank clerk, or the payee?
11. If a person borrows $425 for a period of six months at 4% annually, the principal is _?_, the interest is _?_, and the total amount due six months later is _?_.
12. The interest on $250 for 60 days at 6% equals $_?_; on $375 for 60 days at 6%, the interest is $_?_; on $193 for 60 days at 6%, the interest is $_?_.
13. Can you see a short cut for finding the interest on any principal for 60 days at 6%?
14. What is the interest on $480 for 30 days at 6%? on $620 for 60 days at 3%? Use the short cut.

Keeping in Practice

1. Write the per cent equivalent of each:
   A. $\frac{1}{8}, \frac{5}{8}, \frac{1}{4}, \frac{3}{4}, \frac{1}{3}, \frac{2}{3}, \frac{1}{6}, \frac{5}{6}$ B. $\frac{1}{5}, \frac{2}{5}, \frac{3}{5}, \frac{4}{5}, \frac{1}{10}, \frac{3}{10}, \frac{3}{8}, \frac{7}{8}$

Find the products:

	A	B	C
2.	$\frac{2}{3} \times 16$	$3\frac{1}{2} \times 1\frac{1}{4}$	$2\frac{2}{5} \times \frac{2}{3}$
3.	$.04 \times 12$	$16 \times .8$	$.7 \times 150$
4.	$.02 \times .03$	$.2 \times 320$	$120 \times .05$

Find the quotients:

5.	$\frac{1}{2} \div 4$	$8 \div 1\frac{1}{2}$	$9 \div 2\frac{1}{2}$
6.	$2\frac{1}{2} \div 3$	$3\frac{1}{2} \div 3\frac{1}{2}$	$15 \div \frac{2}{3}$
7.	$.08 \div 2$	$16 \div .4$	$.12 \div 4$
8.	$.06 \div .03$	$20 \div .5$	$3.5 \div .7$

Complete the following:

9. 20% of 50 = ?   25% of 2 = ? $16\frac{2}{3}$% of 72 = ?
10. $12\frac{1}{2}$% of 400 = ? $37\frac{1}{2}$% of 12 = ?   80% of 75 = ?
11. $2\frac{1}{2}$% of 300 = ? $66\frac{2}{3}$% of 150 = ?   6% of 22 = ?

JUST FOR FUN

1. A man drove from his house to the station, a distance of 10 miles, at the rate of 20 miles an hour. He made the return trip at the rate of 40 miles an hour. What was his average rate for the entire round trip? (No, the answer is not 30 miles an hour.) What was the total distance covered in making the round trip? What was the total time required for the round trip?

2. A man spent 20% of his annual income for food, and 10% of the remainder for incidentals. What per cent of his income did he spend for incidentals? If the expenditure for food was $600 more than the expenditure for incidentals, what was his total annual income?

Making Sure

1. The Fairchilds plan to spend 25% of their income for rent, 32% for food, 16% for clothing, and 20% for all other purposes. **A.** What per cent of their income do they plan to save? **B.** If the income is $3800, how much would they save in one year at this rate? 106

2. There are two children in a family. If the yearly family income is $4400, and 15% of this is allowed for clothing, how much is allowed per year for clothing for each member of the family? 107

3. Mr. Bolton pays $85 a month rent for his apartment. If this is 25% of his income, what is his annual income? 108

4. An interest rate of 5% a year on a given principal means that each year the interest is equal to $\frac{1}{20}$ of the __?__. 117

5. Find the interest on $12,000 for 6 months at $2\frac{3}{4}$%. 119

6. What is the interest on $300 for 1 month at 3% a year? 119

7. Find the interest on $750 for 72 days at 5%. 121, 122

8. A tax bill of $125 is paid 18 days after it was due. If interest is charged at the rate of 6% a year, what is the penalty on this bill? 122

9. The interest on $1000 at 2% for 1 year is how many times as great as the interest on $400 at the same rate for 1 year? 118

10. A man borrowed $4000 at $5\frac{1}{2}$% interest. If he had borrowed it elsewhere at $4\frac{3}{4}$% a year, how much less interest would he have had to pay each year? 118

11. The smallest balance in a savings account during a 6-month interest period was $392.75. Find the interest earned for that period if the annual rate is 2%. 125

Photo from National Board of Fire Underwriters

4

SHARING RISKS AND BENEFITS

Fire Insurance

It is always possible that property may be damaged by fire, lightning, a tornado, or other hazards. Owners can **insure** their property against loss by such damage.

Insurance is a cooperative arrangement by which many people pay small sums of money to an insurance company, which, in turn, compensates them in case of property loss or damage. Since most people do not have any losses, the company is able to pay large sums to those who do. In this way, the risk is shared by all who carry insurance. This is the basic idea or principle of all insurance.

For which do you think you would have to pay the higher rate when buying fire insurance:

A. A wooden house or a brick house?
B. A fire-proof building or an ordinary one?
C. A house in a city with an adequate fire department, or a house in the country?
D. A paper box factory or a tin can factory?

When a person insures his property against loss, he receives an **insurance policy** from the company. This is an agreement, or contract, which states the greatest amount the company will pay if there is a loss. This amount is called the **face value** of the policy.

If a fire causes a loss less than the face value, the company pays only the amount of the actual loss, not the entire face value.

Fire Insurance Premiums

When the Lawtons bought a house, they insured it for $7500 against loss by fire.

In return for this insurance, Mr. Lawton paid the company 28 cents for each $100 of insurance. Since the face value of the policy was 75 hundred dollars, the amount he paid for the insurance was 75 × $.28, or __?__. This amount is called the **premium**.

The $.28 per $100 is called the **premium rate**; it can also be expressed as $2.80 per $1000.

Premium rates for fire insurance vary greatly from city to city, and for different types of buildings. The table shows the rates for certain kinds of buildings in two different cities. Explain why the rates are different.

ONE-YEAR PREMIUM RATES PER $100 OF INSURANCE		
KIND OF BUILDING	CITY A	CITY B
Frame house, ordinary roof	$.16	$.50
Frame house, approved roof	.16	.40
Brick house	.10	.30
Retail store	.25	.60
Public garage	.40	.80

1. What is the annual premium on:

　A. A brick house in City A, insured for $12,000?
　B. A retail store in City A, insured for $25,000?
　C. A frame house, with ordinary roof, in City B, insured for $12,000?
　D. A public garage in City B, insured for $18,000?
　E. A frame house, with approved roof, in City A, insured for $14,500?

2. Mr. Carey's house is valued at $13,500. He insures it for 80% of its value for 1 year at $.26 per $100. What annual premium does he pay?

3. A clubhouse valued at $48,000 is insured for $32,000. The house is insured for what per cent of its value?

4. If the premium rate for the clubhouse in Problem **3** is $.72 per $100, what is the annual premium?

Many people buy fire insurance for periods longer than one year, paying the premium for the entire period all at one time. In this way they save money, as you can see from the table below.

PERIOD	RATE
2 years	$1\frac{3}{4}$ times the rate for 1 year
3 years	$2\frac{1}{2}$ times the rate for 1 year
4 years	$3\frac{1}{4}$ times the rate for 1 year
5 years	4 times the rate for 1 year

Example. A house is insured for $9000 for 3 years at an annual rate of $.32 per $100. What is the premium? What is the yearly cost? How much is saved by taking a 3-year policy instead of a 1-year policy?

Premium rate for 3-yr. period = $2\frac{1}{2} \times \$.32 = \$.80$
90 × $.80 = $72, the premium
$72 ÷ 3 = $24, the yearly cost

If a 1-year policy is purchased, the yearly cost = 90 × $.32 = $28.80.
$28.80 − $24 = $4.80, yearly saving
3 × $4.80 = $14.40, amount saved in 3 yr.

5. Mr. Briggs insures his house for $5000 for a 2-year period at an annual rate of $.48 per $100. What is the premium? the yearly cost of his insurance?

6. A building is insured for $12,000 for 5 years at an annual rate of $.22 per $100. Find the premium, and the yearly cost of the insurance. How much is saved by taking a 5-year policy instead of a 1-year policy?

Wide World Photo

Automobile Insurance

To protect himself and others against various risks, a motorist may carry automobile insurance of these types:

1. **Liability for Bodily Injury:** Under this type the insurance company pays the sum for which the car owner would be legally responsible, or *liable,* if persons are injured or killed in accidents involving his car.

2. **Liability for Property Damage:** This type pays the amount of the damage done by the owner's car to another car or other property.

3. **Collision Insurance:** This type repays the car owner in large part for damages to his car resulting from collision.

4. The **Comprehensive Policy:** Pays the car owner for loss due to fire, theft, or other damage.

Liability for bodily injury is the car owner's greatest financial risk. Such claims against the owner may run into many thousands of dollars. A common policy is one that pays up to $25,000 for injury to one person or $50,000 for injury to more than one person in any single accident.

The table below shows typical annual premium rates:

COMMUNITY	LIABILITY FOR BODILY INJURY ($25,000-$50,000)	LIABILITY FOR PROPERTY DAMAGE (Maximum, $5000)	COMPREHENSIVE FIRE AND THEFT
City A	$91	$26.50	$1.30 per $100
Town B	$48	$18.50	$ .80 per $100
Village C	$30	$11.50	$ .55 per $100

1. Using the above rates find the total premium for the three kinds of insurance on each of these cars:

  A. In City A, a convertible valued at $2200.
  B. In Town B, a station wagon valued at $2600.
  C. In Village C, a sedan valued at $2450.

2. A car costing $2375 when new is insured when two years old for 60% of its original value. If the insurance carried is comprehensive fire and theft, what is the premium at $1.60 per $100?

3. Mr. Payne, who carried no automobile insurance, seriously injured a man while driving, and had to pay $20,000 in damages. To secure the money, he was forced to sell his car for $900, his house for $8000, and use his cash savings of $2200. How much did he still have to raise, perhaps over a period of years? Would it have paid him to carry personal liability (for bodily injury) insurance?

4. After paying an average of $36 a year for 12 years on a personal liability policy, Mr. Rollins had an accident in which two people were injured. The company paid the claims, amounting to $8,500. How much did Mr. Rollins save by carrying this insurance?

5. Why would premium rates for theft insurance in large cities differ from those in small towns? Would the same be true of property damage insurance?

Be Careful!

In a single year, 91,000 persons were killed and 9,500,000 were injured in accidents of all kinds. Many of these accidents could have been prevented by following rules of safety.

1. This list shows in what places accidents to children occur and the per cents for each place.

At Home	24%
In School Buildings	19%
On School Grounds	18%
Going to or from School	7%
Other Places	32%
	100%

Draw a bar graph to show these facts.

2. The following list shows the number of fatalities per 100,000 population for six major causes of accidental deaths in a recent year:

Motor Vehicles	23
Falls	17
Burns	6
Drowning	4
Firearms	2
Railroads	3

Draw a bar graph to show these facts.

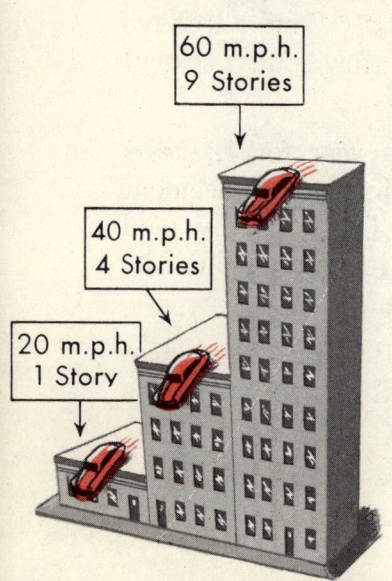

3. The picture and table show the "fall" equivalent to stopping instantly in a crash. **A.** How many times does the "crashing effect" increase when the speed is doubled (from 20 to 40 m.p.h.)? **B.** when the speed is tripled (from 20 to 60 m.p.h.)?

SPEED IN MILES PER HR.	FALL IN FEET
20	13.3
30	30.0
40	54.1
50	83.1
60	120.2

Hospitalization

In many communities hospitalization insurance can be bought. This is a plan to meet the emergency of hospital bills. Usually an entire family joins a hospital insurance plan. The cost of such insurance differs slightly in various communities.

Typical dues for membership are as follows:

	MONTHLY	QUARTERLY	SEMI-ANNUAL	ANNUAL
Self	$1.24	$ 3.72	$ 7.44	$14.88
Husband and wife. .	2.72	8.16	16.32	32.64
Husband, wife, and all unmarried children under 19 years of age	3.56	10.68	21.36	42.72

1. Mr. and Mrs. Jordan have three small children. How much does it cost this family to join a hospitalization plan at the above rates if they pay on a quarterly basis?

2. Would they save by paying annually instead of semi-annually? Would it cost more if they paid monthly?

3. Under this plan, any member of the family is allowed 28 days free hospital treatment in any one year, at a rate up to $5 a day for a room, and 20% of the operating room fee. Mrs. Jordan was in the hospital for 10 days; her hospital room was $8.50 a day. The operating room fee amounted to $35 extra. What was the total hospital bill?

4. How much did the insurance plan pay toward the cost of the room? toward the cost of the operating room fee?

5. How much less did Mrs. Jordan have to pay for hospitalization by carrying this insurance?

Accidents and Their Costs

The greatest number of occupational accidents does not always occur to people who work at dangerous jobs. The type of jobs we usually think of as "safe" can be dangerous if workers are careless.

1. The United States government estimated that, during a recent year, about 1,870,000 persons received disabling injuries while working. These accidents occurred in various industry groups as follows:

INDUSTRY GROUP	THOUSANDS OF ACCIDENTS
Manufacturing	380
Agriculture	340
Wholesale and Retail Trade	330
Construction	180
Transportation	170
All others	470

The number of accidents in each industry group is what per cent (to the nearest tenth) of the total number of accidents?

2. In the same year, the total cost of injuries from occupational accidents was estimated at $1,320,000,000. This amount was accounted for as follows:

COSTS	MILLIONS OF DOLLARS
Wage Loss	750
Medical Expense	120
Insurance Company Expenses and Overhead	450

Find, to the nearest tenth, the per cent that each cost is of the total cost of occupational accidents.

Accident Insurance

Some accidents simply cause inconvenience, while others cause loss of time and income, and an additional money loss for expenses.

1. Mr. Hall, an office worker, bought accident insurance. His policy provided: **A.** $25 per week during the time he was unable to work; **B.** all medical and hospital expenses up to $500; **C.** $5000 for loss of a limb or sight; **D.** $1000 in the event of death.

Mr. Hall was disabled for 6 weeks. The doctor's bills and hospital expenses amounted to $87. How much did the insurance company pay him?

2. Mr. Treadwell carries a similar policy. He was disabled for 9 weeks. His salary is $56 a week, but he received no salary while he was disabled. How much income did he lose?

3. Mr. Douglas, a factory worker, receives a regular weekly wage of $44.25. He was totally disabled for 5 weeks. Through the Workmen's Compensation Law he was paid $\frac{2}{3}$ of his regular wage each week that he was disabled. How much compensation did Mr. Douglas receive?

4. Later it was found that Mr. Douglas (Problem **3**) would always limp slightly as a result of his injury. For this permanent disability he was paid $1250. What was his total compensation?

Life Insurance

The chief purpose of **life insurance** is to protect a person's dependents in case of his death. The purchaser of life insurance pays small premiums into a central "pool," that is, to the life insurance company, from which a **benefit,** or money payment, is made to his dependents in the event of his death.

The person who receives such money from a life insurance policy is called the **beneficiary.** The person whose life is insured is called the **policyholder.**

Life insurance may be bought on many different plans.

KIND OF POLICY	PREMIUMS PAID	BENEFIT PAID
1. Ordinary Life	Until death	Upon death of policyholder
2. 20-Payment Life	For 20 years	Upon death of policyholder
3. 20-Year Endowment	For 20 years	A. To beneficiary if death occurs before the end of 20 years. B. To policyholder if still living after 20 years.
4. 10-Year Term	For 10 years	Upon death of policyholder only if death occurs during the 10-year period.

The premiums below are very nearly average rates:

ANNUAL PREMIUM PER $1,000

AGE	ORDINARY LIFE	20-PAYMENT LIFE	20-YEAR ENDOWMENT	10-YEAR TERM
20	$18.73	$30.30	$49.80	$ 7.84
25	21.20	33.22	50.30	8.57
30	24.23	36.33	51.06	9.64
35	28.10	39.96	52.26	11.34
40	33.01	44.31	54.14	14.17
45	39.34	49.61	57.03	18.51
50	47.59	56.27	61.46	25.17

1. Mr. Saxon, who is 25 years old, decides to buy an ordinary life policy for $3000. What yearly premium must he pay? From the table, page 140, we find age 25 in the "Age" column and read across to the "Ordinary Life" column; the annual premium per $1000 is $21.20. Therefore Mr. Saxon's premium on $3000 is $? .

2. What is the annual premium on an ordinary life policy for $3000, if bought at age 40?

3. An ordinary life policy (Problems 1 and 2) requires that the premium be paid as long as the policyholder lives. When he dies, the beneficiary receives the amount or the **face value** of the policy ($3000). How does the annual rate per $1000 on the policy in Problem 2 compare with the rate in Problem 1?

The older a person is when he takes out a policy, the more he must pay. There is less time for the company to accumulate the money to pay the benefit when he dies. Therefore a larger annual premium must be paid.

4. When he is 25 years old, Mr. Randolph takes out a 20-payment life policy for $3000. What annual premium does he pay? How many payments will he have to make? How much will his beneficiary receive when he dies?

5. If Mr. Randolph should die when he is 36 years old and has paid 12 annual premiums, what amount will he have paid? How much will his family receive?

6. If Mr. Randolph dies when he is 45 years old and has paid 20 annual premiums, how much will he have paid the company in premiums? How much will his beneficiary receive? If he is still living at the age of 45, will he have to pay any more premiums?

7. If Mr. Randolph lives to be 53 years old, will he have to pay premiums during the last 8 years of his life? How much more will his family receive than he paid in?

Protection for the Family

We have just seen that for an ordinary life policy, the premiums must be paid as long as the policyholder lives. For a 20-payment life policy, however, the premiums are paid for 20 years only, no matter how long thereafter the policyholder may live. Under both of these plans, the benefit is paid to the beneficiary only when the policyholder dies. For many families, both plans give protection at economical rates. Which of these plans carries the lower annual premium?

Term insurance gives protection for a limited period or term only, usually 5 to 10 years at most. If the policyholder dies during this term, his beneficiary receives the benefit. If the person is still living at the end of the term, no benefit is paid, and the insurance expires. Such insurance is useful when a large amount of protection is desired or needed for a short time. It carries the lowest premium rates. Can you tell why?

In solving Problems **1-8**, use the table on page 140.

1. Mr. Saunders, a man of 30, has just started his own business. He takes out a 10-year term policy for $10,000. What is the annual premium?

2. Mr. Baldwin, who is 45 years old, took out a 20-year endowment policy for $5000. His annual premium was __?__. How does this premium rate compare with the rates for the other three plans at the same age?

Endowment insurance is different from the other three kinds. Mr. Baldwin must pay the premiums for 20 years. If he dies during these 20 years, his beneficiary receives the benefit ($5000); if he is still living after 20 years, he receives the $5000, and the policy expires.

If a man wishes to carry protection and at the same time build up a savings fund which he himself can collect at a certain time, he may decide to buy 20-year endowment insurance. Can you see why the premium rates are higher for this plan than for other plans?

3. How much will it cost per year for a 20-year endowment policy for $4000 if taken at the age of 25?

4. When he was 20, Fred Hutton took out a 20-year endowment policy for $3000. How much did this insurance cost him per year? About how much insurance could he have bought for the same premium if he had selected an ordinary life policy instead?

5. Find the premium for each of these policies:
   A. $4000, ordinary life policy, taken out at age 20.
   B. $5000, 20-payment life policy, bought at age 35.
   C. $10,000, 10-year term policy, taken out at age 40.
   D. $10,000, 20-year endowment policy, taken out at age 30.

On many policies, small payments called **dividends** are made each year. If the policyholder prefers, he may deduct this dividend from his premium.

6. Henry Payne took out a 20-year endowment policy for $2000 at the age of 25. One year he received a dividend of $6.15. He deducted the dividend from his premium. What was the net cost of his insurance that year?

7. Mr. Taylor, at age 40, took out a 20-year endowment policy for $5000. During one year when the dividend amounted to $5.23, he used it to reduce his premium. What amount of premium did he pay that year?

8. A man of 30 is earning $3500 a year. If he plans to spend 6% of his income for life insurance, how much can he spend for premiums each year? About how much ordinary life insurance can he carry?

Why We Pay Taxes

People who live in cities and towns receive police and fire protection; their streets are paved; their health is safeguarded; they can enjoy parks, playgrounds, libraries, and museums. The state government pays for highways and bridges, for some schools and colleges, and for other services.

The federal government maintains the Army and Navy; assists commerce and agriculture; maintains national parks, forest service, and fisheries; contributes to flood control and irrigation projects; and provides unemployment relief, social security, and many other services.

All these services cost large sums of money, which are obtained either by taxation or by borrowing.

1. Name two benefits provided by your city government which were not mentioned above.

2. Name two benefits provided by your state which were not mentioned above.

3. Name three other benefits or services provided by the federal government.

4. License fees are also taxes. Name three kinds of licenses.

Concert in Robin Hood Dell, Fairmount Park, Philadelphia *Wide World Photo*

Governments Use Budgets

City and state governments, as well as the federal government, use budgets to manage their affairs in a businesslike way. This graph shows how a mid-western large city spent its money in a recent year.

1. Which was the largest item of expense? the smallest?

2. What is the ratio of the amount for schools to the amount spent for health and sanitation?

3. The amount spent for police and fire protection is what part of the total amount spent by the city? What is the ratio of the combined cost of police and fire protection to the cost of schools?

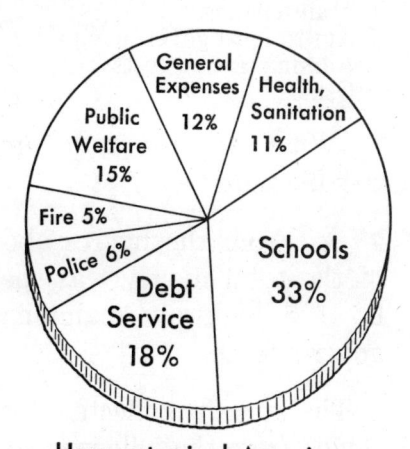

Pie chart: General Expenses 12%, Health, Sanitation 11%, Public Welfare 15%, Fire 5%, Police 6%, Debt Service 18%, Schools 33%

How a typical American city spends the taxpayer's dollar

4. If the total budget expenditures that year were $35,675,000, how much was spent for the city's schools?

5. Name three items that might come under the head of "public welfare." Name three services that might come under the head of "health and sanitation."

6. The "debt service" means the interest which the city must pay on money it has borrowed, as well as sums of money set aside each year to repay loans as they come due. If one year's interest on a city's debt is $25,387.50, and the rate of interest on the debt averages 3%, what is the amount of the debt?

The Nation's Highways

In a recent year, the combined expenditures of the highway departments of the 48 states were approximately as follows:

Construction of highways	$1,100,000,000
Maintenance	500,000,000
Aid to local governments	700,000,000
Administrative costs	100,000,000
Other	500,000,000

1. What was the total amount spent on highways by the 48 states?

2. A. From the figures above, find about what per cent of the total money was spent for highway construction; **B.** for highway maintenance; **C.** for aid to local governments.

The money collected for highway purposes was obtained from the following sources:

License and registration fees, motor vehicle and fuel taxes	$2,100,000,000
Federal aid	400,000,000
Income from bonds	300,000,000
All other sources	200,000,000
Balance from previous year	1,200,000,000

3. A. What per cent of the total collections came from license and registration fees and motor vehicle and fuel taxes? **B.** What per cent came from federal aid? **C.** Compare the total highway expenditures (Problem 1) with the total collections. Which is greater? How much money is left to be used the following year?

4. The total expenditures of the 48 states for all purposes, including highways, were about $10,000,000,000. The total amount expended for highway purposes (Problem 1) was about what per cent of total expenditures?

We Pay Many Kinds of Taxes

Most of the money that governments need is obtained from taxes. A small part of it is obtained by borrowing, but this too must eventually be paid through taxation. A **tax** is a compulsory payment to a government.

City, county, and state governments collect taxes on property, both personal property and real estate. Many states also tax business and personal incomes. All states tax automobiles and gasoline. Many states have a **sales tax**; this means that the purchaser must pay as a tax a certain per cent of the price of the articles he buys.

The federal government receives money from two principal sources: **1. customs duties,** or taxes levied on articles imported from other countries; **2. internal revenue,** which includes both **excise taxes** and **income taxes.** Excise taxes include taxes on certain articles made and sold in this country, such as tobacco and liquor; taxes on luxuries and amusements; taxes on mortgages, stocks, and bonds; etc. About 85% of the total federal income comes from internal revenue.

1. A theater ticket cost $1.80, including a 20% amusement tax. What was the cost, excluding the tax?

2. A wrist watch retails for $47.50, subject to a luxury tax of 20%. How much must the purchaser pay in all?

3. A man bought a suit for $39.75 and a pair of shoes for $8.75. He paid a sales tax of 2%. Find the amount of the tax paid on each article; the total tax.

4. In a certain state the state tax on gasoline is 4¢ a gallon; the federal tax is $1\frac{1}{2}$¢. **A.** If the gasoline retails at 22.8¢, excluding taxes, what must be paid for a gallon of gasoline? **B.** The taxes are what per cent of the total cost?

Income Taxes

A very large share of all the internal revenue collected by our federal government is obtained from a tax on incomes. From time to time, Congress passes **income tax laws** which fix the rates at which business incomes and personal incomes are taxed.

Many states have a tax on incomes, but state tax rates are lower than federal rates.

When computing the amount of income tax to be paid, a taxpayer must consider the following items:

1. **Total income:** With a few minor exceptions, this means all money received.

2. **Personal exemptions:** These are amounts which it is permissible to deduct from one's income on account of family dependents. In a recent year, the federal income tax law allowed $600 each for the head of the family and the wife, and $600 for each child.

3. **Allowable deductions:** These are certain other amounts which it is permissible to deduct from the income—real estate taxes, interest on loans, charitable contributions, bad debts, etc.

People who earn less than $5000 or between $5000 and $10,000 a year may deduct 10% of their total income, instead of listing each deduction.

4. **Taxable income:** This is the amount left after subtracting the sum of the personal exemptions and allowable deductions from the income. It is the amount upon which the tax is based.

5. **Tax rate:** This is the rate, expressed as a per cent, by which the taxable income is multiplied to find the amount of tax.

There are many conditions which determine what the taxable income really is. Income tax rates and exemptions may change from year to year. Tax rates also vary according to the size of the income—the greater the income, the higher the tax rate.

When all or part of an employee's income tax is deducted from his salary by his employer and paid to the government, the tax is known as a **withholding tax**.

1. Miss Clark's withholding tax on her salary of $3,050 was $429.12. To the nearest whole per cent, what per cent of her salary was deducted for taxes?

2. Mr. Paine's annual salary was $3735. The tax withheld that year was $552.96. The amount withheld was what per cent of his salary (nearest whole per cent)?

3. After all allowable deductions, Mr. Cole's taxable income was $3020. His tax is $400, plus 22% of the amount of his taxable income over $2000, if it does not exceed $4000. What is his federal income tax?

4. Mr. Hutchins' annual salary is $5200. On his state income tax he is allowed an exemption of $2500 for himself and his wife, and $400 for each of his two children. He may claim 10% for allowable deductions. Find his state income tax at 2% of the first $1000 and 3% of the second and third $1000 of taxable income.

5. Mr. Russell's total annual income was $7500. On his federal tax that year, he could claim, as personal exemptions, a deduction of $600 for himself and for each of his four dependents. His other allowable deductions amounted to $1250. What was his taxable income? Find his federal income tax at $400, plus 22% of the amount of taxable income over $2000, if this did not exceed $4000.

The Real Estate Tax Rate

When the Burtons bought their house, Mr. Burton inquired at the City Hall about property taxes. He found that the real estate tax rate that year was .062, or 6.2%. He also learned that the assessed valuation of his house was $6200, although the purchase price was $15,000.

The **assessed valuation** means the value that the city or town places upon the property for the purpose of taxation. This value is usually less than the market value.

1. What is the yearly tax on Mr. Burton's house? .062 × $6200 = ? The tax is always computed on the assessed valuation, and not on the purchase price or the market value.

2. How does a city determine the tax rate each year? The community's expenses for the year are estimated according to its budget. Suppose the town in which Mr. Burton lives needs to raise $1,336,720 by taxing property. The total assessed valuation of all the property in the town amounts to $21,560,000. We find what per cent the money to be raised is of the total valuation.

$1,336,720 ÷ $21,560,000 = .062 = __?__ per cent

To find the tax rate, divide the amount of money to be raised by the total assessed valuation.

3. Find the tax rate on each of the following:

	AMOUNT TO BE RAISED	ASSESSED VALUATION
A.	$ 28,000	$ 1,000,000
B.	33,000	660,000
C.	800,000	40,000,000
D.	272,500	12,500,000

How the Tax Rate Is Expressed

The tax rate in a certain town was 3.2%. This rate can be expressed in different ways.

1. 3.2% of $100 = _?_.
2. A tax of $3.20 on $100 is _?_ on $1, or _?_ per cent.
3. A tax rate of 3.2% is the same as a rate of $.032 on $1, or $3.20 per $100, or _?_ per $1000.

A **mill** is one-tenth of a cent, or .1¢. A mill is also one-thousandth of a dollar, or $.001.

4. Complete:
   A. 1¢ = _?_ mills   D. 5¢ = _?_ mills
   B. 3¢ = _?_ mills   E. 3.2¢ = _?_ mills
   C. 10¢ = _?_ mills   F. $.046 = _?_ mills

5. A tax rate of $.032 on $1 is the same as _?_ mills on the dollar.

Do you see that 2.4% means 2.4¢ per dollar, or $2.40 per $100, or $24 per $1000, or 24 mills on the dollar?

6. Express these tax rates in dollars and cents on $1000:
   A. $1.60 on $100   C. 18.6 mills on $1
   B. $2.75 on $100   D. 6.9 mills on $1

7. Express these tax rates in dollars and cents on $100:
   A. $27.50 per $1000   C. 12.36 mills on $1
   B. $.0318 per $1   D. 3.42%

8. Express the following tax rates in mills and decimal parts of a mill on $1:
   A. 4.36%   C. $1.85 per $100
   B. $.0148 on $1   D. $22.56 per $1000

9. The assessed valuation of a city is $30,000,000. The amount to be raised by property taxes is $465,000. Find the tax rate in dollars and cents per $1000 assessed valuation; express this rate in mills per dollar.

Finding the Tax on Property

1. Tax rates vary greatly in different towns, cities, and states.

A. Mr. Butler owns a house assessed at $8,600. If the tax rate is $4.42 per $100, what annual tax must he pay?

B. His friend, who lives in the next town, owns property assessed at $12,900. There the tax rate is $20.60 per $1000. What is his friend's annual tax bill?

C. Mr. Daly lives in a community where the property tax rate is 3.14%. Express this rate in dollars and cents per $1000. His property is assessed at $11,850. What is his total yearly tax?

2. The Chandlers have a house and lot assessed at $16,000. The tax rate is 28.4 mills on the dollar. What is their annual tax bill?

3. In a certain county a discount of 2% is allowed on taxes paid in full on or before January 20. If Mr. Tully owns property assessed at $12,000, and the tax is $2.80 per $100, how much will he save by paying his tax on January 16? What amount will he pay?

4. If the tax is not paid when due, a penalty of 6% of the amount of the tax is sometimes charged. Mr. Carr's semiannual tax bill of $165 was due July 2, but he did not pay it until July 15. What was the charge?

5. Mrs. Johnson's house is assessed at $10,400. The school tax rate in her town is $19\frac{1}{2}$ mills on the dollar. What yearly school tax does she pay?

6. Find the amount of tax on each of the following:

VALUATION	RATE	VALUATION	RATE
A. $ 8,500	$2.61 per $100	C. $13,800	23.8 mills
B. $17,400	$32.45 per $1000	D. $11,750	2.98%

The Cost of Owning a Home

Rather than pay rent, Mr. Lucas wanted to buy a house. Before he bought, he estimated the yearly cost of owning a home, and compared this with the cost of renting.

1. The price of the house was $13,500. He had saved $4000 for the cash payment. At $2\frac{1}{2}\%$ annually, how much interest would he lose by using his savings to purchase the house?

2. Each quarterly payment of principal and interest on the mortgage of the new house will amount to $180.69. How much is this per year?

3. The total premium on a 3-year fire insurance policy would be $27.80. What is the yearly cost of insurance?

4. The previous owner's tax bill for the last 6 months was $91.50. How much should he allow a year for taxes?

5. He remembered that there would be repairs. He allowed 2% of the purchase price for repairs and depreciation. How much is this a year?

6. What will be the estimated total yearly cost of owning this house? (Problems **1-5**) How much is this per month?

7. Mr. Lucas is now paying $84 a month for the rental of a house. How much more per year will it cost him to own his own home?

8. If his yearly income is $4380, how much does he earn in one month?

9. His budget allows 25% of his income for rent. Can he afford his present rent? Would he pay more or less than 25% of his income to own this house?

10. What advantages are there in owning your home? What disadvantages can you think of?

Import Duties

Taxes on raw materials and finished products which are brought into this country are called **customs revenues,** or **import duties.** Another name for import duty is **tariff.**

Not all foreign merchandise is taxed; many items are on the **free list.** Congress decides which merchandise is to be taxed. Congress may also change the tariff rates from time to time.

Import duties are computed in two ways: **1. ad valorem duty,** which means a certain per cent of the value of the goods; **2. specific duty,** which means a fixed amount of tax per article, per yard, per pound, per gallon, etc.

1. A certain type of cotton towel has an ad valorem duty of 40%. If each towel is valued at 45 cents, what is the duty on each?

2. What would the import duty be on 15 tons of crude aluminum, if the duty rate is 2 cents per pound?

3. Tulip bulbs are dutiable at the rate of $3 per thousand. What would the duty be on 75,000 tulip bulbs?

4. One kind of Portland cement is dutiable at the rate of $2\frac{1}{4}$ cents per hundred pounds. What would the duty be on 5200 pounds?

5. Certain types of handkerchiefs are dutiable at the rate of 2 cents each, plus 30% ad valorem. If a company imports 30 dozen of these handkerchiefs valued at $21, how much duty must the company pay?

Taxes and the Consumer

The average consumer pays taxes of many kinds. Let us see what some of them are, and what part of a consumer's income goes to pay taxes.

1. Last year Mr. Bradley's taxable income was $5600. Find his federal income tax at $840, plus 26% of the amount over $4,000.

2. On his state income tax return, Mr. Bradley reported a taxable income of $4500. Find his state tax at 2% of the first $1000 of taxable income, 3% of the second and third $1000, and 4% of the fourth and fifth $1000.

3. Mr. Bradley's house is assessed for $9,500; the tax rate last year was 38 mills. What was his property tax?

4. The annual fee for his automobile registration (license plates) was 50¢ for every 100 lb. of car weight up to 3500 lb. and 75¢ for every 100 lb. over 3500 lb. His car weighs 4000 lb. Find the registration fee.

5. That year he estimated that he had used 800 gallons of gasoline. If the average tax was $5\frac{1}{2}$¢ per gallon, what did he pay in gasoline taxes?

6. Mr. Bradley pays $4.75 a month for local telephone service. To this, a federal tax of 15% is added and a city tax of 2%. What is the total amount of these taxes for one year?

7. He paid $329 for a television set, plus a 10% federal tax, plus a 2% local sales tax. What was the total amount of tax on the television set?

8. The Bradleys spent $1.20 per week for movies. This included an admissions tax of 20%. At this rate, how much tax did they pay per week? how much per year?

9. The total amount of these taxes (Problems **1-8**) was what per cent of Mr. Bradley's total income of $8500?

Understanding Insurance and Taxes

1. What determines the amount of a fire insurance premium?

2. Which is probably the better life insurance plan for a married man of 30 with two small children, ordinary life or 20-year endowment?

3. What is the basic principle underlying insurance?

4. What is the difference between ordinary life insurance and 20-payment life insurance?

5. How is the amount of a life insurance premium affected by the age at which the policyholder buys it?

6. List 5 benefits that a community receives from taxes.

7. Which costs more per year: ordinary life insurance or 20-payment life? Why?

8. In what two ways does the federal government obtain the money it needs?

9. Why is personal liability insurance more important than property damage insurance for the owner of a car?

10. Explain how a tax rate on real estate is determined.

Indicate which answer is correct:

11. The beneficiary of a life insurance policy is (the policyholder; the person who pays the premiums; the person who receives the benefit).

12. The amount of federal income tax is based upon (total income; taxable income; personal exemptions).

13. The benefit provided by a life insurance policy means (the cost of the policy; the premium rate; the amount paid by the company).

14. The tax on real estate is based on (the assessed valuation; the purchase price; the market value).

Making Sure

1. Mr. Perry's house, worth $8500, is insured against fire for 80% of its value at an annual rate of $.45 per $100. What premium does Mr. Perry pay? 132

2. A building is insured for $20,000 for 3 years at an annual rate of $.28 per $100. If the premium on a 3-year policy is $2\frac{1}{2}$ times the annual rate, what is the premium? What is the yearly cost of insurance? 133

3. A 1-year fire insurance policy for $4000 carries a premium of $8.80. What is the annual rate per $100? 132

4. Mr. Adams allows $200 a year for ordinary life insurance. At a premium rate of $21.20 per $1000, how large a policy, to the nearest $1000, can he purchase? 140

5. The town of Oakville has a property tax rate of 34 mills on the dollar. What is the tax on property assessed at $4500? 152

6. Mr. Fay's house cost $8400. It is assessed at 75% of its value. What is the yearly tax, if the rate is $2.98 on $100 of assessed valuation? 151, 152

7. A $45 ring cost the purchaser $54, including the luxury tax. What is the luxury tax rate? 147

8. Mr. Roberts paid 26.8 cents a gallon for gasoline. This included a state tax of 4 cents and a federal tax of $1\frac{1}{2}$¢. To the nearest tenth, what per cent of the selling price was the total tax? 147

9. Express each of these tax rates in dollars and cents per $1000: **A.** $2.38 per $100; **B.** 3.15%; **C.** 24.2 mills on $1. 151

10. If the total assessed valuation of a town is $8,000,000 and the budget requires that $150,000 be raised, what is the necessary tax rate in dollars and cents per $1000? 150

5

MEASURING SURFACES

Finding Areas

We are often concerned with finding areas and measuring surfaces. We must have a measure of the surface of a floor to be varnished, or of the side of a house to be painted, or of a roof to be shingled, in order to know how much covering material to buy. For the same reason, we must know the surface measure of a driveway to be cemented, of a fence to be built, or of a lawn to be sodded.

Many surfaces are rectangular in shape. You will remember that a **rectangle** has four sides and four square corners. The **dimensions** of a rectangle are its length and width. The area of a rectangle equals the product of its dimensions, or $A = lw$.

A **square** is a special kind of rectangle in which all four sides are equal. A square is as wide as it is long.

The Area of a Square

1. How many square feet are there in a square each side of which is 3 ft. long? Do you see that 3 rows, each having 3 sq. ft., make 9 sq. ft. in all?

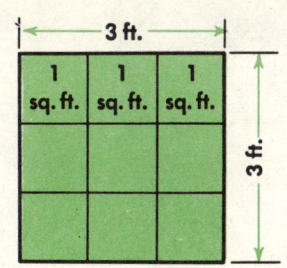

2. How many square feet are there in a square yard?

3. What is the area of a square if each side is 8 in. long? 10 ft. long? 30 yd. long?

4. How many square inches are there in a 6-inch square (6 in. by 6 in.)? in a 5-inch square? a $2\frac{1}{2}$-inch square?

5. The area of a square 4 in. by 4 in. equals 4×4, or 16 sq. in. We can write 4 by 4 as 4^2; we read it, "four squared". What does 3^2 equal? 7^2? 9^2? 10^2? 20^2?

6. If the sides of a square are s units long, then its area, A, equals $s \times s$; or, $A = s^2$.

7. What is the area in square inches of a square 12 in. by 12 in.? How many square inches in a square foot?

8. Each side of a certain square is 4 yd. long. The area is how many square yards? how many square feet?

9. How many square inches are there in a square 2 yd. by 2 yd.?

10. The sides of the shaded square are each $\frac{1}{2}$ in. long; what is its area in square inches? What is the area of the large square?

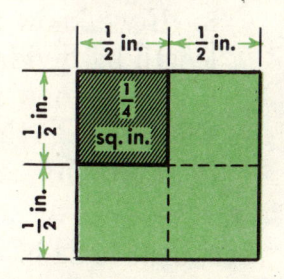

11. If the side of a square is $\frac{1}{4}$ yd. in length, show by drawing a free-hand sketch that its area is $\frac{1}{16}$ sq. yd.

The Area of a Rectangle

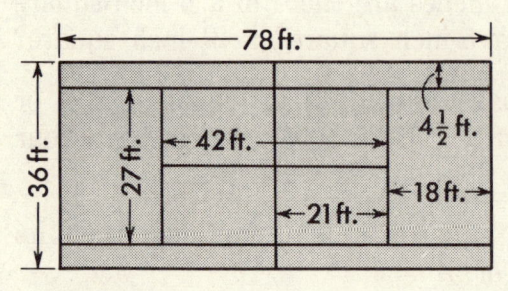

1. Mr. Hall built a tennis court measuring 36 ft. by 78 ft. How many square feet did it cover? Remember, $A = lw$.

2. How many square feet are there in a square yard? How many square yards did the tennis court cover?

3. Complete the following:
   A. The area of a rectangle is equal to the product of its _?_ and its _?_.
   B. If we know the area of a rectangle, we can find the length by dividing the _?_ by the _?_.
   C. If we know the area of a rectangle, we can find the width by _?_ the area by the _?_.
   D. There are _?_ square inches in a square foot.

4. The area of a certain rectangle is 308 sq. in. If the rectangle is 22 in. long, what is its width?

5. A roller-skating rink in the shape of a rectangle covers 900 sq. yd. How many square feet does it occupy?

Everyday Problems with Areas

1. Find the cost of carpet, at $11.20 a square yard, for a hallway 18 ft. long and $6\frac{1}{2}$ ft. wide.

2. Each side of a square is 16 in. long. **A.** Find its area in square inches. **B.** To the nearest tenth of a square foot, what is its area in square feet?

3. Mr. Fisher insulated the ceiling of an attic room, measuring 16 ft. by 12 ft. The insulating tiles were 12 in. by 12 in. How many tiles did he have to use? If the tiles came in cartons of 25 for $2.05, how many cartons did he have to order? What was the cost?

4. The dimensions of a rectangle measuring 6 in. by 8 in. can also be written 6" × 8". Here the sign × means *by*. The rectangle is 6 inches wide and 8 inches long. Find the area of a rectangle measuring 14" × 26"; a rectangle $6\frac{1}{2}" \times 8\frac{1}{2}"$.

5. How many times as large as a 2-foot square is a 4-foot square? What is the difference between their areas?

6. If the side of one square is twice that of another, its perimeter will be how many times as great? Its area will be how many times as great?

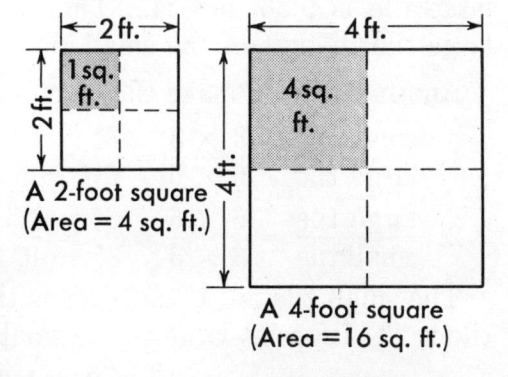

7. Which is larger, a two-foot square or two square feet? How many times as large is it? how much larger?

8. Which is larger, a piece of land in the form of a 5-mile square or a piece of land having an area of 5 square miles? how many times as large? how much larger?

Comparing Areas of Squares

A. Mrs. Philips plans to buy a square tablecloth for her bridge table. One cloth is 3 feet square, and another measures 4 ft. × 4 ft. How many times as large as the first cloth is the second one?

Area of small cloth = 3 × 3 = 9 sq. ft.
Area of large cloth = 4 × 4 = 16 sq. ft.
16 ÷ 9 = $1\frac{7}{9}$ times as large.

The area of the small cloth is what part of the area of the large cloth?

B. One square tile measures 3″ × 3″; another measures 6″ × 6″. What is the ratio of their areas?

Area of the small tile = 3 × 3 = 9 sq. in.
Area of the large tile = 6 × 6 = 36 sq. in.

The ratio of the area of the small tile to that of the large tile is 9:36, or 1:4. The ratio of the area of the large tile to that of the small tile is __?__:__?__, or __?__:__?__.

Another way to make these comparisons is:

1. $\dfrac{\text{small tile}}{\text{large tile}} = \dfrac{3 \times 3}{6 \times 6} = \dfrac{3^2}{6^2} = \dfrac{9}{36} = \dfrac{1}{4}$

2. $\dfrac{\text{large tile}}{\text{small tile}} = \dfrac{6 \times 6}{3 \times 3} = \dfrac{6^2}{3^2} = \dfrac{36}{9} = \dfrac{4}{1} = 4$

The small tile is __?__ as large as the large tile; the large tile is __?__ times as large as the small tile.

1. Compare the area of a 3-inch square with the area of a 1-inch square.

2. Compare the areas of two squares, one of which measures 2″ × 2″ and the other 5″ × 5″.

3. The side of one square is 4 times as long as the side of another square. The area of the large square is how many times as great as the area of the small square?

Measuring Land

1. There are $30\frac{1}{4}$ square yards in a square rod. There are 160 square rods in an acre. How many square yards are there in an acre?

2. How many square feet in a square yard? How many square feet in an acre?

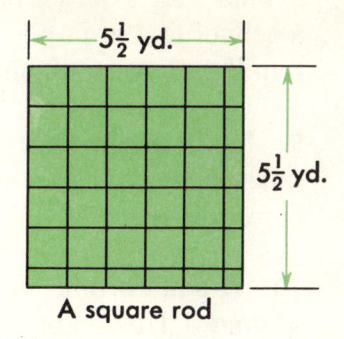

A square rod

3. There are 640 acres in a square mile; how many square rods are there in one square mile?

4. A rectangular city lot 50 ft. × 150 ft. contains how many square feet? This is approximately $\frac{1}{6}$ of an acre, since $\frac{1}{6}$ of 43,560 sq. ft. = 7260 sq. ft.

5. Another lot is 72 ft. × 150 ft. What is its area in square feet? About what fraction of an acre is this?

6. A certain city lot measures 25 ft. × 100 ft. Allowing approximately 45,000 sq. ft. to the acre, about how many such lots are there to an acre?

7. City lots may be measured by the square foot, but the **front foot** (measured along the front of a lot) is often used to tell the size of the lot. If a lot is 25 ft. wide and 100 ft. long (deep), it has a "frontage" of 25 ft. Find the area of a lot 118 ft. deep with a frontage of 26 ft.

It will help you to picture an acre to think that a football field is a little more than 1 acre, and a baseball diamond, excluding the outfield, is about $\frac{1}{5}$ acre.

8. The education department of a certain state recommends that a playground area of 8 acres be provided for a school of 400 pupils. This is how many square feet per pupil? (1 A. = 43,560 sq. ft.)

9. In a certain part of a city there are 10 blocks to the mile each way, east-west and north-south. How many acres are there in one square block (nearest whole acre)?

10. A square mile, or 640 acres, is also called a **section** of land. How many acres in a quarter-section?

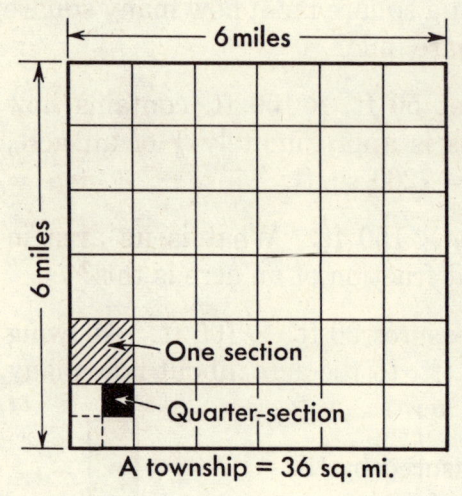

11. In many parts of our country the counties are divided into **townships,** which are squares 6 miles on a side. How many square miles does a township contain? a section?

12. A quarter-section of land contains what part of a square mile? How many quarter-sections are there in a township?

A township = 36 sq. mi.

JUST FOR FUN

1. If one mile of fencing encloses a field of 40 acres, how many acres can 2 miles of fencing enclose?

2. A motorist starts out to travel two miles in his car, covering the first mile at the rate of 30 miles an hour. What rate of speed must he maintain in covering the second mile in order to average 60 miles per hour for the entire trip of two miles?

Finding the Area of a Triangle

A Girl Scout troop has a triangular piece of forest land for its camp. If the land has a base of 540 feet and an altitude of 300 feet, what is the area in square feet?

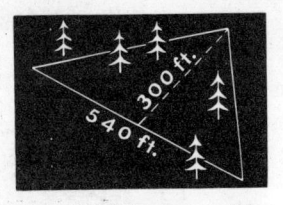

This piece of land is a triangle (Fig. 1) 540 ft. wide (*AB*), and 300 ft. high (*CD*, or *BE*). The **altitude** of a triangle is its **height,** or the line (*CD*) drawn from one corner perpendicular to the side (*AB*) opposite that corner.

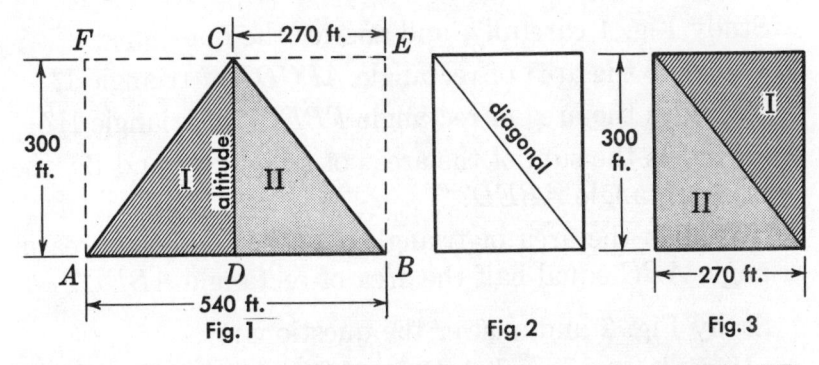

Fig. 1 shows the triangular piece of land, with altitude *CD*. The side (*AB*) of the triangle *ABC* is called the **base**.

You know that the diagonal of a rectangle divides it into two equal triangles (Fig. 2).

Make a drawing like Fig. 3. Do you see that triangles I and II are equal? Since the two triangles make up the rectangle (Fig. 3) the area of triangle *ABC* is equal to the area of the rectangle in Fig. 3, or 270 × 300 = 81,000 sq. ft. The area of triangle *ABC* equals one-half the product of its base and its altitude, or $\frac{1}{2}$ × 540 × 300 = 81,000 sq. ft.

This can be written as a formula, as follows:
Area = $\frac{1}{2}$ × *base* × *altitude*, or $A = \frac{1}{2} b \times h$, or $A = \frac{1}{2} bh$.

Learning More about Triangles

Not all triangles have the same shape as the piece of land, page 165.

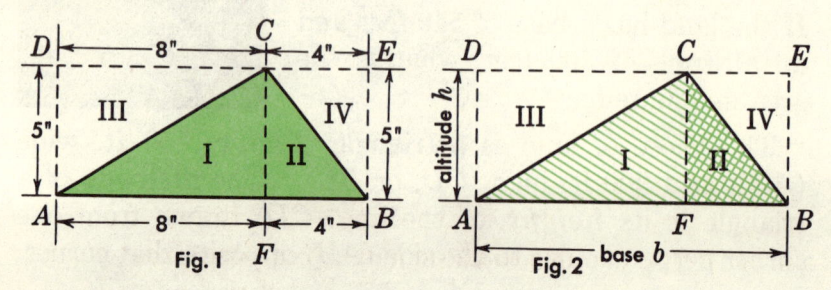

Study Fig. 1 carefully, and answer the questions:

1. What is the area of rectangle *AFCD*? of triangle I?
2. What is the area of rectangle *FBEC*? of triangle II?
3. What is the sum of the areas of triangles I and II? the area of rectangle *ABED*?
4. What is the area of triangle *ABC*? Does the area of triangle *ABC* equal half the area of rectangle *ABED*?

Study Fig. 2 and answer the questions:

5. How else can we label the base *AB* of rectangle *ABED*? the altitude *AD*?
6. What is the area of rectangle *ABED*?
7. How else can we label the base *AB* of triangle *ABC*? the altitude *CF*? Do you see that altitude *AD* equals altitude *CF*?
8. How does the area of triangle I compare with that of triangle III? triangle II with triangle IV?
9. How does the area of triangle *ABC* compare with the area of rectangle *ABED* in Fig. 1? in Fig. 2?
10. What does the formula, $A = \frac{1}{2} bh$, tell us?
11. Find the area of a triangle whose base is 26 inches and whose altitude is 10 inches.

12. Find the areas of the following triangles:

	BASE	ALTITUDE		BASE	ALTITUDE
A.	16 in.	9 in.	E.	600 yd.	120 yd.
B.	14 yd.	8 yd.	F.	11 ft.	8.4 ft.
C.	24 ft.	$6\frac{1}{2}$ ft.	G.	1.8 mi.	1.2 mi.
D.	38 in.	17 in.	H.	$2\frac{1}{2}$ ft.	$\frac{1}{2}$ ft.

13. The triangular sail of a boat is 21 ft. high and 12 ft. along the base. What is the area of the sail in square yards?

14. A certain triangle has a base of 8 ft. and an altitude of 12 ft. Another triangle has an altitude of 8 ft. and a base of 12 ft. Find the area of each triangle.

15. If the base of one triangle equals the altitude of another triangle, and the altitude of the first equals the base of the second, how do their areas compare?

16. Does $\frac{1}{2} bh = (\frac{1}{2} b) \times (h)$? Does $\frac{1}{2} bh = (\frac{1}{2} h) \times b$?

17. If the base of a triangle is twice that of another, but their altitudes are equal, how do their areas compare?

18. If the altitude of a triangle is made one-half as great, while the base remains the same, what can you say of its area?

19. If two triangles have equal bases but different altitudes, which has the greater area? What could you say if they had equal altitudes but different bases?

20. Measure the bases of these triangles; are they equal? If several triangles have equal bases and equal altitudes, what can you say about their areas?

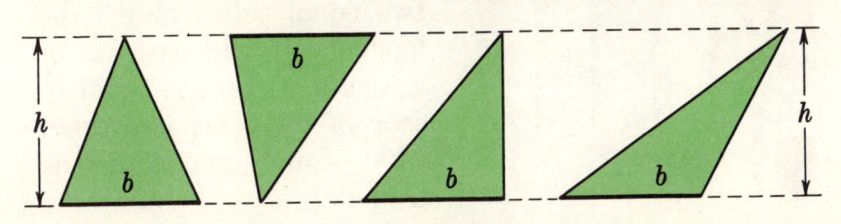

The Sides of a Triangle

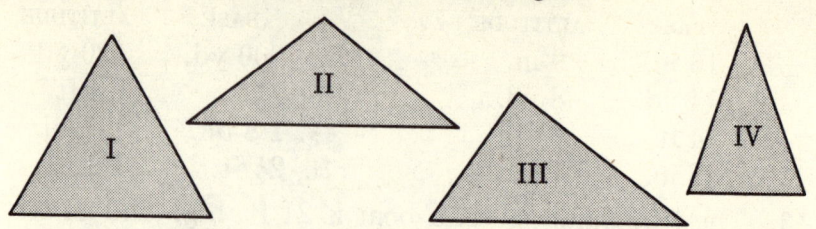

1. In which of these triangles are all three sides equal in length? only two sides equal? all the sides unequal?

2. If two sides of a triangle are equal in length, the triangle is called an **isosceles triangle**; the third side is called the base of the isosceles triangle. If the equal sides of a triangle are each 18 inches, and the base is 10 inches, what is the perimeter of the triangle?

3. If all three sides of a triangle are equal, it is called an **equilateral triangle.** In such a triangle, any one of the three sides may be regarded as the base. What is the perimeter of an equilateral triangle, if each side is 16.8 cm.?

4. Write a formula for the perimeter of a triangle with three unequal sides a, b, and c.

5. Find the perimeter of a triangle with sides 12 in., $14\frac{1}{2}$ in., and $16\frac{3}{4}$ in. long.

6. Study these two pictures. Can you see the isosceles triangles? May the base of an isosceles triangle be shorter than either of the two equal sides? may it be longer? If the base of an isosceles triangle is equal to each of the other two sides, what could you call the triangle?

168

The Meaning of Angle

When two straight lines meet in a point, the figure is called an **angle**. These are angles:

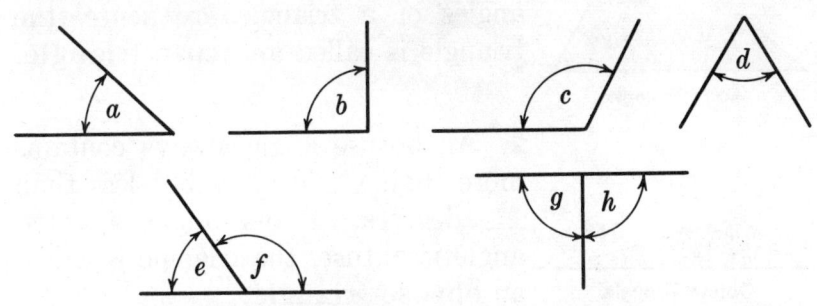

In angle a the two lines are not "opened" as widely as they are in angle b and angle c. We say that angle a is less than angle b; angle b is less than angle c; angle c is greater than either angle a or angle b.

The point at which two lines meet is called the **vertex** of the angle.

1. As the minute hand of a clock makes one complete revolution, it turns through 360 degrees (360°). How many degrees does it turn through in $\frac{1}{2}$ hour? $\frac{1}{4}$ hr.? $\frac{3}{4}$ hr.? 20 min.? 10 min.? 5 min.?

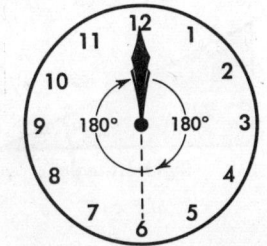

2. A quarter-turn is called a **right angle**. How many degrees in a right angle? Which of the angles at the top of the page are right angles?

3. An angle less than 90° is called an **acute angle**. Which of the angles at the top of the page are acute?

4. Any angle that is greater than 90° but less than 180° is called an **obtuse angle**. Which of the angles at the top of the page are obtuse? Do you see why an angle of 180° is called a **straight angle**?

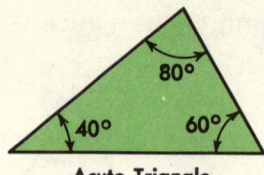

The Angles of a Triangle

1. An acute angle always contains less than __?__ degrees. If all the angles of a triangle are acute, the triangle is called an **acute triangle**.

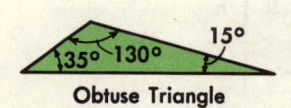

2. An obtuse angle always contains more than __?__ degrees but less than __?__ degrees. If one angle of a triangle is obtuse, the triangle is called an **obtuse triangle**.

3. Do you think a triangle can have more than one obtuse angle? Try to draw a triangle containing two obtuse angles.

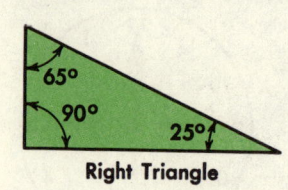

4. If an angle of a triangle is a right angle, the triangle is called a **right triangle**. Can a triangle have more than one right angle? Try to draw a triangle having two right angles.

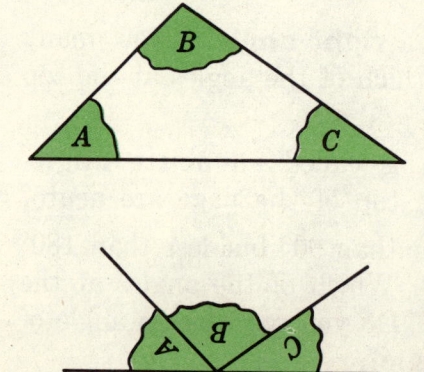

5. Draw a triangle on cardboard, marking the angles A, B, and C. Cut out the triangle. Tear off the "corners", and place these angles together as shown. **A.** How many degrees are there in the sum of these three angles? **B.** What is the sum of the three angles of any triangle?

～ 170 ～

6. Now can you explain your answers to the questions in Problems **3** and **4** on page 170?

7. Name each kind of triangle shown below. What is the sum of all three angles of each triangle? What part of a complete revolution is this sum? How many right angles is this?

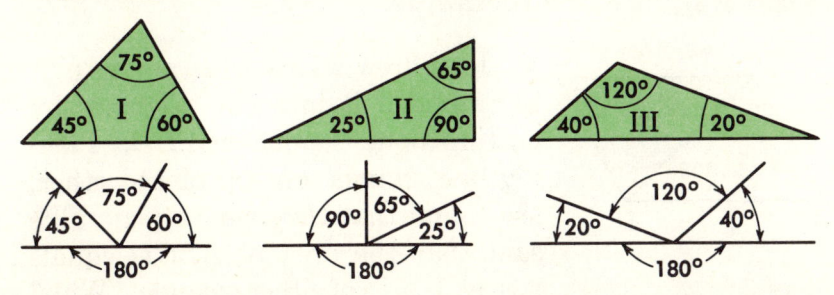

8. There are 29° in one angle of a triangle, and 104° in another angle. How many degrees are there in the third angle of this triangle?

9. Find the missing angles in each of the following:

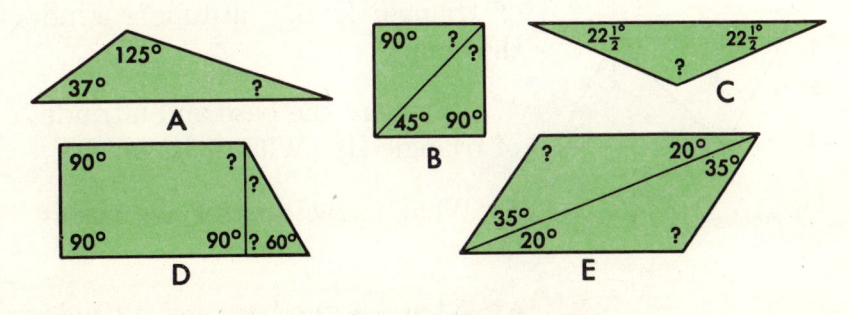

JIFFY QUIZ

1. How many times as great as $\frac{1}{8}$ is 8?
2. Write $\frac{3}{10}$ of 1 per cent as a decimal.
3. What is the ratio of 2 oz. to $\frac{1}{4}$ lb.?
4. Does $12 \times \$.75 = \frac{3}{4} \times \$12$?
5. What ratio is expressed by 2%? 150%? $\frac{1}{2}$%?

Area of a Parallelogram

When lines run in exactly the same direction, they are **parallel**. If both pairs of opposite sides of a four-sided figure are parallel, the figure is a **parallelogram**. If the angles of a parallelogram are right angles, the figure is either a **square** or a **rectangle**.

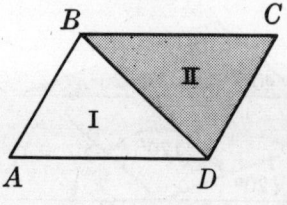

1. Joan drew a parallelogram $ABCD$. She divided it into two triangles by cutting along the diagonal BD. Placing one triangle on top of the other, she found that they were equal. She said that the area of $ABCD$ equals twice the area of either triangle. Why?

2. What can you say about the lengths of the opposite sides of a rectangle? the opposite sides of a parallelogram?

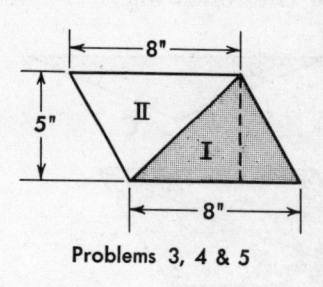

Problems 3, 4 & 5

3. What is the length of the base of triangle I? the altitude? Find the area.

4. What are the base and altitude of triangle II? What is its area?

5. What is the area of the parallelogram?

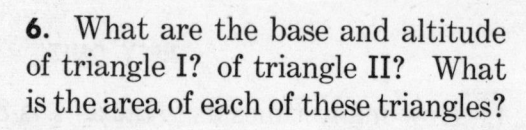

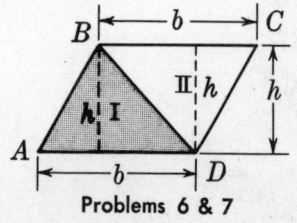

6. What are the base and altitude of triangle I? of triangle II? What is the area of each of these triangles?

Problems 6 & 7

7. Name the base of this parallelogram. Name its altitude. What is its area? State a rule for finding the area of any parallelogram.

Practice in Using Formulas

1. Complete the following table about rectangles, using the formula $A = bh$. Remember that A means area, b means base, and h means altitude.

	A	B	C	D	E
when b = and h = then A =	6 ft. 2½ ft. ?	20 in. 13 in. ?	140 yd. 45 yd. ?	12.2 cm. 4.1 cm. ?	12 in. ? 48 sq. in.

2. The base of a rectangle is 4½ yards and its altitude is 1½ feet. Using the formula, $A = bh$, find the area.

3. You have also used the formula $A = lw$ to find the area of a rectangle. What does the l represent? the w?

4. What does the formula $A = \frac{1}{2}bh$ represent? Does this mean the same as $A = \frac{bh}{2}$?

5. Complete the following table about triangles, using the formula $A = \frac{1}{2} bh$:

	A	B	C	D	E
when b equals: and h equals: then A equals:	4 ft. 2 ft. ?	1 in. 2¼ in. ?	8¼ yd. 6 yd. ?	4 ft. 10 ft. ?	16 yd. 2 yd. ?

6. The base of a triangle is twice its altitude. Its altitude is 3½ yd. Find its area.

7. Each of two triangles has a base of 9 ft. The altitude of one triangle is 12 ft. The altitude of the other is 6 ft. Find the area of each triangle. How do the triangles compare in area?

Area of a Trapezoid

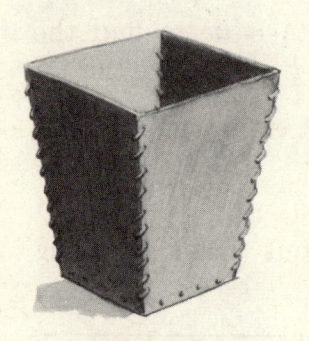

Alice is making a wastebasket. The bottom is in the shape of a square, and the open top is a slightly larger square. The four side pieces, all alike, will have to be made narrower at one end than at the other. Each side of the wastebasket has the shape of a trapezoid.

A **trapezoid** is a four-sided figure having only two of its sides parallel. The figures below are trapezoids.

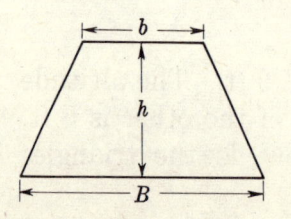

The two parallel sides are called the **bases** of the trapezoid.

The **altitude** (or height) of a trapezoid is the perpendicular distance between its bases.

174

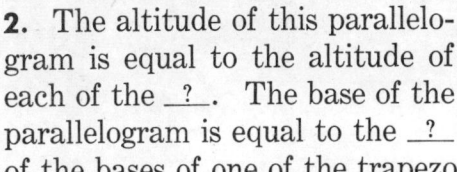

1. Cut out two trapezoids exactly alike from a sheet of cardboard. Place them together as shown. The new figure is a __?__. 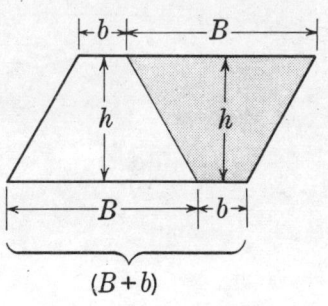
2. The altitude of this parallelogram is equal to the altitude of each of the __?__. The base of the parallelogram is equal to the __?__ of the bases of one of the trapezoids.
3. The area of the parallelogram equals $h \times (B + b)$, or $h(B + b)$. In a formula, when two quantities are enclosed in parentheses, as $(B + b)$, the terms in parentheses must be added first, before multiplying.
4. The area of the parallelogram is twice as great as the area of either trapezoid. Why?
5. Then we may say that the area of one of the trapezoids is equal to $\frac{1}{2}h(B + b)$, or $A = \dfrac{h(B + b)}{2}$.
6. Find the area of each of the following trapezoids:

	b	B	h	A
A	12 in.	18 in.	9 in.	?
B	17 ft.	25 ft.	14 ft.	?
C	$4\frac{1}{2}$ in.	6 in.	$5\frac{1}{4}$ in.	?
D	32.2 cm.	24.6 cm.	12.5 cm.	?

Keeping in Practice

A
1. $10\frac{1}{3} - 8\frac{3}{4} = ?$
2. $66\overline{)3094}$

B
1. $4\frac{1}{4} \div 2\frac{1}{2} = ?$
2. $0.06\overline{)21.6}$

C
1. $.8 \div .04 = ?$
2. $7305 \div 18 = ?$

3. Find the interest on $426 for 2 years at $2\frac{1}{2}\%$.

The Merry-go-round

When Helen and Fred were riding on the merry-go-round in the park, the attendant told them that the big circular platform of the merry-go-round was 40 feet in diameter (distance across) and the **circumference**, or distance around the platform, was about 126 feet.

1. Fred said that the circumference of the platform was about 3 times the diameter. Was he right? Divide the circumference by the diameter and express the quotient to two decimal places.

2. In the park playground for very young children, a small merry-go-round is 5 feet in diameter. The circumference is about 16 feet. This circumference is about how many times the diameter?

3. Do you see that if you know the circumference of any circle you can find its diameter by dividing? If you know the diameter, how can you find the circumference?

4. What is the ratio of the circumference to the diameter, approximately?

Actually, very careful measurement shows that the ratio of the circumference of a circle to its diameter is about $3\frac{1}{7}$, or about 3.14. That is, the circumference of a circle is about $3\frac{1}{7}$, or $\frac{22}{7}$, times its diameter. This ratio is written π—**pi**, and pronounced *pie*.

The Circumference of a Circle

The distance from the center to any point on the circle is called the **radius**. (The plural of radius is **radii**.) Any straight line through the center, cut off by the circle at each end, is called the **diameter**. The **circumference** of a circle is the length of the circle.

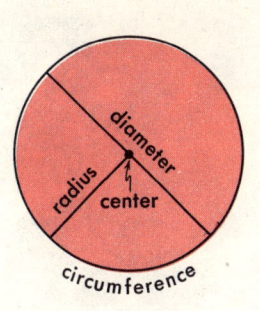

1. **A.** The diameter (D) is __?__ as long as the radius (r).
   B. The circumference is approximately __?__ times as long as the diameter.
   C. A formula for the circumference is $C = \pi D$. Do you see that this could also be written $C = 2\pi r$? If $D = 14$, $C =$ __?__; if $r = 4.2$, $C =$ __?__.
   Remember, $\pi = 3\frac{1}{7}$, or $\frac{22}{7}$.
   D. If $C = \pi D$, then $D = \frac{C}{\pi}$. If $C = 11$, $D =$ __?__.

2. Find the missing values (use $\pi = \frac{22}{7}$):

	A	B	C	D	E
D	28 ft.	3.5 in.	—	10 yd.	—
r	—	—	200 ft.	—	48 cm.
C	?	?	?	?	?

3. The outside diameter of the tire on the wheel of a plane's landing gear is about 4 ft. As the plane taxies down the runway, about how many feet will it move during each revolution of the wheel?

Courtesy Trans World Airline

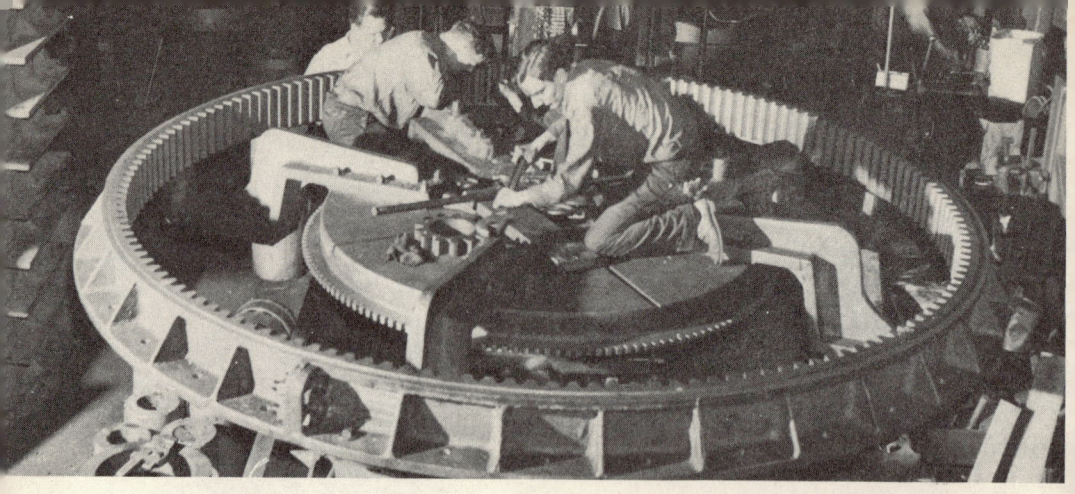

4. These machinists are cutting a gear wheel for a ship of the United States Navy. The huge wheel is 145 inches in outside diameter. What is its circumference to the nearest tenth of an inch?

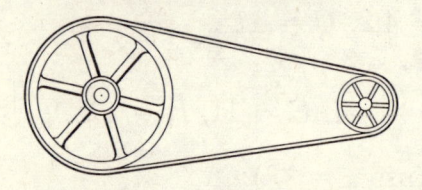

5. Two pulleys are connected by a belt. The diameter of the smaller pulley is 14 in.; the diameter of the larger is 42 in. For each revolution of the larger pulley, how many revolutions will the smaller pulley make?

6. The rear wheel of a tractor is twice as great in diameter as the front wheel. How many times as great is its circumference?

Keeping in Practice

1. Write as per cents: $\frac{7}{8}$, $\frac{4}{5}$, $\frac{3}{20}$, $\frac{5}{6}$, $\frac{1}{12}$.
2. Find: 150% of $3000; $\frac{3}{10}$% of $10,000.
3. Write as decimals: 50%, $2\frac{1}{2}$%, $\frac{94}{100}$, $\frac{1}{4}$ of 1%.
4. What per cent of 4 yd. is 2 ft.?
5. Find: 20% more than $500; 25% less than $80.

Silent Power

Today huge steam turbines drive ocean liners and turn the machines used for making electricity. The picture shows the inside of a turbine. On these disks, or wheels, there may be as many as 1500 tiny blades, forming grooves through which the steam rushes. As the steam pushes against these blades it causes the entire shaft to spin rapidly, much as the wind pushing against the blades of a windmill makes them turn.

1. The tips of the longest blades of a certain turbine move at the rate of 1248 feet per second. Sound travels through air at the rate of about 1088 feet per second. How much faster do the blades move?

2. In another turbine the tip speed of the blades is 1178 feet per second. At this rate, how many miles per hour are they moving?

3. On some turbines the tip speed averages 13 miles per minute. How many feet per second do the blade tips move?

4. A bullet fired by a certain rifle travels 1276 ft. per second. How many miles per minute faster does the bullet move than the blade tips in Problem **3**?

5. At its widest part, the disk of the turbine shown below is 76 inches in diameter. What is its circumference in feet?

Disk wheels inside a steam turbine © *Philip Gendreau*

Finding the Area of a Circle

The circle in Fig. 1 has been divided into **sectors**. Each sector is like a triangle, except that its base is curved. The altitude of each of these sectors is equal to the radius of the circle. The sum of the bases of all these sectors equals the circumference of the circle. (See Fig. 2.)

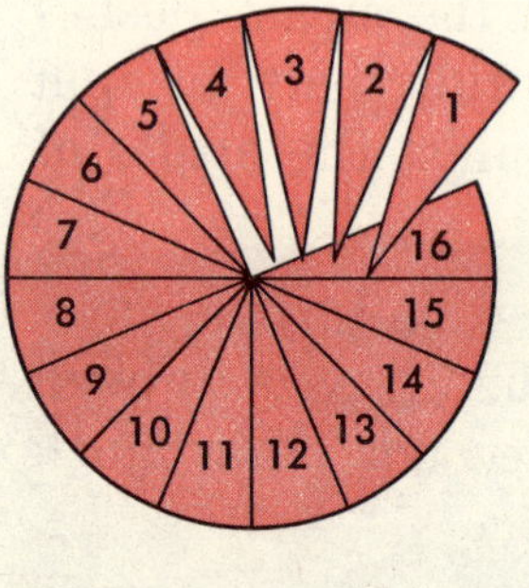

Fig. 1

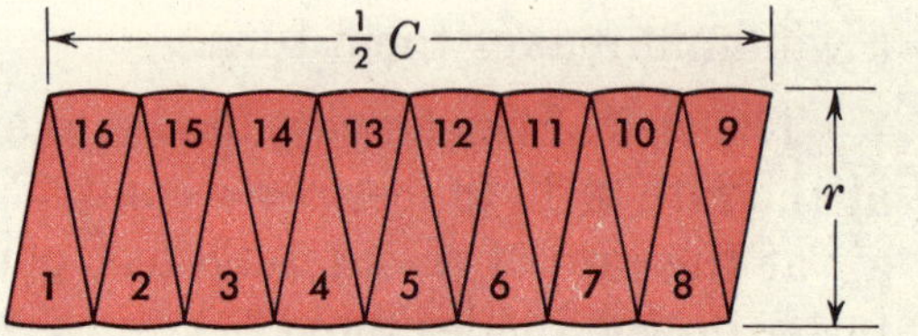

Fig. 2

If we divide the circle into a greater number of sectors, the bases of the sectors will look more nearly like straight lines, and the whole figure will look more like a rectangle.

The **length** of this rectangle will equal half the circumference, or $\frac{1}{2} C$. Why? The **width** of this rectangle will equal the radius of the circle (r). Since the area of a rectangle equals the product of its length and its width, the area of this rectangle is $\frac{1}{2} C \times r$.

We have learned that $C = 2 \pi r$, or $\frac{1}{2} C = \pi r$. Then we may write πr in place of $\frac{1}{2} C$. The area of a circle, A, equals $\pi r \times r$, or $\pi \times r \times r$. But $r \times r = r^2$; so the formula for the area of a circle is: $A = \pi r^2$.

1. Find the area of a circular tray 14 in. in diameter.
2. The radius of a frying pan is $3\frac{1}{2}$ in. Find its area.
3. Find the area of a circular plot 18 ft. in diameter.
4. Find, to the nearest hundred square feet, the area of the surface of a circular pond 200 ft. in diameter.

Problems about Circles

1. A pony is tied to a stake by a rope which allows him to graze over an area with a radius of 17½ feet. Over how many square feet can he graze?

2. What will the labor cost be of laying a tile bottom in a circular wading pool whose radius is 28 feet, if the cost of laying the tiles is 15¢ per square foot?

3. The largest possible circular piece is cut from a square sheet of parchment 28 inches by 28 inches. Find the area of the circle, and also the number of square inches of material wasted.

4. What is the area of a circle whose radius is 7 in.? a circle whose radius is twice as long? The area of the second circle is how many times that of the first?

5. If the radius of one circle is twice the radius of another circle, the area of the large circle will be __?__ times the area of the small circle.

6. Find the area of a semicircular (half a circle) glass window having a radius of 3½ feet.

7. Which is larger in area, a circular opening 14 inches in diameter or a square opening 14 inches on a side? how much larger?

8. A circular flower bed 18 feet in diameter is surrounded by a brick walk 3 feet in width. What is the radius of the smaller circle? the larger circle? How would you find the area of the brick walk? What is the area of the walk?

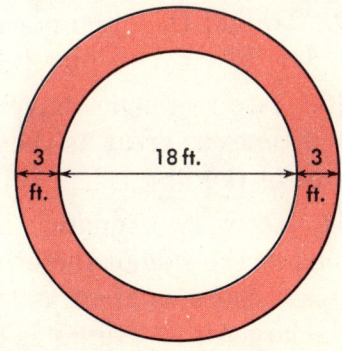

Learning to Solve Problems

Understanding Relations in Geometric Figures

To solve problems about geometric figures, you must know how certain quantities are related. These questions will help you to understand such relations.

In each of the following, select the correct answer:

1. If you know the sides of a triangle, you (add, subtract, divide) to find the perimeter.

2. If you know the perimeter of a square, you (add, subtract, divide, multiply) to find the length of a side.

3. If you know the area of a rectangle and also its length, to find the width you (multiply, subtract, divide).

4. If you know the circumference of a circle, you (divide, multiply) by π to find the diameter.

Complete the following statements:

5. The area of a triangle depends upon the length of its _?_ and of its _?_ .

6. All triangles having equal bases and equal altitudes have equal _?_ s, regardless of their shape.

7. To find the area of a circle, we need to know only one dimension, either its _?_ or its _?_ .

8. The area of a parallelogram depends upon its _?_ and its _?_ .

9. To find the circumference of a circle, we multiply the radius by _?_ ; to find the area, we multiply _?_ by _?_ .

10. Two rectangles have equal bases; the altitude of one is 3 times as great as the altitude of the other. Then the area of the first is _?_ times as great as that of the other.

11. Draw two squares; make the side of one 3 times as long as the side of the other. The perimeter of the larger is _?_ times as great as that of the smaller. The area of the larger is _?_ times as great as that of the smaller.

Learning to Solve Problems

What Facts Are Missing?

To answer the question in a problem, certain facts are needed. If any needed fact is missing, the question cannot be answered.

In each of these problems, tell what fact is missing:

1. The price of butter has increased 5¢ per pound. What is the per cent of increase?

2. A dress is sold at a discount of $33\frac{1}{3}\%$. How much can be saved by buying the dress at this discount?

3. The sales tax on a certain purchase amounts to $.20. The tax is what per cent of the price?

4. A family spends 24% of its yearly income for food. How much money does this family spend for food in one month?

5. Bob's uncle added $100 to his bank account. The next day he withdrew $40. What was the balance?

6. An agent is paid a commission of 6% on all of his sales. What was the agent's commission in two weeks?

7. Mr. Judson borrowed $650 for 6 months. What interest must he pay?

8. Two pints of vinegar were poured out of a jug; how many pints remained?

9. The perimeter of a rectangle is 60 ft.; find its length.

10. The width of a rectangle is $\frac{1}{4}$ of its length. What is the perimeter?

11. A rectangular room is 18 ft. long and 12 ft. wide. What is the area of the four walls?

More Problems about Circles

1. A circular skating rink is 120 feet in diameter. Find the number of square feet of skating surface.

2. The tires of Mr. Dawson's automobile have an outside diameter of 28 inches. What is the outer circumference of each tire? How far will his car travel when the wheels make one complete revolution?

3. How many revolutions will the wheel of Mr. Dawson's car make in going one mile?

4. Find the circumference of a 12-inch phonograph record.

5. The inner diameter of a steel pipe is 8″. If the pipe is $\frac{1}{2}$″ thick, what is its outer circumference?

6. What is the diameter of a telephone pole if its circumference is 44 in.?

7. If the equator is about 25,000 miles in length, find the approximate radius of the earth at the equator. Express the answer to the nearest thousand miles.

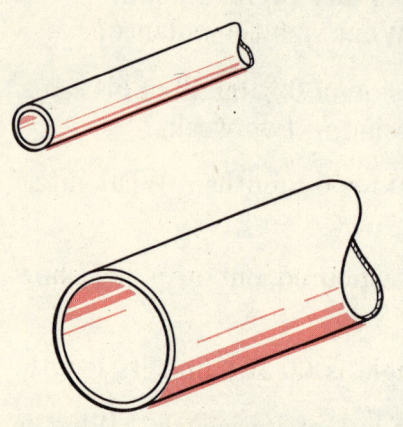

8. The amount of water that flows through a pipe depends upon the area of the open end of the pipe. If the rate of flow is the same for both, a pipe 6 in. in diameter will carry how many times as much water as a pipe 2 in. in diameter? Do you actually have to find the area of each circular opening?

9. Two cylindrical steam pipes have the same length. One has a diameter of 2 in. The other has a diameter of 3 in. The larger pipe provides how many times as much heating surface?

JUST FOR FUN

1. Place two coins side by side as shown in the picture. Without moving the coin at B, roll coin A around B, so that they always touch, until A is in the position of C. Will the head on coin A, when it reaches C, be inverted or the same as in A? How many revolutions has coin A made *about its own center* in going from A to C?

2. Here are five circles having the same center. The "bands" are all equal in width. Which of the two shaded areas is the greater?

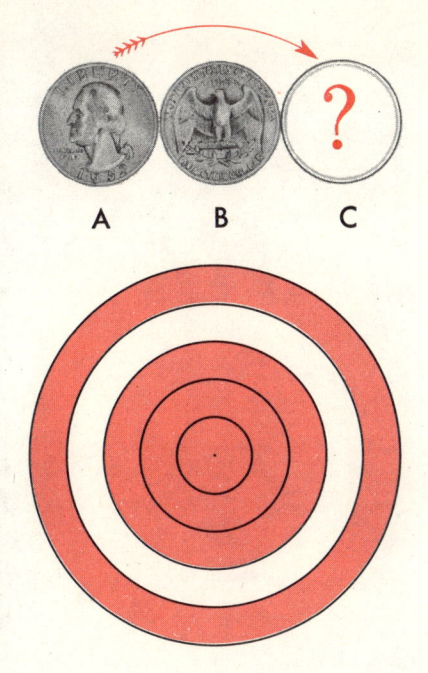

JIFFY QUIZ

1. If a sales tax is raised from 2% to 3%, what is the per cent of increase in the tax?

2. On July 12, Helen's cousin arrived for a visit. She stayed 2 weeks. On what date did she go home?

3. Does $160 \div .125 = 160 \div 8$?

4. The printing press was first used in Europe about the year 1450. In what century was this? About how many centuries ago was it?

5. What is the difference between $\frac{1}{10}$ of $500 and $\frac{1}{10}$% of $500?

6. Does 40% of $20 equal 20% of $40?

7. What is $.003 \times 10{,}000{,}000$?

185

Wheels within Wheels

The first watch, or portable clock, was made by a locksmith of Nuremberg about 1504. It was entirely of iron, and stood half a foot high.

The modern watch is a marvel of precision. The mechanism inside is called the **movement**. Even in the very thinnest of watches, the movement consists of a flat coiled spring and six wheels. Five of these wheels are connected in a "train", since they turn together by means of interlocking "teeth".

1. The balance wheel swings to and fro, causing the watch to tick. A certain watch that is in perfect time ticks five times in a second. How many times will it tick in one hour? in one day?

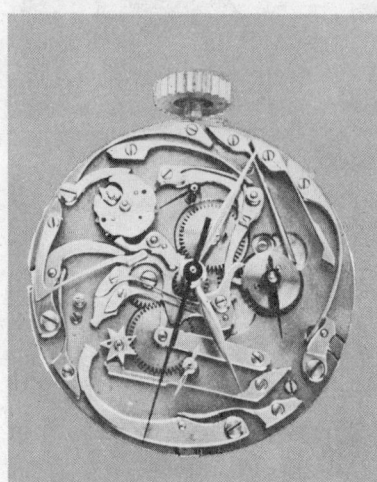

Courtesy The Watchmakers of Switzerland

2. In one day (24 hr.), a point on the rim of the balance wheel of a certain watch travels a total distance of about 10 miles. About how many inches does it travel in one minute? in one second?

3. At five ticks, or swings, per second, through what distance (to the nearest hundredth of an inch) does the rim of the balance wheel move on each swing?

～ 186 ～

Understanding Surface Measure

1. Draw an isosceles triangle; a right triangle; an equilateral triangle; an obtuse triangle; an acute triangle that is not equilateral.

2. If either diagonal of a square is drawn, in what ways are the triangles so formed alike?

3. Explain the difference between the perimeter and the area of any figure.

4. If s represents the side of a square, write a formula for the area of the square.

5. A square measures 10 ft. on each side. Find its perimeter; its area.

6. A circle has a diameter of one foot. Find its circumference; its area.

7. Find the area of the square at the right. What is the radius of the circle within the square? What is its area?

8. What is the difference between the area of the square and the area of the circle in Problem **7**? What is the ratio of the area of the circle to that of the square? The area of the circle is what per cent of the area of the square?

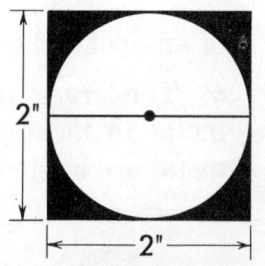

9. If the radius of one circle is twice that of another, the diameter of the first circle is how many times as long as the diameter of the second? The area of the first circle is how many times as great as the area of the second?

10. If the area of one circle is four times as great as the area of another circle, the radius of the first is how many times as long as the radius of the second?

Making Sure

1. If the perimeter of a square is 32 inches, what is the length of a side? What is the area? <small>159, 160</small>

2. A rectangle is 48 yd. by 60 yd. What is the area of one of the triangles formed by drawing a diagonal? <small>165, 167</small>

3. Two circles have diameters of 10 inches and 20 inches, respectively. What is the ratio of their radii? their circumferences? their areas? <small>180</small>

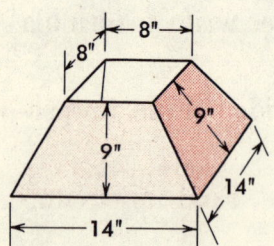

4. Each of the four sides of a parchment lamp shade is in the shape of a trapezoid with the dimensions shown. How many square inches of parchment are required to cover the shade? <small>175</small>

5. What is the total outside surface of an open cubical box measuring 4″ × 4″ × 4″? <small>159</small>

6. The largest possible circle is cut from a square piece of metal 14 inches on a side. How many square inches of metal are wasted? What per cent is wasted? <small>180</small>

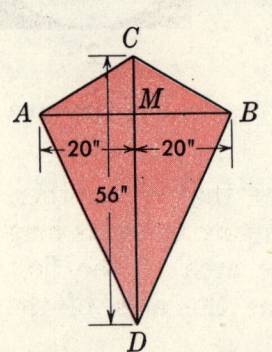

7. A kite frame is made in the shape of two isosceles triangles. The crosspiece AB measures 40 in., and the long piece CD measures 56 in. What is the area of the paper needed to cover this frame? First find the area of triangle ACD, using CD as the base. <small>166, 168</small>

8. The area of a certain parallelogram is equal to that of a rectangle which measures 24 in. × 8 in. If the base of the parallelogram is 32 in., what is its altitude? <small>172</small>

9. $A = \frac{1}{2}bh$; if $b = 36$ and $h = 16$, find A. <small>165, 167</small>

Gaining Skill in Arithmetic

Compare the two methods, A and B, used in each example:

Example 1. At 3 for 10¢, how many oranges can you buy for 50¢?
A. 10¢ ÷ 3 = $3\frac{1}{3}$¢; 50 ÷ $3\frac{1}{3}$ = 50 ÷ $\frac{10}{3}$ = 50 × $\frac{3}{10}$ = 15
B. How many 10's in 50? Five. 5 × 3 = 15

Example 2. Find the cost of 24 boxes at $62\frac{1}{2}$¢ each.

A. $\quad$ \$.62½
$\quad\quad\times\ 24$
$\quad\quad\overline{12}$
$\quad\quad\ 248$
$\quad\quad\ 124$
$\quad\quad\overline{\$15.00}$

B. \$.62½ = \$.625 = \$⅝

$\overset{3}{\cancel{24}} \times \$\frac{5}{\cancel{8}} = \$15$
1

Example 3. What is 75% of \$640?

A. $\quad$ \$640
$\quad\quad\times\ .75$
$\quad\quad\overline{\$480.00}$

B. 75% = ¾
$\quad$¾ of \$640 = \$480

Example 4. A man bought 95 acres of land at \$150 an acre and sold them at \$225 an acre. How much did he gain?

A. $\quad$ \$150 $\quad\quad$ \$225 $\quad\quad$ \$21,375 $\quad$ B. $\quad$ \$225 $\quad\quad$ \$75
$\quad\quad\ \times\ 95 \quad\quad\ \times\ 95 \quad\quad -14{,}250 \quad\quad\quad\ -150 \quad\quad \times\ 95$
$\quad\quad\overline{\$14{,}250} \quad \overline{\$21{,}375} \quad \overline{\$\ 7{,}125} \quad\quad\quad \overline{\$\ 75} \quad \overline{\$7125}$

If these problems can be solved in more than one way, use the simpler method, and solve each problem.

1. Find the cost of 48 articles at \$.87½ each; the cost of 36 articles at $16\frac{2}{3}$¢ each.

2. What is $37\frac{1}{2}$% of \$980? $66\frac{2}{3}$% of \$2775?

3. A dealer bought 1320 tons of coal at \$15.50 a ton and sold them at \$17.50 a ton. What was his profit?

4. At the rate of 3 for 25¢, how many bottles of pop can be bought for \$1.75? How much will 150 bottles cost?

© *Philip Gendreau*

Sphere-shaped tanks for storing butadiene, used in the manufacture of synthetic rubber

6

MEASURING SOLIDS

Some Common Solids

Objects such as building blocks, baseballs, tops, balloons, boxes, and ice-cream cones have definite shapes. Other objects, such as a piece of stone, a lump of clay, or a stick of wood, may be irregular in shape. All of these objects are solids.

1. A solid having six flat sides, or surfaces, each of which is a rectangle, is a **rectangular prism**. Name three objects which are rectangular prisms or solids. They may be empty or hollow like a box, or "solid" like a brick.

2. A **cube** is a special kind of rectangular prism. All the surfaces of a cube are squares. Name two objects having a cubical shape.

3. A **cylinder** is illustrated by an ordinary can of peas or a drum. Some cylinders are much taller than others; a flat cylinder like a coin, is called a **disk**. Name three objects having the shape of a cylinder or disk.

4. A. Name three objects shaped like a **sphere**. **B.** Name four objects shaped like a **cone**.

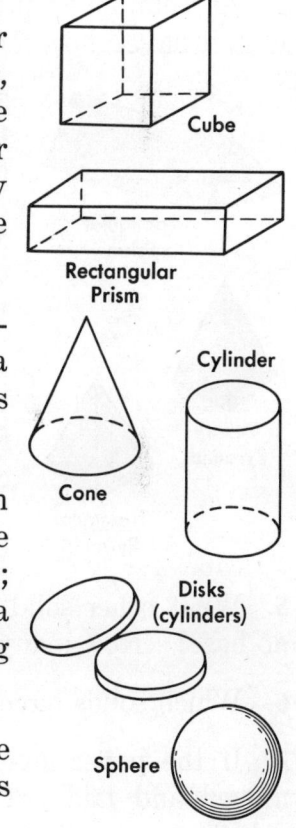

~ 191 ~

Getting Acquainted with Solids

A solid has thickness. The surfaces of a solid do not have thickness. A surface has only area.

Some surfaces are flat, others are curved. The flat surfaces of a solid are called **faces**.

1. A cube has 6 faces. How many edges does a cube have? how many corners? A "corner" of a solid is called a ***vertex***; it is the point where three or more edges meet. The plural of vertex is ***vertices***.

2. A rectangular prism has 6 faces. How many edges does it have? how many vertices?

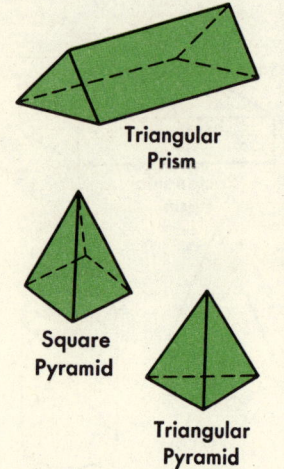

3. How many faces does a **triangular prism** have? how many edges? how many vertices?

Triangular Prism

4. How many faces, edges, and vertices does a **square pyramid** have? a **triangular pyramid**?

Square Pyramid

Triangular Pyramid

The face upon which a solid rests is called a ***base***. If there is an equal face opposite the base, it is also called a base. For example, a rectangular prism has two bases; a pyramid has only one base.

5. What other solid has only one base? What solid has no base? How many bases has a cylinder?

6. Which solids have curved surfaces?

7. If the paper label around a cylindrical can were removed and laid out flat, what geometric figure would it be?

Surface of a Prism

The top and bottom surfaces (bases) of this rectangular box have been removed. The box has been slit open along one edge and laid out flat.

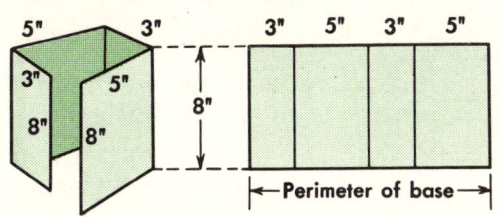

1. If the bases of the box are rectangles 5 in. by 3 in., what is the length of the four bottom edges (perimeter of base) when straightened out?

2. If the height of the box is 8 in., what is the total area of the four sides of the flattened box?

3. The area of the sides of a prism is called the **lateral area**. What is the lateral area of this prism?

4. Complete: The lateral area of a prism equals the perimeter of its base multiplied by its __?__.

5. Find the area of each base of the box.

6. What is the total surface (total area) of the box, including its bases?

7. Find the total surface of a block 10 in. × 6 in. × 4 in.

8. A rectangular prism is 12 in. high; its bases are 5 in. by 6 in. What is its lateral area? the area of the two bases? the total area?

9. Find the lateral surface of each prism at the right.

10. When finding the total surface of a rectangular solid, does it matter which faces are the bases?

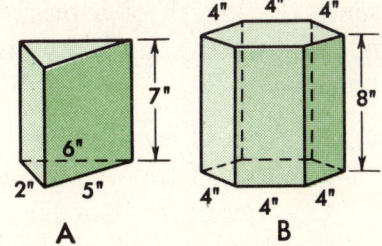

A B

The Surface of a Rectangular Prism

A rectangular prism, you will remember, is a solid with six flat sides, each of which is a rectangle. A chalk box and a cigar box are rectangular prisms.

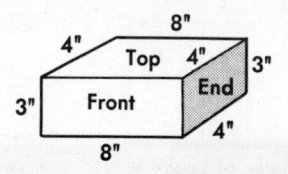

A rectangular prism has three pairs of sides: two ends; top and bottom; front and back. In each pair the rectangles are equal.

Study this rectangular prism, which is 8 in. long, 4 in. wide, and 3 in. high, and complete these statements:

1. A. The area of one end = 4 × 3 = _?_ sq. in.
   B. The area of both ends together = 2 × 4 × 3 = _?_ sq. in.

2. A. The area of the top = 8 × 4 = _?_ sq. in.
   B. The area of the bottom = 8 × 4 = _?_ sq. in.
   C. Area of top and bottom together = _?_ × 8 × 4 = _?_ sq. in.

3. A. The area of the front = 8 × 3 = _?_ sq. in.
   B. The area of the back = _?_ × _?_ = _?_ sq. in.
   C. Area of front and back together = _?_ × _?_ × _?_ = _?_ sq. in.

4. What is the area of the entire surface of the prism?

In this diagram, l represents the length of a prism; w, its width; and h, its height.

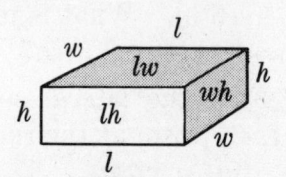

5. A. Area of each end = _?_.
   B. Area of top or bottom = _?_.
   C. Area of front or back = _?_.
   D. Total surface of the prism = _?_ + _?_ + _?_.

6. Here is a rectangular prism 6" by 4" by 2", which has been opened out. Name the three pairs of surfaces which have equal areas.

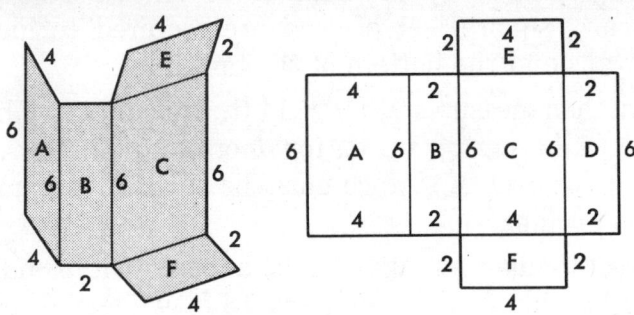

7. What is the area of rectangle **A**? of rectangle **B**? of rectangle **E**? What is the total surface of the prism?

8. Find the total surface of each of these rectangular prisms:

    A. $l = 8"$, $w = 6"$, $h = 3"$
    B. $l = 4$ ft., $w = 3$ ft., $h = 1\frac{1}{2}$ ft.
    C. $l = 12$ ft., $w = 8$ ft., $h = 3$ in.

9. Making no allowance for waste, how many square feet of boards are needed for a rectangular packing case 2 ft. by 3 ft. by 5 ft.?

10. A rectangular living room is 22 ft. long and 12 ft. wide; the height is $9\frac{1}{2}$ ft. What is the area of the floor surface? the area of the ceiling? the area of the four walls (disregarding doors and windows)?

11. If a cube measures 5 inches along each edge, the total surface of the cube equals __?__ square inches.

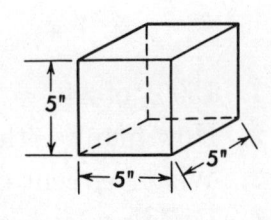

12. If a rectangular prism is placed in a different position, so that its ends, for example, become the top and bottom, will the total surface of the prism be changed? Explain.

Practical Problems

1. An open rectangular tank is 16 ft. × 8 ft. × 6 ft. How many square feet of lead are required to line the inside walls and the bottom of the tank?

2. A kitchen measures $9\frac{1}{2}$ ft. × 14 ft., with a ceiling height of 8 ft. Allowing 38 sq. ft. for doors and windows, how many square feet of surface must be covered to paint the walls and ceiling?

3. A rectangular storage bin in a basement is built of wood. The bin is 28 ft. long and 18 ft. wide, and reaches from the floor to the ceiling. If the basement is 9 ft. in height, how many square feet of lumber were required for the four side walls of the bin? How much did the lumber cost at 14¢ a square foot?

4. If a cube measures e inches on each edge, the area of each of the six sides of the cube equals $e \times e$, or e^2 square inches. What is the total area of all the sides of the cube? Write a formula for the total surface of a cube.

5. Two packing cases have the same capacity. One is 8 ft. long, 4 ft. wide, and 2 ft. high; the other is a cube 4 ft. on an edge. Which has the larger surface? how much larger?

6. Two cubes have edges of 6″ and 18″, respectively. The ratio of their total areas is __?__.

JIFFY QUIZ

1. 150% of $40 = __?__; $1\frac{1}{2}$% of $40 = __?__.
2. How many 16ths of an inch are there in $\frac{3}{8}$ inch?
3. What per cent of 200 is 1?
4. Dividing by $\frac{1}{3}$ is equivalent to multiplying by __?__.
5. How much is 1 × 1? 1 ÷ 1?

Surface of a Cylinder

We found the lateral surface of a prism (page 193) by flattening out a box. We can find the lateral surface of a cylinder by removing the label from a tin can.

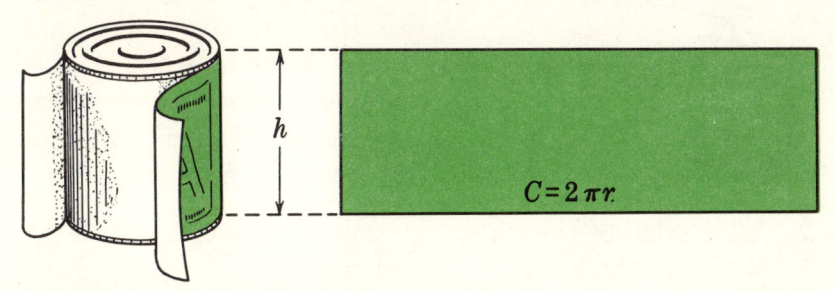

$C = 2\pi r$

1. When unrolled and laid flat, what shape is the label?
2. What does the width of the rectangular label equal?
3. What does the length of the label equal?
4. If the length of the label is $2\pi r$ and its width is h, what is its area?
5. Complete: The lateral surface of a cylinder equals the _?_ of its base multiplied by its _?_.
6. The lateral surface of a cylinder may be written as $A = 2\pi rh$. Use this formula to find the lateral surface of a cylinder 14 in. high with a radius of 5 inches.
7. What is the lateral surface of a cylinder 2 ft. in diameter and $3\frac{1}{2}$ ft. high?
8. Find the lateral surface of a closed cylindrical tank which is 16 ft. high and 7 ft. in diameter. What is the area of its two bases (top and bottom)? What is the total surface of the tank?
9. A cylindrical can is 12 in. in diameter and 20 in. high. What is the area of its curved surface? of the bottom?
10. A steam pipe $3\frac{1}{2}$ in. in diameter is 60 ft. long. This would provide how many square feet of heating surface?

Volume of a Rectangular Prism

While playing with his little brother, Bob built a rectangular prism with some small wooden cubes, like the one shown in the picture.

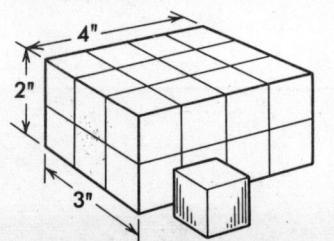

1. How many cubes are there in each layer of this prism? How many layers are there? How many cubes are there in the entire prism?

2. Each edge of the cubes in Problem 1 is one inch long. Each small cube is a unit of volume, or 1 cubic inch. How many cubic inches of space does Bob's prism occupy? What is the volume of Bob's prism?

Turn back to page 42 and read it again to see how we discovered the number of cubic inches in a cubic foot. Do you see that to find the volume of a rectangular prism we find the product of the *length,* the *width,* and the *height?*

3. Tell what each of the letters means in the formula:
$$V = l \times w \times h, \text{ or } V = lwh$$

4. Use the formula to find the volume of each of these rectangular prisms:
  A. $l = 8$ in.; $w = 4$ in.; $h = 7$ in.
  B. $l = 9$ ft.; $w = 6$ ft.; $h = 1\frac{1}{2}$ ft.
  C. $l = 4$ yd.; $w = 3$ yd.; $h = 1$ yd.
  D. $l = 16$ cm.; $w = 6$ cm.; $h = 2$ cm.
  E. $l = 4\frac{1}{2}''$; $w = 2''$; $h = 2\frac{1}{2}''$

5. A cube has edges of 4 inches; its volume is $4 \times 4 \times 4$, which equals 64 cu. in. A short way of writing $4 \times 4 \times 4$ is 4^3; this is read "four cubed." What is a short way of writing $5 \times 5 \times 5$? $10 \times 10 \times 10$? What does 6^3 equal?

6. Tell what the formula, $V = e^3$, means.

Volume of Any Prism

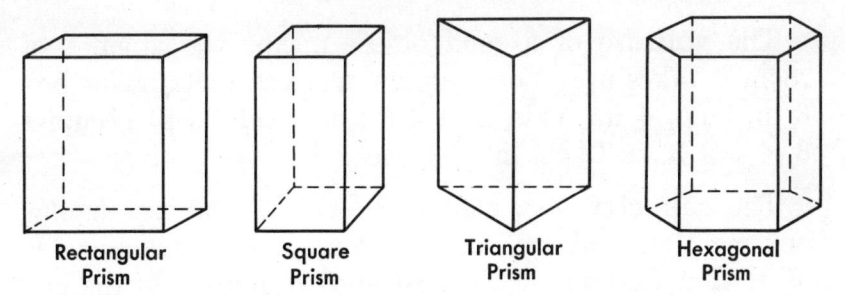

Rectangular Prism Square Prism Triangular Prism Hexagonal Prism

In a rectangular prism the sides and the bases are rectangles. If the area of the base is represented by B, then $B =$ length $\times$ width, or lw. We have just learned that $V = lwh$. This formula can also be written:

$$V = B \times h, \text{ or } V = Bh$$

In other words, the volume of a prism equals the product of the area of its base and its height. This is true of all prisms, even if the bases are not rectangles.

1. Find the volume of each of these prisms:

	KIND OF SOLID	BASE AREA	HEIGHT
A.	Rectangular prism	36 sq. in.	$4\frac{1}{2}$ in.
B.	Rectangular prism	$12\frac{1}{4}$ sq. in.	20 in.
C.	Square prism	25 sq. in.	$8\frac{1}{2}$ in.
D.	Triangular prism	16 sq. in.	$6\frac{1}{8}$ in.
E.	Hexagonal prism	43.3 sq. in.	$1\frac{1}{2}$ ft.

2. Find the volume of a triangular prism whose height is 16 cm.; the base is a right triangle in which the two sides forming the right angle are 6 cm. and 9 cm. long.

3. What is the volume of a glass paperweight in the shape of a cube 2 inches on a side?

4. Find the volume of a wastepaper basket having the shape of a hexagonal prism with a base area of $2\frac{1}{2}$ sq. ft. and a height of 18 inches.

Volume and Capacity

The **volume** of a solid object means the amount of room it takes up. For example, a closed rectangular box 6 in. long, 4 in. wide, and 3 in. high (or deep) occupies 6 × 4 × 3, or 72 cu. in. of space.

The **capacity** of a container, such as the rectangular box mentioned above, means the amount of space inside of it. For example, if the *inside dimensions* of the box were 6 in., 4 in., and 3 in., the box would have a capacity of 72 cu. in. It could hold 72 cu. in. of water or sand, and so on.

To measure the capacity of a container accurately, we must use its inside dimensions. Why?

1. A carton measures $5\frac{1}{2}$ ft. × 3 ft. × 2 ft. What is its capacity in cubic feet?

2. A cedar chest is 44 in. × $18\frac{3}{4}$ in. × 18 in., inside dimensions. How many cubic feet does it hold?

3. A rectangular container measures 8 in. × $2\frac{3}{4}$ in. × $2\frac{3}{4}$ in. Its capacity is about __?__ cu. in. If 1 pint is approximately equal to 29 cu. in., how much milk can this container hold?

4. What is the capacity in cubic feet of a refrigerator 15 in. × 24 in. × 36 in., inside measurements?

5. The body of a truck for hauling shelled corn is 12 ft. by $5\frac{1}{2}$ ft. by $3\frac{1}{2}$ ft. What is its capacity in cubic yards?

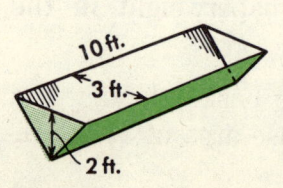

6. What is the area of each end (base) of this water trough which has the shape of a triangular prism? What is the length (altitude) of the prism? Find its volume.

Problems about Prisms

1. Peter's fish tank is 18 inches long and 10 inches wide. How many cubic inches of water will the tank hold when filled to a depth of 9 inches?

2. There are 231 cubic inches in a gallon. To the nearest gallon, how much water will Peter's tank hold when the depth of the water is 9 inches?

3. Find the number of cubic feet of air space in a classroom 36 feet long, 24 feet wide, and 12 feet high.

4. Allowing 300 cubic feet of air space for each pupil, about how many pupils could use the classroom in Problem **3**?

5. A water tank is 8 ft. long, $2\frac{1}{2}$ ft. wide, and 18 in. deep. How many gallons can it hold? (1 cu. ft. = $7\frac{1}{2}$ gal.)

6. Ground is to be excavated to build the basement of a house. The excavation will be 36 ft. long, 21 ft. wide, and 6 ft. deep. How many cubic yards of earth must be removed? How much will the excavating cost at $1.75 a cubic yard?

7. The inside of a freight car measures 36 ft. by $9\frac{1}{2}$ ft. by 9 ft. Find the number of cubic feet of storage space.

8. What is the weight of a block of ice, 4 ft. by 2 ft. by 6 in., if one cubic foot of ice weighs $57\frac{1}{2}$ pounds?

Measuring Lumber

George and his father are building a chicken house. They need 72 boards, each 6 in. wide, 16 ft. long, and ¾ in. thick. When they bought the boards at the lumber yard, the clerk said, "That will be 576 board feet." How did he figure this?

If a board is 1 ft. long, 1 ft. wide, and 1 in. (or less) thick, it contains **1 board foot**. To find the number of board feet in a piece of lumber, then, we find the area of the surface in square feet and multiply by the thickness in inches. If it is less than 1 in. thick, we count it as 1 inch.

Each of the boards for the chicken house contains
$$1 \times \tfrac{6}{12} \times 16 = 8 \text{ board feet}$$
The 72 boards contain 72 × 8 = 576 board feet.

1. How much did these 72 boards cost at $140 per thousand board feet?

    576 board feet = .576 ***thousand*** board feet
    .576 × $140 = $80.64

2. George's father said they also needed 16 pieces, 2″ × 4″, and 16 ft. long. How many board feet are there in one of these pieces? (Notice that these pieces are *two* inches thick.) How many board feet, to the nearest board foot, are there altogether?

3. At $130 per **M** (per thousand), how much will these pieces cost?

4. How much lumber is there in a plank 8 in. wide, 10 ft. long, and 2 in. thick?

5. How many board feet are there in a board $\frac{3}{4}$ in. thick which is 18 ft. long and 10 in. wide?

6. A board 1 in. thick is 6 in. wide and 14 ft. long. Find the number of board feet.

7. A piece of lumber measuring 2 in. by 4 in. is 9 ft. long. How much lumber is contained in 20 such pieces?

8. Strips of lumber $\frac{5}{8}$ in. thick and 1 in. wide can be obtained in 18-foot lengths. How many board feet are there in one dozen strips?

9. How much lumber is there in a beam 6 in. thick, 8 in. wide, and 18 ft. long?

10. Ordinary plywood, usually made of Douglas fir, is sold in standard size sheets, 4 feet by 8 feet. The price varies with the thickness. What is the cost of 40 sheets of this plywood, $\frac{1}{2}$ inch thick, at 35¢ a square foot?

11. How much must be paid for 12 sheets of pressed wood, 4 ft. by 8 ft., at 11¢ a square foot?

JIFFY QUIZ

1. How much is $\frac{1}{2}$ of $\frac{1}{2}$ of $\frac{1}{2}$?

2. If the year were divided into 12 months of equal length, how many weeks would there be in each month?

3. How many $\frac{1}{2}$-inch squares are there in a 2-inch square?

4. Which is greater in area, a circle with a 10-inch radius or one with a 10-inch diameter? How many times as great is it?

5. A certain amount of money is increased by 200%. Is it now two or three times the original amount?

6. $9 \times 125 + 5 \times 125 - 4 \times 125 = ?$

Volume of a Cylinder

Many common objects used as containers—for example, gas tanks, steam boilers, ash cans, pipes, cisterns, silos, milk cans—are cylinders in shape.

1. Name three cylindrical objects that you have seen in school, in the kitchen, in the shop, or in a store.

2. The bases of a cylinder are equal circles, just as the bases of a prism are equal squares, or equal rectangles, or equal triangles. How do you find the volume of a prism?

3. We find the volume of a cylinder just as we find the volume of a prism—multiply the area of the base by the altitude. Write this sentence as a formula in which B represents the area of the base of the cylinder.

4. How do you find B, the area of the base, if the base is a circle?

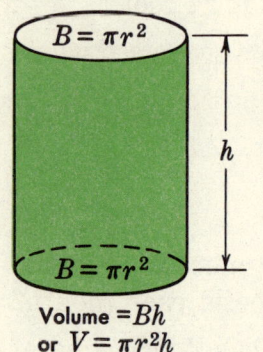

$B = \pi r^2$

h

$B = \pi r^2$

Volume $= Bh$
or $V = \pi r^2 h$

5. Now we can write the formula for the volume of a cylinder as $V = \pi r^2 h$. State this formula in words.

6. If the radius or diameter of a cylinder is expressed in inches, in what unit is the area of the base expressed? If the altitude is also given in inches, in what unit is the volume expressed?

7. In the shop, John uses a metal can in the shape of a cylinder. The can has a diameter of 9 in. and is 14 in. high. What is its volume in cubic inches?

$V = \pi r^2 h$
$r = \frac{9}{2};\ h = 14$
$V = \frac{22}{7} \times \frac{9}{2} \times \frac{9}{2} \times 14$
$V = 891$ cu. in.

8. Household gas is stored in cylindrical tanks whose height can be changed to hold more or less gas, as desired. If such a tank has a diameter of 49 feet, how many cubic feet of gas does it hold when its height is 60 feet?

9. A silo 30 ft. high has an inside diameter of 12 ft. How many pounds of silage will it hold when full, if 1 cu. ft. of silage weighs 35 lb.?

© Ewing Galloway
Gas tanks, New York waterfront

10. Two cylindrical cans have equal bases. Each can has a diameter of 7 inches. One can is 4 in. high and the other is 8 in. high. How do the cans compare in volume?

11. If the height of one cylinder is twice that of another, but the diameter of the base of each cylinder is the same, the volume of one is _?_ times that of the other.

12. Two cylinders have the same height, 8 inches. The radius of one of them is 3 in.; the radius of the other, 6 in. How do their volumes compare?

13. If the diameter of one cylinder is twice that of another, but the height of each cylinder is the same, the volume of one is _?_ times that of the other.

14. A railroad tank car, 56 ft. long, has an inside diameter of 5 feet. How many gallons of oil, to the nearest 100 gallons, will it hold?

Railroad tank cars   *© Link, from Frederic Lewis*

The Capacity of a Cylinder

1. A cylinder has a diameter of 7 in. and is 10 in. high; another cylinder is 14 in. in diameter and 20 in. high. What is the ratio of their volumes?

2. If the diameter and the height of one cylinder are double the diameter and the height of another, the volume of the first cylinder is __?__ times that of the second.

3. The diameter and the height of one cylindrical can are double the diameter and the height of another can. If the second can holds $5\frac{1}{2}$ fluid ounces, how much does the first can hold?

4. A certain brand of facial cream is packed in a cylindrical jar. The inside height of the jar is $1\frac{1}{8}$ in. and the inside diameter is $1\frac{1}{2}$ in. Find the volume of the jar to the nearest cubic inch. If there are 2 cu. in. to 1 oz. of facial cream, about how many ounces does the jar contain?

5. The facial cream is also packed in a cylindrical jar with double the height and diameter of the jar in Problem 4. How many ounces of facial cream does the larger jar contain?

6. A cylindrical water tank on top of a building is 20 ft. in diameter. How many gallons does it hold when the tank is filled to a height of 21 ft.? (1 cu. ft. = $7\frac{1}{2}$ gal.)

Learning to Solve Problems

Looking Up the Necessary Information

When solving a problem, some needed fact which is not given in the statement of the problem may be found by referring to a table of measures, an encyclopedia, or some other reference book.

In solving the problems below, refer to the tables in the back of this book.

1. A flour barrel is $\frac{3}{4}$ full. How many pounds of flour have been removed?

2. A rectangular coal bin measures 9 ft. $\times$ 7 ft. $\times$ 5 ft. How many tons of coal can it hold?

3. At $2.50 per bushel, what is the cost of one pound of apples?

4. A tank contains 1200 gallons of water. What is the weight of this water in tons?

5. A container having a capacity of 2 gallons can hold how many liters?

6. A block of ice is 2 ft. $\times$ 1$\frac{1}{2}$ ft. $\times$ 1 ft. What is the weight of the block in pounds?

7. A pitcher contains 2$\frac{1}{4}$ pints of lemonade. How many ounces does the lemonade weigh?

8. The capacity of a storage bin is 120 cubic feet. How many bushels can it hold?

9. A milk bottle holds one quart. What is its volume in cubic inches?

10. What is the weight in ounces of 1$\frac{1}{2}$ cups of butter?

11. A farmer shelled 1000 bushels of ear corn before he sold it. How much did the cobs weigh?

12. An article imported from France weighs 227 grams, according to the label. How many pounds does it weigh?

Cones and Pyramids

In one store a soda was served in a conical cup; in another store a soda was served in a cylindrical glass. Paul and his friend wondered which container held more soda. They tried this experiment.

They made a hollow cylinder and a hollow cone of cardboard, both equally high and both with bases equal in diameter. Then they filled the cone with sand, leveling off the top, and poured the sand into the cylinder. When they measured the height of the sand in the cylinder, they found that the cylinder was just $\frac{1}{3}$ full.

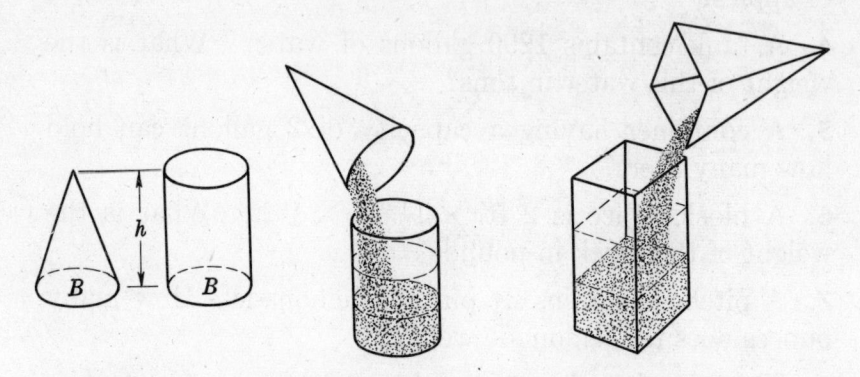

Then they repeated the experiment, using a square pyramid and a square prism with equal bases and equal altitudes. Again, when they poured the sand from the filled pyramid into the empty prism, the prism was $\frac{1}{3}$ full.

1. The volume of a cone is what part of the volume of a cylinder equal in base and altitude to the cone?

2. Write the formula for the volume of a cylinder.

3. The formula for the volume of a cone is $V = \frac{1}{3} \pi r^2 h$. Explain.

4. What is the formula for the volume of any prism?

5. Do you see that the formula for the volume of a pyramid must be $V = \frac{1}{3} Bh$? Why?

6. Find the volume of each of these pyramids:
   A. Area of base = 36 sq. ft.; altitude = 8 ft.
   B. Height = 6 cm.; square base = 4 cm. × 4 cm.
   C. Height = 24 in.; base 5 in. square.

7. Find the volume of each of these cones:
   A. Altitude = 12 ft.; base area = 25 sq. ft.
   B. Height = 6 in.; radius of base = $3\frac{1}{2}$ in.
   C. Area of base = 9 sq. yd.; altitude = 5 yd.
   D. Diameter of base = 14 cm.; height = 18 cm.

8. Find the volume of a pyramid, 18 ft. high, having a rectangular base 9 ft. long and 4 ft. wide.

9. The altitude of a triangular pyramid is 20 in.; the area of the base is 48 sq. in. Find its volume.

10. What is the volume of a cone 9 inches high and 14 in. in diameter?

11. What is the volume of a cone equal in diameter but having twice the height of the cone in Problem **10**?

© McManigal, from Philip Gendreau

12. A conical heap of wheat 6 ft. high measures 28 ft. in diameter at its base. Find the number of cubic feet in the heap. If a cubic foot contains .8 of a bushel, how many bushels are there in the heap?

Surface of a Sphere

Dick experimented with a sphere. He cut a cork ball in half. He wound a piece of cord on the curved surface of one of the hemispheres, as shown in the picture, after first fastening it to the pin. He noted how long a piece of cord was required. Then he wound a piece of cord about a pin fastened at the center of the *flat surface* of the other hemisphere; this piece of cord was only about *half* as long as the first piece.

1. If the radius of the sphere is r, the area of the flat surface of the hemisphere equals __?__.

2. The area of the curved surface of a hemisphere therefore equals __?__, and the surface of the entire sphere is __?__.

This may be written as a formula: $A = 4\pi r^2$

The surface of a sphere is exactly four times as great as the area of the flat surface through its center.

Find the surface of each of these spheres ($\pi = 3\frac{1}{7}$):

3. $r = 14$ in.   **5.** $r = 10\frac{1}{2}$ ft.   **7.** $r = 1$ in.

4. $D = 20$ cm.   **6.** $r = 3\frac{1}{2}$ yd.   **8.** $D = 8$ in.

9. Considering the earth as an approximate sphere with a radius of about 4000 miles, find the approximate area of its surface. (Use $\pi = 3.14$)

10. Compare the surface of a sphere having a 5-inch radius with that of a sphere having a 10-inch radius.

11. One sphere has a 6-inch radius; another, a 6-inch diameter. What is the ratio of their areas?

Volume of a Sphere

Suppose you had a cubical box, of such a size that a sphere just fitted into it "perfectly". The radius of this sphere is r. Why is the length of any edge of the box $2r$?

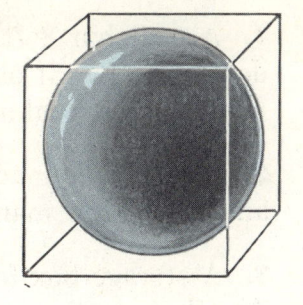

1. The volume of the cube is equal to $2r \times 2r \times 2r$, or $8r^3$. What does r^3 mean?

2. What is the volume of the cube when the radius of the sphere is 2 inches? 3 inches?

3. Look at the diagram. Is the volume of the sphere greater or less than the volume of the cube? The volume of the sphere is only a little more than half as great as the volume of the cube.

The formula for the volume of a sphere is $V = \frac{4}{3}\pi r^3$.

4. Find the volume of a sphere whose radius is 6 feet.

$V = \frac{4}{3}\pi r^3$ $\qquad V = \frac{4}{3} \times \frac{22}{7} \times 216$
$r = 6$ $\qquad\qquad\quad V = \frac{6336}{7} = 905.1$
$r^3 = 6 \times 6 \times 6 = 216$ $\quad$ The volume is 905 cu. ft.

5. Find the volume of each of these spheres:

A. $r = 2$ in. $\qquad$ B. $r = 3\frac{1}{2}$ ft. $\qquad$ C. $D = 20$ cm.

6. How many cubic inches of cork are there in a solid cork ball 21 inches in diameter?

7. What is the capacity of an ice-cream scoop in the shape of a hemisphere 2 inches in diameter?

8. How does the volume of a sphere with a radius of 4 inches compare with that of a sphere 8 inches in radius?

9. If the radius of one sphere is twice that of another, the volume of the first sphere is how many times as great as the volume of the second?

Problems about Solids

1. A coal bin 8 ft. wide and 10½ ft. long is filled to a depth of 5 ft. If one ton of coal occupies 35 cu. ft., how many tons of coal are there in the bin?

2. A mechanic made an open cubical tin box 6 inches on an edge. How many square inches of tin did he need?

3. A storage box for sand is 10 ft. wide and 12 ft. long. To what depth must it be filled to hold 420 cu. ft. of sand?

4. A storage bin is 9 ft. wide, 12 ft. long, and 4½ ft. deep. How many bushels of wheat, to the nearest 10 bushels, will it hold if 1 bushel of wheat occupies 1¼ cu. ft.?

5. A cone-shaped pile of coal is 5 ft. high, and its base is a circle whose area is 168 sq. ft. How many tons of coal are there in the pile?

6. A marble monument in the shape of a square pyramid is 12 ft. high, with its base 5 ft. on a side. If 1 cu. ft. of marble weighs 170 lb., what is the weight of the monument?

7. A conical pile of gravel stands 9 ft. high, and the distance across its circular base is 40 ft. How many cubic yards of gravel are there in the pile?

8. We can find the volume of an irregular object, say a lump of coal, by letting it sink in water and measuring the volume of water it pushes up. What is the volume of an object that causes a rise of 1 inch in a cylinder having a diameter of 2 inches?

9. Find the capacity in cubic feet of this water trough whose ends are trapezoids with the dimensions given. How many gallons will it hold when full?

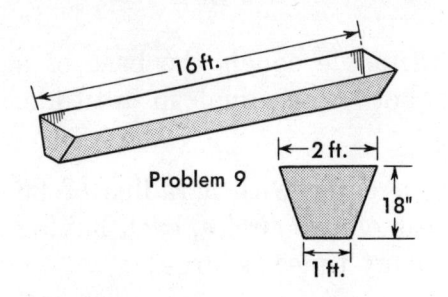

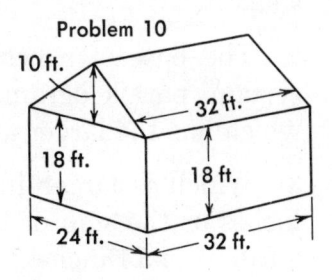

10. In a certain locality, the cost of building a frame house is roughly estimated at 80¢ per cubic foot of space within the house. At this rate, find the approximate cost of construction of the house pictured above.

11. The concrete walk in front of a house is made with slabs (rectangular blocks) of concrete 4 inches thick. If the walk is 3 ft. wide and 36 ft. long, how many cubic yards of concrete are required?

12. Boxes of dried fruit are delivered to grocery stores packed in large cartons. One brand comes in a carton with approximate inside dimensions of 6″ × 12″ × 12″. How many boxes 2″ × 3″ × 6″ does the carton contain?

Keeping in Practice

A	B	C
1. 260 × 490 = ?	44 × 8½ = ?	7½ ÷ 1½ = ?
2. 1⅔ + 2¾ = ?	2.4 × 3.35 = ?	12⅝ − 9⅞ = ?
3. 15)7̄	.24)9.6̄	90)2.7̄
4. 36 is 75% of ?	80 is _?_% of 120	200% of 18 = ?
5. 39 is 1% of ?	1.5% of $500 = ?	50% of 20 = ?
6. ½% of $800 = ?	60 is _?_% of 40	60 is 125% of ?

Learning to Solve Problems

Thinking with Measures

1. Is an area of one square foot necessarily square in shape?

2. The base of a certain rectangle equals the base of a certain parallelogram. If both are equal in altitude, which has the larger area?

3. Which is larger in area, a circle with a radius of 28 inches or the sum of the areas of two circles, each having a radius of 14 inches? how many times as large?

4. If the radius of one circle is one-half that of another circle, how does the circumference of the first circle compare with the circumference of the second?

5. How many square centimeters are there in a square that is 100 cm. on a side?

6. Which is greater:
   A. One dry quart or one liquid quart?
   B. 10 fluid ounces or $\frac{1}{2}$ pint?
   C. 2 inches or 4 centimeters?
   D. A liquid quart or a liter?

7. In each case, which answer is most nearly correct?
   A. 15 kilometers equal (9, 15, 25) miles.
   B. 50 kilograms equal (90, 100, 110) pounds.
   C. 10 liters equal (9 qt., 11 qt., 3 gal.).

8. A foot is _?_ times as great as an inch; a square foot is _?_ times as great as a square inch; a cubic foot is _?_ times as great as a cubic inch.

9. A cube containing 1 cubic yard measures how many feet on each edge? How many cubic feet does it contain?

10. The edge of one cube is twice as long as the edge of another cube. What is the ratio of their volumes?

Using What You Have Learned

Complete these statements:
1. A cube has _?_ faces, each of which is a _?_.
2. The lateral faces of a pyramid are _?_.
3. The lateral faces of a prism are _?_.
4. A triangular prism has _?_ edges.
5. The surface of a sphere is _?_ times as great in area as the area of a circle of equal diameter.
6. The volume of a cone is _?_ as great as the volume of a cylinder of equal height and diameter.
7. A prism and a pyramid have equal bases and equal heights. The volume of the prism is _?_ times as great as the volume of the pyramid.
8. One cubic foot is equal to _?_ gallons.
9. One gallon is equal to _?_ cubic inches.
10. The total surface of a cube is _?_ times the area of one of its faces.
11. A cube 4 inches on an edge is equivalent in volume to _?_ cubes each 2 inches on an edge.
12. A sphere 6 inches in diameter has a surface _?_ times as great as that of a sphere 3 inches in diameter, and its volume is _?_ times as great.

JIFFY QUIZ

1. Will dividing 17.319 by 4 give the same result as multiplying 17.319 by .25?
2. Does 17% of 49 equal 49% of 17?
3. If $1\frac{1}{2}$ pounds of candy cost 75¢, how much does one pound cost?
4. How much is 20% more than $15? 20% less than $15?
5. If 6 oranges cost 28¢, how much will $1\frac{1}{2}$ dozen cost?

215

Understanding Solids

1. Does the surface of a solid have thickness?
2. Are all rectangular prisms cubes? Are all cubes rectangular prisms? Are all prisms rectangular?
3. If all the faces of a rectangular prism are exactly alike, what kind of solid is it?
4. Can a cylinder have a diameter that is 10 or 20 times its altitude? an altitude 10 or 20 times its diameter?
5. If the height of one cylinder is twice that of another cylinder but the diameter of the base is the same, the volume is _?_ times the volume of the other cylinder.
6. If the diameter of one cylinder is twice that of another cylinder but the height is the same, the volume is _?_ times the volume of the other cylinder.
7. The radius of one sphere is twice that of another. The surface of the first sphere is _?_ times as great as the surface of the second.
8. If the radius of one sphere is twice that of another sphere, the volume of the first sphere is _?_ times the volume of the second.

Give the formulas for:

9. Volume of a cube; area of a cube.
10. Volume of a cylinder; volume of a cone.
11. Volume of a rectangular prism.
12. Volume of a sphere; area of a sphere.

Complete these statements:

13. The total surface of a rectangular prism is equal to _?_ + _?_ + _?_.
14. The lateral, or curved surface, of a cylinder equals _?_.
15. The volume of a pyramid equals one-third the product of its _?_ and its _?_.

Making Sure

1. How many boxes, one foot on each side, can be packed in a carton 4 ft. long, 2 ft. wide, and 3 ft. deep?   198

2. A box with a square base is 8 in. high; its volume is 288 cu. in. What is the length of each edge of the base?   199

3. A storage room in a warehouse covers a floor space 48 ft. by 66 ft. If the room has an 18-foot ceiling, how many cubic feet of space are there in the room? how many cubic yards?   200

4. A rectangular tank is 4 ft. long, $2\frac{1}{2}$ ft. wide, and 21 in. high. How many gallons of water will it hold when $\frac{2}{3}$ full? (1 cu. ft. = $7\frac{1}{2}$ gal.)   201

5. The edge of one cube is twice as long as the edge of a second cube. The volume of the first cube is how many times that of the second?   198

6. Find the volume of a cone having a diameter of 20 in. and an altitude of 9 in.   208, 209

7. What is the lateral area of a cylinder whose altitude is 14 ft. and whose radius is 4 ft.?   197

8. Find the volume of a cylinder that is 20 in. in diameter and 14 in. high.   204

9. If a brick measures 8 in. × 4 in. × 2 in., how many of these bricks are there in a cubic foot?   198, 213

10. The dimensions in this table are those of rectangular prisms. Complete the table.   198, 199

	LENGTH	WIDTH	HEIGHT	AREA OF BASE	VOLUME
A	10″	?	6″	40 sq. in.	?
B	12″	8″	?	?	288 cu. in.
C	?	10″	?	180 sq. in.	720 cu. in.
D	16″	?	4″	?	384 cu. in.

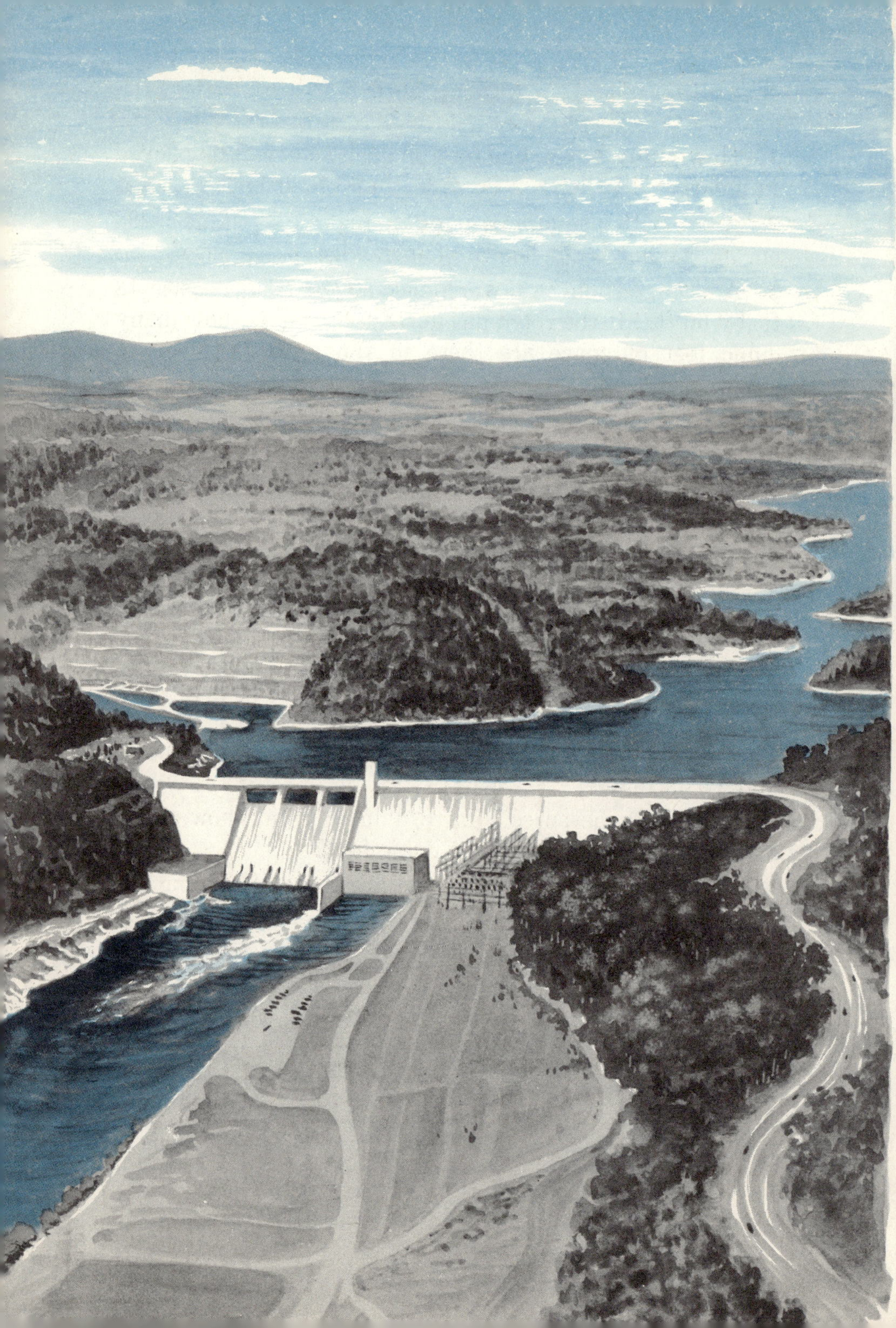

7

THE WORLD WE LIVE IN

Understanding Important Facts about the World

Every day, in the newspapers and on radio and television, large numbers are used to tell us important facts. We should know what such numbers mean.

Often we are asked to find how one large number is related to another large number. There is a simple method of doing this.

One year, imports totaling 68,078,000 tons passed through the principal ports of the United States. Of this amount, 19,678,000 tons passed through New York Harbor. This was what per cent of the total?

If we were to complete this division example it would be long and difficult:

$$68,078,000 \overline{) 19,678,000.000} \quad .289 \text{ or, } 28.9\%$$

A simpler way of doing this example is, first, to round each of the numbers to the nearest tenth of a million.

68,078,000 = 68.1 million
19,678,000 = 19.7 million

Now you can divide 19.7 by 68.1. What is the quotient? Do you see that we can work with rounded numbers more easily? When we work with rounded numbers, they must all be rounded to an equivalent place value, that is, to tenth of a million or tenth of a billion, etc.

Complete, rounding to the nearest tenth of a billion:

1. 50,794,000,000 = 50.8 billion   **3.** 120,708,000,000 = ?
2. 27,640,200,000 = ?   **4.** 962,666,000,000 = ?

Courtesy Standard Oil Co., (N. J.)

Our Nation's Farms

Of the 150,000,000 people in our land, only a little more than 15% live on farms. Yet, the farmers of the United States produce more than enough food to supply the basic needs of the entire population.

1. The per cent of farm population has been decreasing steadily in recent years. The table below shows the total population and the farm population as reported by the Census at the end of three ten-year periods.

YEAR	TOTAL POPULATION	FARM POPULATION
1930	122,775,000	30,445,000
1940	131,669,000	30,547,000
1950	150,697,000	23,577,000

A. Make a table similar to the one above, but round each population figure to the nearest tenth of a million.

B. Using your table, find (to the nearest tenth) what per cent the farm population is of the total population for each of the three years.

2. An easy way to compare the amount of farm products grown each year is by the use of **index numbers.** The average annual volume of all farm production from 1935 to 1939 is represented by the number 100. The index number for any year shows whether production for that year was above or below normal. For example, if the index number for a year is 90, production for that year was 10% lower than for a normal year.

A. What per cent above or below an average year was the agricultural production in: 1935, 1940, 1945?

B. How many times as great as the production in 1930 was that in 1950 (to the nearest tenth)?

YEAR	INDEX NUMBER
1930	98
1935	91
1940	110
1945	134
1950	138

3. Corn and wheat are the major American grain products. In a recent year, wheat production was about 1.14 billion bushels and corn production was about 3.37 billion bushels. The ratio of wheat to corn was about 1 to __?__.

4. About 153 million tons of wheat were produced in the world in a recent year. Of this, the United States produced about 35 million tons. What per cent was this?

5. The total net cash income for a Kansas wheat farm in a certain year was $13,371. Not all of this income came from the sale of wheat. The table on the right shows the various sources of income in per cents. Find, to the nearest dollar, the amount from each source.

SOURCE OF INCOME	PER CENT OF INCOME
Wheat	73%
Other crops	3%
Livestock	16%
Livestock products	5%
Government payments	3%

Producing Our Nation's Meat

1. The United States leads all other countries in reported meat production. Argentina ranks second and Brazil third. The table shows how production was distributed in a recent year.

COUNTRY	PRODUCTION IN BILLIONS OF POUNDS			
	BEEF AND VEAL	PORK	MUTTON AND LAMB	TOTAL
United States	10.86	10.41	.61	21.88
Argentina	4.27	.34	.49	5.10
Brazil	2.20	.51	.04	2.75

A. The United States produced how many times as much beef and veal as Argentina and Brazil combined? how many times as much pork? how many times as much mutton and lamb? (Nearest tenth.)

B. Draw a bar graph to show the total production of meat in each of the three countries. Round the totals to the nearest billion before you make your graph.

2. In one year the total number of cattle sold by a small Idaho cattle ranch was 67, at an average price of $138.57 per head. What was the total amount the ranch received from the sale of cattle?

3. If this represented 87% of the ranch's total income that year, what was the total income to the nearest dollar?

Farmers and Forest Conservation

1. The United States government spent $48 million for conservation purposes in a recent year. In the same year, about $33 million was lost through forest fires. The population of the nation in that year was about 150 million. **A.** The amount spent by the government for conservation represented an average of about what amount per person? **B.** The amount lost through forest fires was what per cent of the total spent for conservation that year?

2. Farmers are becoming increasingly aware of the need for restoring our forests. Listed below are the number of trees planted on farm lands in each of three years.

Round each number to the nearest million. About how many times as great as the number of trees planted in 1935 was the number planted in 1940? in 1949?

YEAR	NUMBER OF TREES PLANTED
1935	26,150,000
1940	87,468,000
1949	102,903,000

3. Tree seedlings, used in reforestation, may be bought from state tree nurseries. The trees are often planted 6 feet apart (see diagram). This means that each tree takes up about __?__ square feet of land. How many trees can be planted to an acre? (1 acre = 43,560 sq. ft.) At an average cost of $4.46 per thousand, about how much would it cost to buy enough seedlings for one acre?

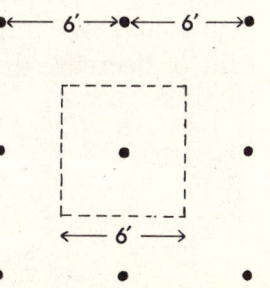

Some Foods We Import

1. In one year the sugar production of the United States was 2,084,000 tons. An additional 5,682,000 tons were imported. Using rounded numbers, find what per cent of the United States sugar supply was imported.

2. Of the sugar produced in the United States, 1,564,000 tons was beet sugar. What was the per cent of beet sugar? of cane sugar?

3. We also import bananas in great quantities, mostly from Central America. Bananas are usually transported in specially designed ships which can carry about 85,000 bunches of bananas. The average weight of a bunch of bananas is 50 lb. About how many tons of bananas can one of the ships carry?

4. In a recent year, the coffee we imported would supply each person in the nation with 17.8 lb. Figuring 2 tablespoons to each cup of coffee, on the average, how many cups would 17.8 lb. provide each person in one year? (1 lb. of coffee = 80 tbsp.)

5. The cost of the cocoa we import has increased greatly. In 1940 the price in foreign markets averaged 4.4¢ per pound. The price, 10 years later, had increased to 35.4¢ per pound. What was the per cent of increase?

6. The United States does not import as much cheese as in the past. In 1939, we imported 55,291,000 lb. Eight years later we imported 25,135,000. What was the per cent of decrease during the eight-year period?

Food for the Family

1. In a recent year, the people of this country spent about $58,600,000,000 for food alone. If the population was about 150,000,000, the average expenditure for food per person was about how much during that year?

2. At this rate (Problem **1**), how much would it cost to buy food for a family of four for one week?

3. Food prices sometimes are a good guide to the value of money. For example, in 1941 the average price of eggs was 39.7¢ per dozen. In 1949, the price was 69.6¢. What was the per cent of increase in price?

4. During the same period, the average price of butter rose from 41.1¢ to 73.5¢ per pound. To the nearest tenth, how many pounds of butter would one dollar buy in 1941? in 1949?

5. Cost of food is the largest item in the family budget. In one year, a certain family spent $1570 for food. This was 36.5% of the family's total income. What was the family's income that year?

Courtesy Snow Crop

Making frozen orange juice—fruit passing into rotary juice presses

Processing Food

Before they are offered for sale in food stores, most foods must be processed. Processing differs for various foods and is intended to make them easier to prepare, taste better, and keep longer.

1. One method of processing food is quick freezing. The frozen food industry has grown rapidly. In 1939, there were only 3,334 workers in this industry. Eight years later, there were 15,770. How many times as many workers were there in 1947?

2. In making frozen orange juice, most of the water is removed from fresh orange juice and the concentrate is canned and frozen. To prepare it for drinking, 3 cans of water are added to one can of juice. The added water forms what per cent of the prepared orange juice?

3. The amount of frozen fish consumed each year has increased greatly. In 1939, 183 million pounds of frozen fish were produced. Ten years later, 286 million pounds were produced. What was the per cent of increase during the ten-year period?

4. A popular way of buying canned grapefruit juice is in the large can holding 1 quart 14 fluid ounces of juice. How many gallons of juice are there in a case of 12 cans?

5. One type of grapefruit yields about 1 gallon of juice from 25 lb. of fruit. About how many pounds of grapefruit are needed to produce the case of 12 large cans of juice?

6. To make evaporated milk from whole milk, about 60% of the water is removed. At this rate, how many gallons of evaporated milk can be made from a can of whole milk containing 10 gallons?

7. Using your answer to Problem **6**, find how many cans may be filled with the evaporated milk if each can holds 13 fluid ounces. (16 fluid ounces = 1 pint)

8. About $10\frac{1}{2}$ lb. of milk are needed to provide sufficient cream for 1 lb. of butter. The huge churns used in a modern dairy produce 1000 lb. of butter at one time. How many pounds of milk are needed to supply the cream for this amount of butter? How many quarts is this, to the nearest quart, if one quart of milk weighs 2.15 lb.?

9. In making white bread, wholesale bakeries use, on the average, 3.42 lb. of milk solids for every 100 lb. of flour. About 8 lb. of whole milk are needed to make 1 lb. of milk solids. How many pounds of whole milk are needed for every 100 lb. of flour used in making bread? How many quarts is this to the nearest whole quart?

Courtesy Continental Baking Co.

Courtesy General Motors

Transporting Food

The people of the United States eat better and more varied foods than the people of most other lands. This is due, in part, to our rapid, efficient transportation system which can deliver food from the producer to the consumer in a few days over distances of thousands of miles.

1. In 1910, the average amount of citrus fruit eaten per person in the nation was 17.8 lb. In 1950 the average was 41.0 lb. This increase was due largely to swift and inexpensive transportation. What was the per cent of increase from 1910 to 1950?

2. Our transportation system provides us with many different kinds of food. This is one reason why potato consumption decreased from 197 lb. per person in 1910 to 104 lb. per person in 1950. What was the per cent of decrease?

3. Refrigerated trucks often transport loads of strawberries from Plant City, Florida to Chicago, Illinois, a distance of about 1200 miles. If these trucks average 35 miles an hour, about how long does it take to make this trip?

4. Strawberries are packed in crates with 36 pints to each crate. If the market value of strawberries is 30¢ a pint, what would a truckload of 356 crates be worth?

5. A truck farmer has 4 acres of carrots. The farm price of carrots recently averaged $1.32 per bushel, and production averaged 362 bushels per acre. At these rates, what amount can this farmer expect to receive when he markets his crop?

6. A tank truck carrying milk from a rural community to a large city holds 16,000 quarts of milk. If 1 qt. weighs 2.15 lb., how many pounds does the truck carry? If the wholesale price in a certain large city is $6.14 per 100 lb., how much is the truckload of milk worth?

7. Increase in the price of food is due partly to rises in the cost of transportation. In 1939, the total cost of transporting farm food products was $950,000,000. Ten years later, it was $2,130,000,000. At the end of the ten-year period, the cost was how many times as great as the cost in 1939?

8. In one year, the railroads hauled 254,991 carloads of potatoes weighing a total of 5,161,652 tons. Round these numbers to the nearest thousand, and find about how many tons of potatoes were carried per carload.

9. In the same year, the wholesale price of potatoes in a large New England city was $3.76 per hundred pounds. At this rate, how much would an 18-ton carload be worth?

Courtesy Milk Industry Foundation

Food Gives Us Energy

Most of the heat and energy we need for work and play comes from two substances in our food, fats and carbohydrates. These are often called fuel foods because they supply our bodies with heat and energy. The heat energy they furnish is measured in special units called **calories**. Foods differ in the number of calories they provide.

1. If ham furnishes 1344 calories per pound, how many calories will be obtained from three slices of baked ham, each weighing $\frac{1}{2}$ oz.?

2. George drinks two pints of milk a day. An average glass, holding half a pint, furnishes 165 calories. Find how many calories George obtains from the two pints.

3. A quart of ice cream weighs about 2 lb. If there are 953 calories in a pound of ice cream, how many calories are there in half a pint of ice cream?

4. One medium-size egg furnishes 75 calories, and one slice of white bread, 100 calories. Find the number of calories obtained from an egg sandwich on white bread.

5. How many calories are furnished by the egg sandwich (Problem **4**) and a glass of milk (Problem **2**)?

6. A boy 13 to 15 years old needs about 3200 calories per day, while a girl of the same age needs about 2800. A boy needs what per cent more calories than a girl?

Food Builds Our Bodies

In addition to fats and carbohydrates, food contains protein, another essential substance. Protein is often called the building food because it builds and repairs muscles and tissue, and helps insure growth.

1. About .3 gram of protein is needed each day for each pound of body weight. How many grams would a 110-lb. boy need? Is this more or less than an ounce? (1 gram = .0352 oz.)

2. Meat is one of the best sources of protein. The protein content of 1 lb. of frankfurters is 69 grams. If there are 6 frankfurters to one pound, how many grams of protein are there in one frankfurter?

3. A pound of frankfurters furnishes 912 calories. How many calories will one frankfurter provide?

4. An average serving of pot roast gives about .84 oz. of protein. If a 110-lb. boy requires about 1.16 oz. of protein daily, what per cent of his requirement does an average serving furnish?

5. A pound of cottage cheese supplies 87 grams of protein but only 24 grams of fats and carbohydrates. How many times the amount of fats and carbohydrates is the amount of protein?

6. Cottage cheese supplies 459 calories. Cheddar-type cheese (made from whole milk) supplies 1784. The number of calories in cottage cheese is what per cent of the number in Cheddar-type cheese (nearest whole per cent)?

7. A pound of bananas contains about 3.6 grams of protein, .6 gram of fat, and 69.9 grams of carbohydrate. Bananas contain how many times as much carbohydrate as protein? how many times as much carbohydrate as fat?

Learning to Solve Problems

Estimating with Measures

When solving a problem, it is always helpful to estimate the answer. You may make your rough estimate before or after you work the problem. Such estimates help to prevent ridiculous answers.

Tell which answer, of those given for each problem, is correct, or most nearly correct.

1. At the rate of 21¢ a quart, the cost of 2 gallons of milk is about: $.40, $.85, $1.65.

2. At a speed of 11 miles an hour, a boy riding a bicycle can travel, in $2\frac{1}{4}$ hours, about: 20 mi., 25 mi., 5 mi.

3. A bridge $\frac{3}{8}$ mile long has a length of about: 1000 ft., 2000 ft., 4000 ft., 5000 ft.

4. Nine boys, weighing on the average 112 lb., altogether would weigh about: 2 tons, 1900 lb., 1000 lb.

5. At the rate of $3\frac{3}{8}$¢ a mile, the cost of a railroad trip of 410 miles is about: $16, $12, $14, $13.

6. Two hundred letters, each weighing $1\frac{1}{2}$ oz., would weigh in all about: 1 lb., 100 lb., 10 lb., 20 lb.

7. The cost of sending a trunk a certain distance by express is $1.15 a hundred pounds. If the trunk weighs 228 lb., the express cost will be about: $250, $22.80, $2, $2.50.

8. At $1.78 an hour, a mechanic who works 40 hours a week will earn each week about: $44, $50, $70, $100.

9. At 2 for 27¢, $1\frac{1}{2}$ doz. cans of fruit juice will cost about: $3, $2.50, $6, $2.

10. Mr. Munsey built a fence 255 feet long. He placed the fence posts $8\frac{1}{2}$ feet apart. About how many posts did he need: 10, 15, 30, 50, 100?

David W. Corson from A. Devaney, N.Y.

Making Cloth

Primitive man used as clothing, the skins of animals, pieces of bark, or woven grass. Later, man discovered how to weave cloth from the hair of certain animals and from the fibers of certain plants. Today, in addition to these natural fibers, modern industry produces artificial, or synthetic fibers, such as rayon and nylon.

1. Different breeds of sheep give varying quantities of wool. A merino sheep usually yields about 8 lb. of raw wool at a shearing. If it takes about $3\frac{1}{2}$ lb. of raw wool, on the average, to make a man's suit, about how many such suits could be made from the wool of 100 sheep?

2. On most ranches, sheep are sheared once a year. An expert can shear one sheep in about 3 minutes. Working eight hours in one day, he will shear about how many sheep?

3. The production in a certain year of four leading wool-producing nations is given below. Total world production in that year was 3,780.0 million pounds.

COUNTRY	PRODUCTION IN MILLION POUNDS	COUNTRY	PRODUCTION IN MILLION POUNDS
Australia. . . .	1095.0	New Zealand . .	255.0
Argentina . . .	400.0	United States. .	258.6

A. What per cent of the world total did each country produce? **B.** What per cent did the four countries together produce?

4. Cotton is the most important plant fiber used in making cloth. In a recent year, world production of cotton was 27,315,000 bales, of which 14,685,000 were produced in the United States. What per cent did the United States produce?

5. Cotton pickers dump the seed cotton (unginned cotton) into wagons which stand in the fields. A wagonload of 1500 pounds of seed cotton produces one 500-pound bale of cotton and 1000 pounds of seed. How many pounds of seed cotton would have to be ginned to provide a truckload of 56 bales?

6. Cottonseed is made into cooking oil, paints, plastics, and other useful products. In one year, the farm value of the cotton crop was $2,549,874,000, which included $286,965,000 worth of cottonseed. Rounding these numbers to the nearest million, find what per cent the cottonseed was of the total crop value.

7. Rayon, the first of the synthetic fabrics, is made from chemically-treated cotton or wood. A more recently developed fabric is nylon, made from plastic substances. The table shows the United States production of these fabrics in recent years. How many times as much rayon as nylon, to the nearest tenth, was produced each year?

YEAR	PRODUCTION IN THOUSANDS OF YARDS	
	RAYON	NYLON
1946	1,713,364	21,539
1947	1,976,836	21,881
1948	2,180,890	32,654
1949	1,929,621	87,399

Spinning rayon filaments into thread © Ewing Galloway

The Clothing Industry

Before the invention of cutting and sewing machines, clothing manufacture was slow and costly. Today, the garment industry can produce well-tailored clothing rapidly and inexpensively.

1. A garment worker using a chopper (machine cutter) can cut the pieces for 50 garments at one time. If a woman's dress is cut from a $3\frac{1}{2}$-yard piece of cloth, how many yards are needed for 50 dresses? At 87¢ a yard, how much would the material for 50 dresses cost?

2. Surveys show that men's suits are normally bought as shown in the table. Using the per cents shown, find about how many suits of each kind a manufacturer would produce out of a total of 7500 suits.

SIZE	PER CENT OF SUITS BOUGHT
Regular	54.3
Short	31.3
Stout	4.7
Long	5.6
Short-stout	4.1

3. Recently, the average weekly earnings for workers making shirts and collars were $39.22. How much would this be per year? The average number of hours worked per week was 37.0. What was the average hourly rate of pay?

4. Recently, the number of persons in all industries was 57,588,000. Of this total, 1,181,000 were engaged in clothing production. What per cent was this?

The Cost of Clothing

1. In a recent year, the total personal expenditures of the people of the United States were $178,832,000,000. Of this amount $18,435,000,000 was spent for new clothing. What per cent of the total was this?

2. In one year, the Wilson family spent $462 of its total income for essential clothing. If this was 13.3% of the family income, what was the total income to the nearest dollar?

3. The table shows how the Wilson family's clothing costs were distributed. What per cent of the total amount spent for clothing did each member of the family receive?

FATHER $149
MOTHER 134
BOY 89
GIRL 90

4. Clothing costs have risen rapidly in recent years. In 1944, the retail clothing index was 138.8. By 1949, it had gone up 51.3 points. This increase was what per cent of the 1944 index?

5. Wages and salaries have increased also. In 1944, the average annual salary of bank employees was $2069; in 1949 it was $3163. What per cent of increase is this? Which is greater, the per cent of increase in salary or the per cent of increase in clothing costs (Problem **4**)?

Shipping Goods

Every day, many thousands of tons of material are transported by train, truck, ship, airplane, or pipeline. Each of these methods of transportation plays an important role in keeping the people in all parts of our nation supplied with the materials they need.

A **ton-mile** means a ton of freight carried one mile. Five tons of freight hauled 3 miles equal 15 ton-miles. Three tons of freight hauled 5 miles also equal 15 ton-miles.

Ton-miles = number of tons × number of miles

1. An average-length freight train has 57 freight cars. If a train of this length is made up entirely of gondolas and hopper cars (coal cars), each carrying 50 tons of coal, what will be the total number of ton-miles on a 250-mile haul?

2. Freight cars average 858 ton-miles per day.

A. If the average daily mileage per freight car is 42.9 miles, how many tons, on the average, are carried each day per freight car (nearest tenth)?

B. What per cent less than capacity do freight cars usually carry if the average capacity is 51.5 tons?

3. The table shows how inter-city freight was transported in a recent year. To the nearest hundredth, find what per cent of the total of 870.3 billion ton-miles was carried by each method.

METHOD	BILLIONS OF TON-MILES
Railroads . . .	534.4
Waterways . .	132.3
Pipelines . . .	109.7
Highways . . .	93.7
Airways . . .	.2

4. More and more of the nation's freight is carried by trucks each year. This increase is shown by the greater numbers of trucks registered. **A.** Express the number of trucks registered in each year in millions and tenths of a million. **B.** Using these rounded numbers, draw a broken line graph showing the number of trucks registered each year.

YEAR	NUMBER REGISTERED
1925	2,483,215
1930	3,518,747
1935	3,675,865
1940	4,590,386
1945	4,834,742
1950	8,604,448

5. Canals and inland waterways make useful routes for carrying bulk materials. The Sault Sainte Marie Canal system (the "Soo"), connecting Lake Superior and Lake Huron, carries more cargo than any other canal in the world. Its eastbound cargoes are mostly iron ore and grain; its westbound cargoes are mostly coal. Freight tonnage in a recent year totaled 115,000,000 tons; 95 million of this was eastbound. What per cent of the total was eastbound traffic?

Freighters from the Great Lakes passing through the "Soo" locks
Courtesy National Film Board of Canada

Transporting Oil and Natural Gas

Since the building of the Big Inch pipeline during World War II, pipeline construction has increased much as railroad building did in the last half of the 19th century. Extending underground for hundreds of miles, pipelines carry petroleum to refineries and natural gas to centers of population.

1. Thirty-inch pipeline, that is, a pipeline having a diameter of 30 inches, is usually made in sections 40 ft. long. How many of these sections would there be in 1 mile of pipeline?

2. Find the area of the cross section (open end) of a 30-inch pipe to the nearest tenth of a square foot.

3. How many gallons of oil would a single section (40 ft.) of the pipeline in Problem **2** hold? ($7\frac{1}{2}$ gal. = 1 cu. ft.)

4. At $12.00 a foot, what would it cost to build a 30-inch pipeline 320 miles long?

5. One of the longest pipelines in the world carries natural gas 1,840 miles from Texas to New York City. It cost $240,000,000 to build this pipeline. To the nearest dollar, what was the cost per mile?

Measuring Energy

Energy in the form of heat, light, and mechanical power is required to do the work of the world today. This energy is obtained mainly from coal, water, petroleum, and natural gas.

1. The table shows the per cent of energy for all purposes supplied by each of the four sources. **A.** The ratio of the total energy supplied by coal to that by water was about _?_ to 1. **B.** The ratio of the total energy supplied by petroleum to that supplied by natural gas was about _?_ to 1.

SOURCE OF ENERGY	PER CENT SUPPLIED
Coal	46%
Petroleum	35%
Natural Gas	15%
Water	4%

2. A common unit of measuring power is the **horsepower** (**H.P.**). A horse at work pulling a load will actually furnish about $\frac{3}{4}$ H.P. A small automobile can furnish about 80 H.P. How many times as much power as the horse does the automobile furnish?

3. Men doing light work each furnish about $\frac{1}{10}$ H.P. **A.** If each man earns $1 per hour, what is the cost per hour for 1 H.P.? **B.** Electric washing-machine motors often furnish $\frac{1}{4}$ H.P. If it costs 4¢ per hour to run one of these motors, what is the cost per hour for 1 H.P.? **C.** At these rates per hour for 1 H.P., the cost of manpower is how many times as great as the cost of machine power?

4. Electric power is usually measured in units called **watts** and **kilowatts**. A **kilowatt (kw.)** is a thousand watts. One horsepower equals 746 watts. How many horsepower are equal to 1 kilowatt (to the nearest tenth)?

5. A certain gasoline engine supplies 120 H.P. How many kilowatts is this (to the nearest tenth)?

6. The United States leads the world in the production of coal, our main source of energy. On the average, one of our miners, using modern machinery, produces 6.30 tons of coal per day. In Great Britain, a miner produces 1.15 tons; in Germany, a miner produces 0.95 ton. A United States miner produces how many times as much coal as the British miner? as the German miner?

7. A solid block of a certain kind of coal, containing 1 cu. ft., weighs 81 lb. If burned at a power plant, it would produce enough electricity to supply an average home for about 19 days. How long would a ton of this coal keep the home supplied with electricity?

8. About 90% of our annual coal production is bituminous, or soft coal. In one year, our bituminous coal production was 546 million tons. Of this, 113 million tons were used to run our railroads and 86 million tons were used to produce electricity. What per cent was used by the railroads? What per cent was used to produce electricity?

9. Our nation's coal fields are rich but not inexhaustible, and we conserve wherever possible. In 1920, the railroads used one ton of coal to move 11,627 tons of freight one mile. Today, due to better practices, a ton of coal moves 17,505 tons of freight one mile. How many times as much freight can be moved per ton of coal today?

Petroleum and Natural Gas

The products of our nation's oil fields—petroleum and natural gas—rank second to coal as sources of energy.

1. Gas, such as that which we burn in kitchen stoves, can be natural or manufactured. Natural gas is usually found in oil wells. Manufactured gas is made largely from coal. The amount of natural gas used in the United States in one year totaled 2,985 billion cubic feet; the amount of manufactured gas totaled 442 billion cubic feet. The amount of natural gas used was how many times that of manufactured gas?

2. By a process known as "cracking," petroleum is made into fuel oil, gasoline, and many other useful products. If 18 gallons of gasoline are made from a 42-gallon barrel of petroleum, what per cent of the petroleum is the gasoline produced?

Courtesy Standard Oil Co., (N. J.)
A petroleum "cracker"

3. The use of fuel oil to drive engines has made important changes in the amount of cargo a ship can carry. A coal-burning ship with a total capacity of 8000 tons allows 1000 tons of this total for coal. Another ship, with the same total capacity, using oil, allows only about 250 tons for fuel. What per cent more cargo can the second ship carry?

4. Although the amount varies with climate, about 1200 gallons of fuel oil will heat an average 6-room house during one year. If 100 gal. of petroleum produce 39 gal. of fuel oil, how many gallons of petroleum are needed to produce the fuel oil for heating the house?

5. Water cannot be used as a fuel, but it is useful as a producer of electricity (hydroelectric power). Of the total electricity produced in the United States in a recent year, about 31% was hydroelectric power; the remainder was produced by fuels. The ratio of electricity produced by fuels to hydroelectric power was about __?__ to 1.

6. Giant generators change the power of rushing water into electricity. Bonneville Dam, on the Columbia River in Oregon, has a capacity of 518,000 kilowatts. How many horsepower is this? (1 H.P. = 746 watts.)

7. Hoover Dam, on the Colorado River between Arizona and Nevada, has a capacity of 1,034,800 kilowatts. The total capacity of all hydroelectric plants in the United States is about 16,595,000 kilowatts. Hoover Dam has what per cent of the total capacity?

8. Recently, two 65,000 H.P. motors were built for Grand Coulee Dam in Washington. They are used to drive pumps supplying water for irrigation. If the total power capacity of the dam is about 2,632,000 H.P., what per cent is needed to drive the two motors?

9. It is not always necessary to build dams to produce hydroelectric power. For example, large power plants, built at Niagara Falls, generate nearly 1,500,000 H.P. for use in the United States and Canada. If all of the power of the falling water were used, it would generate about 4,000,000 H.P. Find what per cent of the possible power of Niagara Falls is being used?

© *Philip Gendreau*

Electricity in the Home

Electricity is one of the most important forms of energy produced from coal, water, petroleum, and gas. Most families "buy" electricity from the local power company, paying according to the number of kilowatt-hours used.

A **kilowatt-hour** (**kwh.**) is the amount of electric energy provided in 1 hour at the rate of 1 kilowatt. It may take more or less than an hour to use 1 kilowatt-hour. An electric appliance using 2 kilowatts may only be operated for $\frac{1}{2}$ hour on one kilowatt-hour. An appliance using $\frac{1}{2}$ kilowatt (500 watts) may be used for 2 hours.

$$\text{kilowatt hours} = \text{kilowatts} \times \text{hours} \quad \text{or,} \quad \frac{\text{watts} \times \text{hours}}{1000}$$

1. Stamped on the end of light bulbs is the number of watts they require. A 100-watt bulb will use 1 kilowatt-hour of electricity in 10 hours:

$$\frac{100 \times 10}{1000} = 1 \text{ kwh.}$$

A. Find the number of kilowatt-hours used by a 100-watt bulb in 35 hours; **B.** the number of kilowatt-hours used by a 75-watt bulb burning 4 hours per day for 30 days.

2. Electric appliances are "rated" by the number of watts on which they operate. A certain type of electric fan is rated at 90 watts. How many kilowatt-hours would this fan use, running 8 hours each day for 6 days?

3. Electricity provides us with large amounts of energy at a very low cost. Families using electricity for light, electric appliances, and refrigeration consume about 100 kwh. per month per family. In a recent year, in large cities the average bill for 100 kwh. was $3.64 per family. What was the cost per kilowatt-hour?

4. Power companies usually charge lower rates per kilowatt-hour when large amounts of electricity are used. The table shows recent average bills in large cities for 25 kwh. and 250 kwh. **A.** What was the cost per kilowatt-hour when 25 kwh. were used? when 250 kwh. were used? **B.** How many times as great was the cost per kilowatt-hour when 25 kwh. were used as when 250 kwh. were used?

AMOUNT OF ELECTRICITY USED	AVERAGE BILL
25 kwh.	$1.24
250 kwh.	6.81

5. At 3.6¢ per kilowatt-hour, what is the monthly cost of using an electric toaster 10 minutes every day for 30 days, if the toaster is rated at 700 watts?

6. An average-size home freezer requires $2\frac{1}{2}$ kwh. per day to operate. Find the cost of operating such a freezer for one year at 2.7¢ per kilowatt-hour.

7. A home electric milk pasteurizer often used on farms requires 300 watts. The machine has a capacity of 1 gallon and is operated for approximately half an hour. If electricity costs 4¢ per kilowatt-hour, what is the cost of pasteurizing a gallon of milk?

8. A certain radio used 3 kwh. when operating continuously for 40 hours. What was the rating of the radio in watts?

Use of Raw Materials

1. The manufacture of steel requires large amounts of iron ore. World production of iron ore in a recent year was estimated at 232,522,000 tons, of which the United States produced about 113,346,000 tons. What per cent of the total world production was the United States production?

2. Coal, in the form of coke, is essential in steel production. In one year, the United States used about 15.7% of its coal supply in making coke. The total coal supply was about 478,000,000 tons. About how many tons were made into coke?

3. Tungsten is a metal which is needed to make steel harder. The table shows the production of tungsten, in a recent year, as reported by certain countries.

If the total world production that year was about 32,000 tons, about what per cent of the total did each of these countries produce?

COUNTRY	TONS
China	13,410
United States. . .	4,005
Portugal	3,220
Bolivia	2,735
Australia.	1,340

4. The United States must import its entire supply of natural rubber. The output of principal rubber-producing lands in a recent year is shown below.

COUNTRY	TONS
Malaya	782,000
Indonesia	484,000
Ceylon	106,000
Indo-China	49,000
Africa	47,000

Total world production that year was 1,702,000 tons. What per cent was produced by Malaya? by Indonesia? What per cent was produced altogether by the other three principal rubber-producing lands?

Courtesy U. S. Rubber Company

5. In order to be more independent of foreign sources, the United States now manufactures synthetic rubber in large quantities. In a recent year, total consumption of rubber in the United States was 1,094,290 tons, of which 455,840 tons were synthetic. What per cent of the rubber used was synthetic?

6. Tin resources in the United States are scanty. The value of one recent year's domestic production was $13,000. The value of the tin imported was $212,289,000. The value of the imports was how many times as great as the value of the domestic production?

Keeping in Practice

I.

	A	B	C	D
1.	39.2 × 16	$4.85 × 24	638 × .32	$12.95 × 18
2.	4093.6 − 628.7	$5000.00 − 1875.24	2,380,620 − 1,781,590	$100 − 18.98
3.	47)903	72)2960	58)11,852	64)31,000

4. $\frac{2}{3} \div \frac{4}{5} = ?$ $1\frac{3}{8} + \frac{5}{6} = ?$ $3\frac{3}{4} - 2\frac{7}{8} = ?$ $12\frac{1}{2} - 8\frac{1}{4} = ?$

5. $\frac{3}{8} \div \frac{3}{4} = ?$ $2\frac{1}{4} \times \frac{2}{3} = ?$ $16 \div \frac{1}{8} = ?$ $7\frac{1}{2} \div 2\frac{1}{2} = ?$

II.

	A	B	C
1.	6% of $72 = ?	$\frac{1}{4}$% of $1000 = ?	$98\frac{1}{2}$% of $400 = ?
2.	18 is __?__% of 27	18 is __?__% of 9	18 is __?__% of 18
3.	150% of $200 = ?	110% of 60 = ?	225% of $800 = ?
4.	16 is 50% of ?	12 is 25% of ?	24 is 80% of ?

III.

1. Express as decimals:

$\frac{7}{8}$ $\frac{3}{5}$ $\frac{5}{6}$ $\frac{3}{16}$ $\frac{1}{20}$

2. Express as fractions in lowest terms:

1.5   .025 $4\frac{1}{2}$%   2%   .2%

3. Express as per cents:

$\frac{3}{4}$ $\frac{3}{10}$ $1\frac{1}{4}$ 2.1   1

4. Express as decimals:

5%   50%   .5%   1.5%   55%

5. Arrange in order of value from smallest to largest:

.40   40.0   4.04   .040

Three Kinds of Per Cent Problems

A problem in per cent asks one of these questions:
1. What is the *percentage?*
2. What *per cent* is one number of another?
3. What is the *base?*

If we call the base B, the rate R, and the percentage P, then we know that P = R × B.

1. **A.** Which of the three questions above does the formula, P = R × B, answer?

   B. What is 20% of 40? 40% of 20? 100% of $25?

2. **A.** How do you find what per cent one number is of another?

   B. Do you see that you can do this by using the formula, $R = \frac{P}{B}$?

   C. What per cent of 90 is 45? What per cent of 20 is 30? What per cent of 50 is 50?

3. **A.** How do you find a number when you know that a given number is a certain per cent of it?

   B. Do you see that you can do this by using the formula, $B = \frac{P}{R}$?

   C. A man's salary is increased by $3 a week. If this represents a rate of increase of 6%, what was his weekly salary before it was increased?

4. An increase from $4 to $5 is an increase of what per cent? A decrease from $5 to $4 is a decrease of what per cent?

5. How much is $500 increased by 10%? $400 decreased by 25%?

6. The interest for 1 year at 4% on a certain principal is $20; find the principal.

Public Education in Our Nation

In each of the forty-eight states free education is available to all children. This fact is an important reason why the United States is one of the most advanced nations of the world. Continued progress depends, in part, upon further improvements in our educational systems.

1. In a recent year, the total number of elementary and secondary schools in the United States was 197,698. Of these, 184,541 were public schools; the remainder were private. The ratio of public schools to private schools was about _?_ to 1.

2. In 1940, the total public school enrollment was 25,434,000. The total number of teachers was 875,000. How many pupils were there per teacher?

3. In 1950, there were 25,185,000 pupils and 904,000 teachers. How many pupils were there per teacher in this year?

4. In recent years there has been a serious shortage of teachers in elementary schools. It was estimated that in one year 150,000 additional teachers were needed. In that year the nation's teachers colleges graduated only 28,000 elementary school teachers. The number of teachers needed was how many times as great as the number of teachers graduated?

Courtesy the American Music Conference through Scholastic Magazine

A modern high school   © *Ewing Galloway*

5. Although 12 years of schooling are available in most states, the usual number of years completed is only about 9 at present. Listed below is the total enrollment in high schools for certain years and the number of graduates for each of the years.

What per cent of the total enrollment in the high schools in each of the years graduated? What was the increase in the per cent graduating between 1930 and 1950?

YEAR	HIGH SCHOOL ENROLLMENT	GRADUATES
1930	4,799,867	666,904
1940	6,601,444	1,221,475
1950	5,585,000	1,067,000

6. In recent years, school enrollment has increased in most states. Listed below are the total school enrollments for certain large states as reported by the 1940 and 1950 Census. Find the per cent of increase or decrease in school enrollment for each of these states.

STATE	SCHOOL ENROLLMENT 1940	SCHOOL ENROLLMENT 1950
Pennsylvania	2,076,000	2,499,000
California	1,264,000	1,831,000
Illinois	1,463,000	1,484,000
Texas	1,341,000	1,438,000
Michigan	1,123,000	1,286,000

Paying for Education

Everyone in a nation benefits when the citizens are well educated. For this reason the costs of operating our nation's schools are shared by all the taxpayers.

1. Each year greater amounts of money are required to build and operate public schools. The table shows the total school expenditures of state and local governments for certain years.

The expenditures in 1950 were how many times as great as in 1930?

YEAR	TOTAL EXPENDITURES
1930	$2,317 million
1940	2,344 million
1950	4,492 million

2. The costs of constructing a school building were recently estimated as being 186% of the 1939 costs. If it cost $125,000 to construct a certain school building in 1939, how much would it cost to build such a school at the new rate?

3. During a recent year, the average amount spent in the nation per public school student was estimated at $213. **A.** In that year the greatest amount spent by any state for education averaged about $300 per pupil. This was what per cent more than the national average? **B.** The smallest amount spent by any state averaged about $75 per pupil. This was what per cent of the national average?

4. Transporting students to and from school is a large item of expense in modern education. The total reported costs in one recent year were $129,756,735. If the average cost was $25.66 per student, about how many students received free school transportation?

5. The proposed budget in a town of 22,000 people, in a recent year, was $1,621,738. This was an increase of $241,981 over the previous year. What was the per cent of increase?

6. Of the total budget, $939,898 was to be spent on the operation of the town's public school system. What per cent of the total amount of the budget was this?

7. To meet the rise in the cost of living, each employee in the school system was to have an increase of $400 in his yearly salary. If there were 163 employees, what was the total amount of increase?

8. The minimum salary for most beginning teachers in the town is $2200. Salary is increased $150 each year until the maximum of $3850 is reached. How many years does it take to reach the maximum salary?

9. In 1942, for the nation, the average annual salary in the field of public education was $1515. In 1950, the average was $2826. What per cent increase is this?

10. During the same period, the average annual salary of all workers in the United States rose from $1719 to $2869. What per cent increase is this?

11. The present average salary in public education is what per cent of the average salary of all workers?

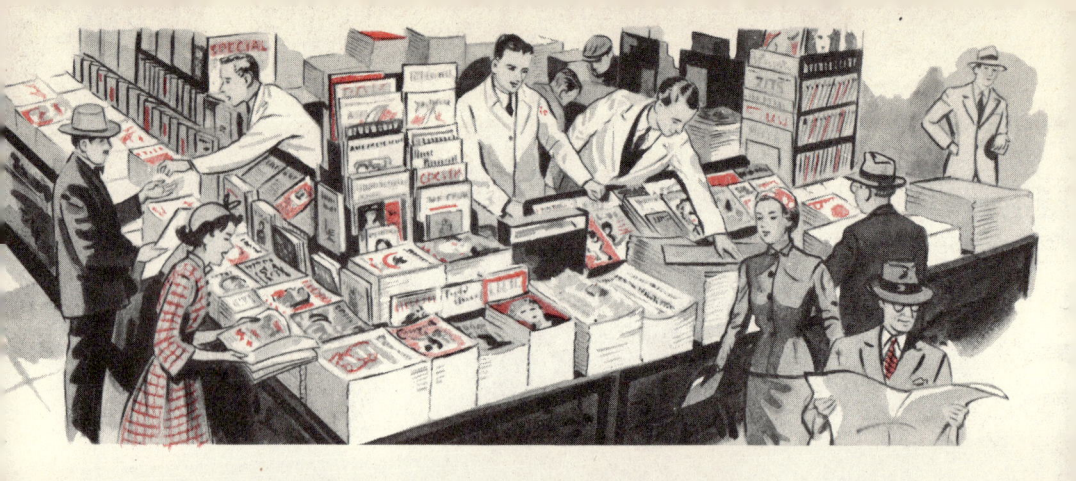

Communication in Our World

The first great advance in mechanical means of communication was the invention of the printing press. Today, man has developed additional ways of sharing his ideas. What are some of these ways?

1. Before people can enjoy the benefits made available by the printing press, they must know how to read. The table below gives the number of illiterates (persons over 14 years old who are unable to read) and the population for that age group in certain countries.

COUNTRY	POPULATION OVER 14 YEARS OLD	NUMBER OF ILLITERATES
United States	106,000,000	2,800,000
Brazil	24,000,000	13,300,000
Sweden	5,000,000	6,000
Egypt	10,000,000	8,400,000

A. What per cent of the population over 14 years old was illiterate in each of these countries?

B. The rate of illiteracy in the world has been estimated at 50%. How much less than the world rate was the rate of illiteracy in the United States? How much more than the world rate was the rate of illiteracy in Egypt?

2. This table shows the number of daily newspapers printed per thousand inhabitants in each country. **A.** The ratio of the newspapers per 1000 inhabitants in the United States to those in Egypt is about _?_ to 1. **B.** Sweden has about _?_ times as many newspapers per 1000 inhabitants as Brazil.

COUNTRY	NEWSPAPERS PER 1000 INHABITANTS
Sweden . . .	382
United States	357
Brazil	31
Egypt	18

3. The table below shows the reported annual production of electric power and the total number of radios in certain nations in recent years.

COUNTRY	POPULATION	ANNUAL PRODUCTION OF ELECTRICITY IN KILOWATT-HOURS	NUMBER OF RADIO SETS
United States . .	150,000,000	345,066,000,000	83,000,000
Mexico	24,000,000	4,328,000,000	750,000
Austria	7,000,000	5,112,000,000	1,250,000
India	340,000,000	4,920,000,000	268,000

A. About how many kilowatt-hours of electricity were available annually per person in each of these countries?

B. In each of the countries there were about how many people per radio set?

Courtesy Radio Corporation of America

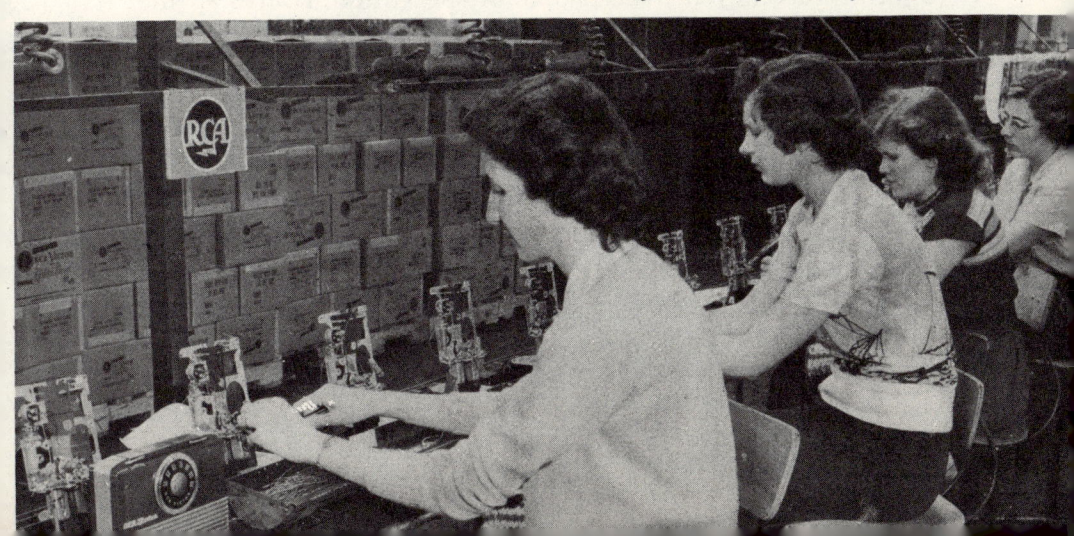

Motion Pictures and Television

1. Motion pictures bring entertainment to people of all lands. The table shows how many times per year, on the average, persons in various nations attend the movies.

COUNTRY	NUMBER OF TIMES ATTENDED
United States	32
United Kingdom	29
Brazil	3
Indonesia	.7

A. The people of the United States attend movies how many times as often as do the people of Brazil?

B. The people of the United Kingdom attend movies how many times as often as do the people of Indonesia?

2. Today there are enough motion picture theatres in the world to seat 44,000,000 people at one time. The theatres of the United States will seat 12,000,000 people at one time. What per cent of the total seating capacity does the United States have?

3. In a recent year, the people of the United States spent $1,802,000,000 in admissions for the major spectator amusements. The three most popular amusements and the amount spent for each were as follows:

What per cent of the total spent for admissions was spent for each of these three most popular amusements?

AMUSEMENTS	SPENT
Motion pictures	$1,342,000,000
College football	106,000,000
Opera and theatrical productions	92,000,000

4. During one year, Mr. Anderson kept a record of the number of times his family attended the motion pictures. There were 34 admissions for the adults in his family at an average price of 65¢ per ticket and 56 admissions for children at 25¢ per ticket, including tax. How much did the family spend in all during the year?

5. It was recently estimated that, during one year, 6,500,000 television receivers were sold in the United States with a total retail value of $2,000,000,000. To the nearest hundred dollars, what was the average price paid per set?

6. In 1951, there were about 12 million television receivers in use. It was estimated that the number would eventually total about 30 million. This is what per cent more than the number in use in 1951?

7. At the beginning of 1950, there were 98 television transmitters in the United States. A year later there were 109. What was the per cent of increase during the year?

8. It is not possible for a television transmitter to send a signal for great distances. A certain transmitter has a range of approximately 75 miles in all directions. How many square miles will such a transmitter cover?

9. In a recent year, it was estimated that television covered areas in which 90,000,000 people of our 150,000,000 population lived. Television was available to what per cent of the population?

Television antenna
Courtesy Radio Corporation of America

Using Longitude

The earth is like a huge globe. It is approximately a sphere 8000 miles in diameter.

1. Imaginary circles that go around the earth and pass through the North and South Poles are called **meridians.** If these meridians are drawn 1° apart, how many of them can be drawn on the surface of the earth? Why?

2. The meridians are counted east and west from Greenwich (London), England. The meridian which passes through Greenwich is called the **prime meridian,** or 0° meridian. Halfway around the world in either direction from Greenwich measures 180°. Why?

3. Distances measured in degrees east from the prime meridian are called **east longitude.** Distances measured west from the prime meridian are called **west longitude.** East longitude and west longitude meet halfway round the world. East longitude and west longitude each measure from 0° to __?__°.

4. The longitude of all places on the prime meridian is 0°. What is the greatest longitude a place can have? What part of the way around the earth from the prime meridian would such a place be?

5. The earth makes one complete turn (360°) every 24 hours. **A.** Through how many degrees does it turn in 1 hour? **B.** How long does it take the earth to turn one degree of longitude? fifteen degrees? five degrees?

6. The distance around the earth at the equator is about 25,000 miles. Find the number of miles in one degree at the equator, to the nearest 10 miles.

Telling Time

On any particular day, when the sun is at its highest, it is noon. It is noon at exactly the same time at all points lying on any particular meridian. When it is noon on one meridian, it is earlier or later than noon on any other meridian.

Courtesy Pictograph Corp. and New York Times

The shadows fall on the same meridian. It is the same time at **A** as at **B**.

1. It takes the earth 1 hour to turn through 15° of longitude. What is the difference in time of two places that are 30° of longitude apart? 45°? 10°?

2. If London is on the 0° meridian, and New York is approximately at the 75° meridian, what is the difference in time between these two cities?

3. Rome is about 15° east of Greenwich. Since the earth rotates, or turns, from west to east, is it earlier or later in Rome than in Greenwich? When it is 8 A.M. in Greenwich, what time is it in Rome?

4. The longitude of Moscow is about 37° East. Does the sun set earlier or later in Moscow than in London? How much earlier or later?

5. A radio broadcast is heard in London at 10 P.M. At what time is this broadcast heard in New Orleans, which is 90° west of London?

Courtesy Pictograph Corp. and New York Times

6. When it is noon in London, what time is it along the 180° meridian?

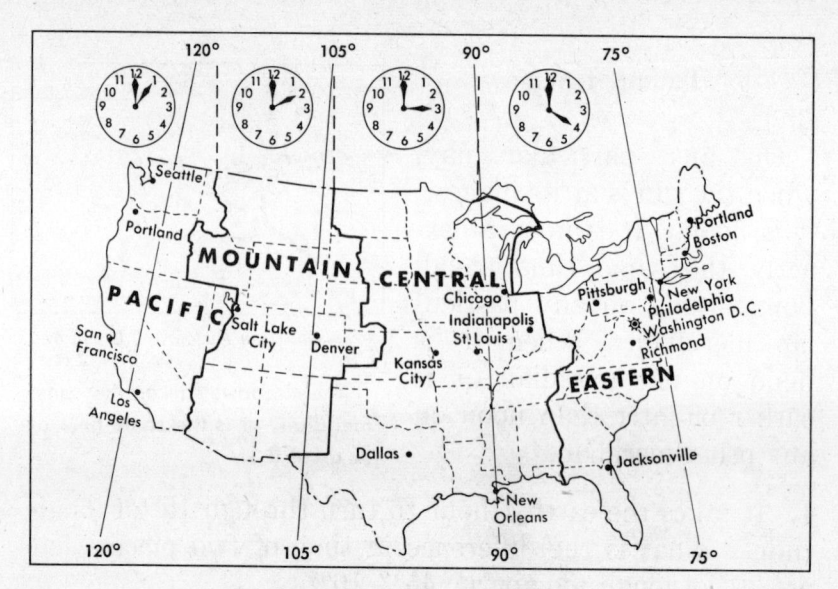

Standard Time Zones

If the clocks in every locality in the United States were set exactly by the sun, the time at one place would be different from the time at every other place east or west of it. This would cause great confusion, especially with railroad timetables and plane schedules.

To avoid such confusion, the United States is divided into four **standard time zones,** as shown above. Each zone covers about 15° of longitude. The time everywhere in a given zone is agreed upon as being the same, that is, **standard time.**

For example, San Francisco is about 2600 miles, or 50° of longitude, west of New York. Since the earth turns from west to east, sunrise in San Francisco is about $3\frac{1}{3}$ hours later than in New York; or, *sun-time* is always about 3 hr. 20 min. earlier in New York than in San Francisco. But, as you see from the map, the difference in *standard time* between these two cities is always just 3 hours.

1. When it is noon on the 75th meridian, what time is it in New York? in Washington, D. C.? in Jacksonville?

2. When it is 10 A.M. in Philadelphia, what time is it in Chicago? in Denver? in Seattle?

3. When it is 8 P.M. in St. Louis, what time is it in Los Angeles? in Pittsburgh? in Dallas?

4. When people on the Pacific coast of the United States are eating breakfast at 7:30 A.M., what time is it along the Atlantic coast?

5. If you should travel from Denver, Colorado to Richmond, Virginia, how many times would you change your watch? Would you move it ahead or set it back?

6. In many parts of the United States, clocks are set forward 1 hour during the summer months, and the time is then called **Daylight Saving Time.** In the summer, Chicago is on Daylight Saving Time; Denver is not. At 9 A.M. in Chicago on a day in July, what time is it in Denver?

7. New York City has Daylight Saving Time, but Kansas City, Missouri, does not. When it is 6 P.M. in Kansas City on a summer day, what time is it in New York?

8. A plane makes overnight flights between New York and San Francisco. If the speed is the same, will the night be longer on an eastbound or a westbound flight?

9. In what time zone is your home? What time is it now in your school? What time is it in New York? St. Louis? Denver? Seattle? New Orleans? Salt Lake City?

10. One morning, two automobiles started from Indianapolis at sunrise, one going east, the other going west. At 6 o'clock Central Time that evening, one car was in Pittsburgh and the other in St. Louis. What time was it then in Pittsburgh? in St. Louis? If each car traveled until sunset, which car stopped first?

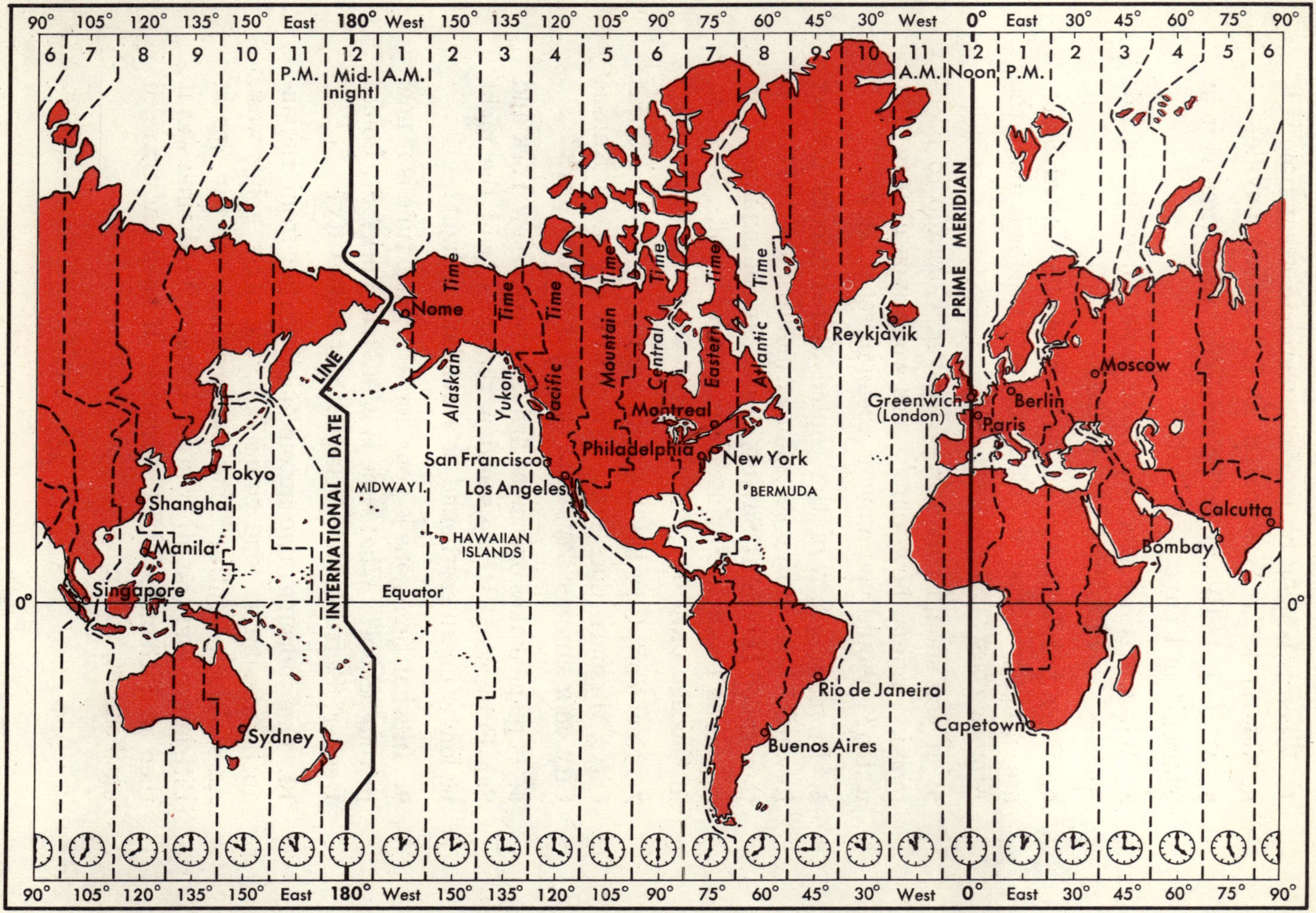
90° 105° 120° 135° 150° East 180° West 150° 135° 120° 105° 90° 75° 60° 45° 30° West 0° East 30° 45° 60° 75° 90°
6 7 8 9 10 11 12 1 2 3 4 5 6 7 8 9 10 11 12 1 2 3 4 5 6
P.M.
Mid-night
A.M.
A.M.
Noon
P.M.
INTERNATIONAL DATE LINE
PRIME MERIDIAN
Alaskan Time
Yukon Time
Pacific Time
Mountain Time
Central Time
Eastern Time
Atlantic Time
Nome
Tokyo
Shanghai
Manila
Singapore
Sydney
MIDWAY I.
HAWAIIAN ISLANDS
Equator
San Francisco
Los Angeles
Montreal
Philadelphia
New York
BERMUDA
Reykjavik
Greenwich (London)
Berlin
Paris
Moscow
Calcutta
Bombay
Rio de Janeiro
Capetown
Buenos Aires
0°
0°
90° 105° 120° 135° 150° East 180° West 150° 135° 120° 105° 90° 75° 60° 45° 30° West 0° East 30° 45° 60° 75° 90°

What Time Is It in the Rest of the World?

To avoid confusion, nearly all the countries in the world have agreed to divide the world into 24 time zones, since there are 24 hours in a day. In general, each zone differs by one hour from the one next to it. Within each zone every place has the same time. However, there are a few places where the time change is not a full hour; for example, time on the Hawaiian Islands is $2\frac{1}{2}$ hours, instead of 2 hours, earlier than Pacific Standard Time.

1. Study the simplified map on the opposite page. What is the width in degrees of most of the zones?

2. When it is 10 A.M. Eastern Standard Time in New York, what time is it in Reykjavik, Iceland? in Capetown? in Bermuda? Rio de Janeiro? Berlin? Buenos Aires?

3. A radio program is broadcast from New York at 8 P.M. What time is it heard in San Francisco? in Moscow?

4. A speaker in London began his broadcast at 3 P.M. What time was it in Philadelphia? in Singapore?

5. When it is sunset at Long. 90° W., how long after sunset is it at Long. 75° W. in the same latitude? at Long. 45° W.?

6. When it is noon on the 75th meridian west, what time is it on the 120th meridian? the 90th meridian?

7. What is the difference in longitude of two places if the difference in their sun-time is 2 hr.? 3 hr. 20 min.?

8. It is 11 A.M. at one place when it is 2 P.M. at another place; how many degrees apart are they?

9. Midway Island in the Pacific is about 54° of longitude west of San Francisco. If his watch indicates correct sun-time when he leaves Midway, will a navigator have to set his watch forward or backward to indicate correct sun-time when he arrives in San Francisco? by how much?

Using a Timetable

1. Study Table 1. How long does it take to go from New York to Buffalo? from New York to Albany? from Buffalo to Cleveland?

2. How long does the train stay in Albany? in Buffalo? in Cleveland?

3. How long does it take to go from New York to Chicago? from Cleveland to Chicago? (Remember the change from E.S.T. to C.S.T.)

TABLE 1

STATION	P.M.
Lv New York, N.Y. (E.S.T.)	6 15
Ar Albany, N.Y. "	9 05
Lv Albany, N.Y. "	9 10
Ar Buffalo, N.Y. "	2 20
Lv Buffalo, N.Y. "	2 27
Ar Cleveland, O. "	5 47
Lv Cleveland, O. "	6 05
Lv Toledo, O. "	8 15
Lv South Bend, Ind. (C.S.T.)	10 10
Ar Chicago, Ill. "	11 59

Figures showing time are in *light-face* type for A.M., and **heavy-face** type for P.M.

4. Study Table 2. How far is it by rail from Columbus to Philadelphia? from New York to Pittsburgh?

5. How long does it take to travel from St. Louis to Indianapolis? from Pittsburgh to Philadelphia? from Pittsburgh to New York?

TABLE 2

MILES	STATION		A.M.
0.0	St. Louis, Mo. (C.S.T.) Lv		9 00
240.0	Indianapolis, Ind. " Lv		**1 07**
420.4	Columbus, O. (E.S.T.) Lv		5 40
611.3	Pittsburgh, Pa. " Ar		**10 00**
611.3	Pittsburgh, Pa. " Lv		**10 05**
856.0	Harrisburg, Pa. " Lv		3 01
964.7	Philadelphia, Pa. " Lv		4 57
1050.6	New York, N.Y. " Ar		6 30

Figures showing time are in *light-face* type for A.M., and **heavy-face** type for P.M.

6. When changing from Central Standard Time (C.S.T.) to Eastern Standard Time (E.S.T.), how must the traveler's watch be changed?

7. How long does it take to go from St. Louis to New York? (Remember the change from C.S.T. to E.S.T.)

In the cab of a Diesel locomotive *Courtesy General Motors*

By Land and Sea

Distances on the sea are measured in **nautical miles**; distances on land are measured in **statute miles**. A statute mile is an ordinary land mile of 5280 feet.

1. Since 1000 nautical miles are about equal to 1152 statute miles, a nautical mile is how many times a statute mile?

2. What per cent more than the land mile is the nautical mile? What per cent of the nautical mile is the land mile?

3. About how many feet are there in one nautical mile?

4. When asked how fast a ship is moving, the navigator answers in "knots". A **knot** means a speed of one nautical mile per hour. It is wrong to say "knots per hour," because "knot" means a rate of speed per hour. If a ship is making 20 knots, what is its rate in land miles per hour?

On the bridge of the S. S. "America"
Courtesy United States Lines

5. If a speed boat is moving at the rate of 50 land miles per hour, at about how many knots is it traveling?

265

Learning to Solve Problems

Using Per Cents in Problems

1. Is 100% of a quantity more or less than the quantity?
2. If 60% of a certain amount of money is $75, what is the entire amount?
3. The price of an article is reduced from $5 to $4. Is this a decrease of 20% or 25%?
4. Is $\frac{3}{8}$ of something more or less than 35% of it?
5. Does 125% of a sum of money mean the same as 25% more than that amount?
6. If a paste is made by mixing 3 cups of water with 2 cups of flour, what per cent of the mixture is water? What per cent is flour?
7. Does 10% of a quantity mean the same as 10% less than the quantity?
8. A reduction of 2% on a certain bill amounts to $9. Find the amount of the bill before the reduction.
9. If an automobile has depreciated 25%, its value now is what per cent of its original value?
10. An increase in weight from 60 lb. to 80 lb. is an increase of what per cent?
11. Which represents the smaller per cent: 9 out of 15, or 10 out of 16?
12. If the ratio of two quantities is 2:3, the smaller is what per cent of the larger, and the larger is what per cent of the smaller?
13. A vacuum cleaner was sold for $68. If this is 80% of the original price, what was the original price?
14. Does 100% of $50 equal 50% of $100?
15. Can a quantity ever be decreased by more than 100%? increased by more than 100%?

Making Sure

1. Write these numbers in another way:
198.6 million, 13.5 billion, 71.85 billion.   219

2. The index number of department store sales in a large city rose from 216.9 to 220.2. The increase was what per cent of the lower index number?   221

3. A stick ($\frac{1}{4}$ lb.) of butter is sliced into 10 pats. If 1 lb. of butter contains 3475 calories, about how many calories are there in 2 pats?   230

4. In traveling from Portland, Oregon to Chicago, Illinois, would you set your watch forward or back?   260

5. An electric motor furnishes $\frac{1}{2}$ H.P. How many watts is this? how many kilowatts (nearest tenth)?   240, 241

6. When it is noon at 60° west longitude, what time is it at 105° west longitude? at 30° west longitude?   262, 263

7. An electric sign has 200 bulbs of 100 watts each. How many kilowatt-hours are consumed if the sign is illuminated 6 hours on each of 30 nights?   244

8. An electric heater rated at 850 watts is used an average of 5 hours a day. What is the daily cost at 4¢ per kilowatt-hour?   244

9. If 8,500 tons of freight are hauled 250 miles, how many ton-miles is this?   237

10. Dick weighs 120 lb. He drinks $1\frac{1}{2}$ pints of milk daily. One pint of milk supplies about 16 grams of protein. What part of Dick's daily protein requirement does the milk provide?   231

11. When it is noon in London, England, is it morning or afternoon in Cairo, Egypt?   262, 263

12. If a ship is sailing at a speed of 30 knots, what is its speed in miles per hour?   265

© *Thomas Airviews, from Gendreau*

Rockefeller Center, New York City, where more than 32,000 people are employed

8

EARNING A LIVING

Working for a Salary

In most communities there are many ways in which people earn a living. Some work in stores or offices, and receive weekly or monthly salaries.

1. Sally is a secretary in a business office. Her monthly salary is $190, from which $24.24 is withheld as income tax and $1\frac{1}{2}\%$ for social security. How much does she actually receive each month?

2. Arthur is a salesman in a hardware store. He earns $250 a month, from which $14.88 is withheld as income tax and $1\frac{1}{2}\%$ for social security. **A.** What is his monthly take-home pay? **B.** How much does he receive in a year?

3. A. Helen is a salesgirl in a dress shop. She is paid $142 a month, less $15.60 withholding tax and less $1\frac{1}{2}\%$ for social security. What does she actually receive in salary each month? **B.** She also receives a bonus of 5% of all sales above $400. Last month her sales amounted to $3278.40. What was her bonus if $25.91 of it was withheld for income tax and $1\frac{1}{2}\%$ for social security? **C.** What did she receive, in all, that month?

4. If an office worker's weekly salary has been increased from $50 to $56, what is the percent of increase? Are the annual earnings increased by the same per cent?

Going to work © *Ewing Galloway*

Working for Wages

Workers in a shop or a factory are usually paid on an hourly basis. This is also true of transport workers, many mechanics, and workers in other trades.

1. Frank Harris is a mechanic's helper in an automobile machine shop. He is paid at the rate of 88¢ an hour. If he works an 8-hour day, five days a week, what are his weekly earnings?

2. Larry Stevens is a foreman in an airplane factory. He receives $2.25 an hour. If he works an 8-hour day, five days a week, what does he earn in a week?

3. In a certain week a machinist worked 8 hours a day Monday through Thursday, and 4 hours on Friday. At $1.86 an hour, how much did he earn that week?

4. If Mr. Howard's hourly wage rate is raised from $1.60 an hour to $1.84 an hour, what per cent of increase does he receive? On the basis of a 40-hour week, how much more does he earn in one week at the new rate?

5. Ted works in a paper box factory. He receives $49.20 a week for 40 hours' work. Find his hourly wage rate.

6. A building trades mechanic receives $24 a day in wages. What did he earn in a period of 4 weeks when he worked 5 days in each of the first two weeks, 4 days the next week, and 3 days the last week?

Farming Is a Business

A farmer has to consider many items of cost and expenses before he can tell what profit he makes on a crop.

1. A farmer planted 60 acres in corn. If he used $75 worth of fertilizer and 9 bu. of seed corn at $6.75 a bushel, how much did he spend on these two items?

2. Since the farmer (Problem 1) did the work himself, he allows himself wages of $12 a day. From plowing to harvest time he worked 24 days. Find the total wages.

3. To tide him over until he could market his crop, he had to borrow $1200 for 6 months at $4\frac{1}{2}\%$. What interest did he pay?

4. He figured that the $3400 worth of farm machinery he used in raising the corn crop had depreciated $12\frac{1}{2}\%$. What was the amount of depreciation?

5. The acreage planted produced 85 bu. of corn per acre. A. Find the total number of bushels produced. B. It cost the farmer 4¢ a bushel to get the corn hauled to market. How much did he pay for transportation?

6. The farmer sold his crop at $1.65 per bushel. What did he receive for the crop? Using your answers to Problems 1-5, find the farmer's profit.

Iowa farmer at work in his cornfield © Gates, from Frederic Lewis

Selling on Commission

1. Charles sells evening newspapers at 5¢ each, and receives 1¢ on each paper he sells. He sells an average of 60 papers a day, 6 days a week. How much does he receive? How much does he give to the newspaper office?

2. Since he receives 1¢ on every 5¢ he collects, his rate of commission is $1 \div 5 = \frac{1}{5}$, or __?__ per cent.

3. On Sundays, Charles delivers the Sunday papers to his customers at their homes. He receives 3¢ for every 15-cent paper he delivers. At this rate, what per cent commission does he receive?

4. An agent sells magazine subscriptions. He receives $1.80 for each $6 yearly subscription that he sells. What is his rate of commission?

5. At this rate, how much commission will the agent receive for the sale of 24 subscriptions at $5 each?

6. A real estate agent sold a house for $11,490. If he received a commission of 5% of the selling price of the house, how much commission did he receive for this sale?

Commission Merchants

Livestock and other farm products are often sold by agents called **commission merchants,** who receive the products, make the sales, and collect the money. For doing this, they receive *commissions.* The amount of the commission is deducted from the money received for the products, and the remainder is sent to the person whose products were sold. The amount received by this person is called the **net proceeds.**

1. An applegrower in Oregon sent 400 bushels of apples to his agent, who sold them for $3.72 a bushel, charging 6% commission. What net proceeds were sent to the applegrower?

2. The owner of an orange grove in Texas sold, through a commission merchant, 300 boxes of oranges at $7.18 a box. The agent's commission was 5%. What was the amount of his commission?

3. In Problem **2,** the cost of shipping the oranges amounted to $126.68. If this expense was also deducted from the selling price, what were the net proceeds received by the orange grower?

4. A commission merchant received a shipment of cattle weighing 18,250 pounds, which he sold at $24.50 a hundred pounds. How much did he receive for the cattle? At the rate of $2\frac{1}{2}\%$, what was his commission?

5. A farmer sent 36 head of cattle to market. The agent charged a commission of $5 a head for his services; what was his commission? If the cattle were sold at an average price of $220 a head, what was the rate of commission?

© Ewing Galloway

The Retail Merchant

Most articles that people use—such as clothing, food, and furniture—are bought in retail stores. The retail merchant buys goods from manufacturers and wholesale dealers, and sells them to the consumer—to you and me.

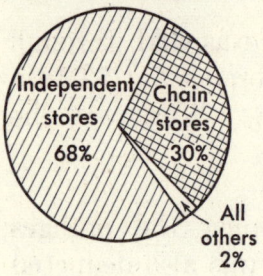

1. The circle graph shows how the total retail business in the United States was divided, in a typical year, among the main kinds of retail stores. The independent stores did about how many times as much business as the chain stores?

Independent stores 68%
Chain stores 30%
All others 2%

2. This table shows sales in billions of dollars for different kinds of retail business. Round these figures to the nearest billion; then draw a horizontal bar graph.

RETAIL BUSINESS	BILLIONS OF DOLLARS
Food stores . . .	31.0
Auto dealers . .	18.4
Restaurants . .	10.7
Department stores	10.6
Clothing stores .	9.8
Building supplies	8.8
Furniture dealers	6.9
Drug stores . . .	4.0
All other	30.3
	130.5

Paying Bills: Cash Discount

If a merchant pays promptly for the goods he purchases, he is frequently allowed a discount. Such a discount is called a **cash discount**.

1. The Triangle Hardware Store bought goods amounting to $261.50. A cash discount of 2% was allowed for prompt payment. What was the actual amount paid?

$.02 \times \$261.50 = \$5.23$, cash discount
$\$261.50 - \$5.23 = \$256.27$, amount paid

The actual amount paid is the **net cost** of the merchandise.

2. A merchant's bill for goods purchased amounted to $582.15. He was allowed a 2% discount for cash. What was the net cost of the goods?

3. A dealer bought $2440 worth of furniture. He was allowed a 3% cash discount if he paid the bill within 10 days, or 2% if he paid it within 30 days. How much did the furniture cost him if he paid the bill three weeks after he received it?

4. How much more could have been saved by paying the bill two weeks earlier?

JIFFY QUIZ

1. How many slices, each $\frac{3}{8}$ inch thick, can be cut from a 9-inch loaf of bread?

2. Which is larger, .625 or $\frac{3}{5}$? how much larger?

3. Write 7.8 billion dollars in another way.

4. After spending $\frac{1}{3}$ of his money, a boy had $7.50 left. How much did he spend?

5. If the temperature rises from 6 below zero to 19 above zero, how many degrees does it rise?

The Merchant's Discount

Merchants sometimes order their goods from trade catalogs which describe the merchandise and give the prices. These prices are known as **list prices**. But when a merchant receives his bill, he is often allowed to deduct a **trade discount**. This is different from the cash discount that you learned about on page 275.

1. A department store ordered 200 pairs of gloves, at a list price of $3 a pair. A trade discount of 40% was allowed. What was the amount of the purchase? the amount of the discount? the net cost of the gloves?

$200 \times \$3 = \$600 =$ amount of the purchase
40% of $\$600 = \$240 =$ amount of discount
$\$600 - \$240 = \$360 =$ net cost of gloves

2. A dealer bought an automatic washer listed in the catalog at $195. The trade discount was 35%. What was the amount of the discount? the net cost?

3. A camera is sold to a sporting goods shop for $24.75, less a trade discount of $33\frac{1}{3}\%$. What is the net cost?

4. A retail store purchased 6 electric refrigerators from the manufacturer for $234 each, less 25%. What was the net amount of the bill?

Chicago's Merchandise Mart, the largest commercial office building in the world

© *Fulton, from Philip Gendreau*

5. A wholesale dealer in hardware received an order for tools from a retail store, amounting to $264.85. The wholesaler allowed the retail merchant a trade discount of 40%. What was the amount of the discount? How much did the wholesaler receive for the tools?

More Than One Discount

Sometimes a manufacturer offers two or more trade discounts on an article.

Example. The list price of an article is $120. There is a trade discount of 40%, and also 25%. What is the net cost? What is the total discount allowed?

$.40 \times \$120 = \$48$, amount of first discount
$\$120 - \$48 = \$72$, net amount after first discount
$.25 \times \$72 = \$18$, amount of second discount
$\$72 - \$18 = \$54$, final net cost
$\$48 + \$18 = \$66$, total discount allowed

▶ If a cash discount is also offered, the cash discount is figured on the net cost.

1. Tennis rackets are priced at $8 each, less 25% and 10%. What is the net cost? the total discount?

2. Flashlights are listed in a catalog at $1.80, less $33\frac{1}{3}\%$ and 20%. Find the net cost.

3. A sun lamp is priced at $24, less trade discounts of 10% and 10%. Find the net cost and the total discount.

4. A wholesale furniture dealer sold $645 worth of bookcases to a retail merchant, allowing a discount of 40% and 10%. How much did the wholesaler receive?

5. A dealer in auto accessories bought $822.50 worth of merchandise, subject to a trade discount of 40%, and 2% for cash. If he paid his bill promptly, what was the net cost?

6. A retail shoe dealer buys shoes at $6 a pair, less 20% and 10%, and 2% discount for cash. What is the net cost of a pair of shoes?

7. Is a trade discount of 25% and 10% equivalent to a trade discount of 10% and 25%?

Selling Price and Margin

We can readily see that to make money a merchant must receive more for his goods than he pays for them. The difference between what he receives for his merchandise and what he pays for it is called his **margin.**

$$\text{margin} = \text{selling price} - \text{cost, or,}$$
$$\text{selling price} = \text{cost} + \text{margin}$$

1. A pair of shoes cost a merchant $4.15. He sold the pair for $10.95. What was his margin?

2. If pocketknives cost $8 a dozen and sell for $1.25 each, what is the margin on a dozen knives?

3. Bottles of cleaning fluid sell for 25¢ each. They cost $1.80 a dozen. What is the margin on two dozen bottles?

4. If the cost of a fishing rod is $2.80 and the margin is $1.95, what is the selling price?

5. An all-wool blanket is priced at $17.95; if the margin is $7.20, what is the cost?

Find the missing quantity in each of the following:

	SELLING PRICE	COST	MARGIN
6.	$2.50	$1.72	?
7.	$3.95	?	$1.65
8.	?	$1.76	$ .69
9.	$2.98	?	$1.44
10.	$5.50	$2.88	?

11. A certain camera sells for $49.75. It cost the merchant $32.50. What is the margin?

Expenses and Profit

Bill helped in his uncle's toyshop. He noticed a sailboat that sold for $2.50. His uncle said it cost $1.50. "Well," said Bill, "that's $1 profit."

His uncle said, "That $1 isn't all profit. Remember, it costs something to operate the store. There is the salary I pay the sales clerk; that has to come out of the sales. Then, there are rent, taxes, electricity, telephone service, fire insurance, and the shipping charges, which are all part of my cost.

"So, you see, the $1 isn't all profit. The $1.50 I pay for the boat is the wholesale price; the $2.50 is the retail price, or my *selling price*; and the difference, $1, is the *margin*. All my expenses must be paid out of the margin on all my sales. The *profit* is what is left after the cost and all expenses have been paid."

profit = margin − expenses, or,
profit = selling price − cost − expenses

1. During the month of July, Bill's uncle had sales amounting to $1250. The merchandise sold cost him $732. What was his margin?

2. That month, Bill's uncle said that the expenses were rent, $60; salaries (including the salary he allows himself), $175; other expenses, $26. What was his profit for the month?

3. During a certain period a merchant sold $645 worth of goods. This merchandise cost $260. His expenses during that time were $158. What was his profit?

4. A week's sales in a dress shop amounted to $1475. The goods sold cost $865. The expenses were 25% of the sales. What was the margin? the profit?

What the Selling Price Includes

Bill wanted to know more about the businessman's profit. This is how his uncle explained it. "Suppose I sell a Boy Scout knife, for which I receive $1. This is my 'sales dollar.' The knife costs me $.65; so my margin is $1.00 − $.65 = $.35. This means that 65% of that sales

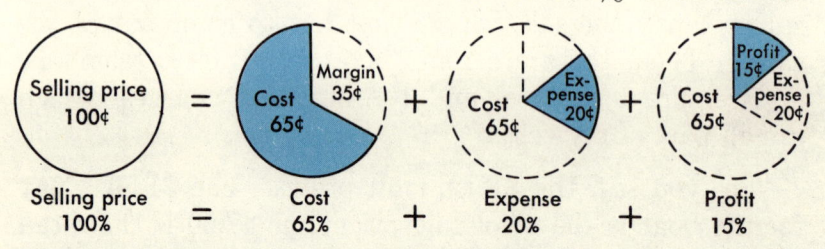

Selling price 100¢ = Cost 65¢ + Margin 35¢

Cost 65¢ + Expense 20¢

Cost 65¢ + Profit 15¢ + Expense 20¢

Selling price 100% = Cost 65% + Expense 20% + Profit 15%

dollar represents the cost of the article, and 35% of that dollar represents my margin. But my total expenses amount to 20% of all my sales. So 20% more of that sales dollar must be paid out. That leaves me 15% of the dollar, or $.15, which is my profit."

1. An article costs a merchant $1.50 wholesale. His expenses are $.50, and his profit is $.25, what is the selling price of the article?

2. What are the three items which together make up the selling price of an article?

3. If cost, expense, and profit are each expressed as a per cent of the selling price, what is their sum?

4. What per cent does the selling price represent?

5. Find the missing per cents in each of the following:

	COST	MARGIN	EXPENSE	PROFIT
A	60%	?	18%	?
B	56%	?	?	14%
C	?	?	22%	13%
D	?	50%	?	20%

The Per Cent of Profit

Most merchants express the profit as a per cent of the selling price, or as a per cent of the total sales.

1. Mr. Robinson's sales amounted to $500. The goods sold cost $275, and his expenses were $150. What was the amount of his profit? What per cent was his profit, based on his sales?

$$\begin{array}{l}\underline{\$500 = \text{sales}} \\ \underline{\$275 = \text{cost}} \\ \$225 = \text{margin} \end{array} \quad \begin{array}{l}\$225 = \text{margin} \\ \underline{\$150 = \text{expenses}} \\ \$\ 75 = \text{profit} \end{array} \quad \frac{\$75}{\$500} = .15, \text{ or, } 15\% \text{ profit}$$

2. The sales of the Gem Candy Shop amounted to $950. The profit on these sales was $114. What was the per cent of profit, based on sales?

3. During one week before Christmas the sales of a gift shop were $1400. The margin amounted to $580, and the expenses were $380. What was the profit? Find the per cent of profit, based on sales.

4. A clothing merchant bought garments costing $1600. He sold them for $3000. His expenses during that time were $900. What profit did he make? What per cent of the sales was his profit?

5. A furniture dealer buys cabinets costing $780. His expenses average 15% of his sales. If he sells the cabinets for $1200, what per cent profit does he make on his sales?

6. If a toy that costs $2.40 sells for $4, what per cent of the selling price is the cost? What per cent of the selling price is the margin?

7. A bathing suit costs $4.50 wholesale, and sells for $6. What per cent of the selling price is the cost? What per cent of the selling price is the margin?

Determining the Selling Price

A businessman knows the cost of his goods, and also how much his expenses are. He usually knows what per cent of profit he wishes to make, and then determines the price at which he must sell the goods to make that profit.

1. A merchant bought hats at $3 each. The expenses of selling a hat amount to $1. To make a profit of 20% on the selling price, at what price should he sell the hats?

$$\text{cost} + \text{expenses} + \text{profit} = 100\% \text{ of selling price}$$
$$\text{profit} = 20\% \text{ of selling price}$$
$$\text{cost} + \text{expenses} = 80\% \text{ of selling price}$$
$$\text{cost} + \text{expenses} = \$3 + \$1 = \$4$$

$$80\% \text{ of selling price} = \$4$$
$$1\% \text{ of selling price} = \$4 \div 80 = \$.05$$
$$100\% \text{ of selling price} = 100 \times \$.05 = \$5$$

2. A fountain pen costs the merchant $4; his selling expenses are $2. At what price should he sell the pen to make a profit of 25%?

3. The cost of a certain coat to the merchant is $25. It costs him $10 to sell the coat. What price must he get for the coat to make $12\frac{1}{2}\%$ profit?

4. Goods costing $2200 are sold at an expense of $800. What must be the total sales to make a profit of 15%?

5. A retail dealer buys a radio for $15. If his expense in selling the radio is $5, and he wants a profit of 20%, what must he sell it for?

6. A piece of furniture costs $80 wholesale. If the retail dealer's margin is 60%, what should be the retail price of the furniture?

Estimating Decimals and Per Cents

It is helpful to estimate answers to problems about commission, discount, and profit, just as it is in solving all problems in which decimals and per cents are used.

Tell by estimating, which answer is correct or most nearly correct; then find the exact answer:

1. $3\frac{1}{2}\%$ of $1600 equals ($25, $75, $55, $30).

2. The product of .015 × $2100 equals ($300, $30, $40, $3.15).

3. A cash discount of 3% on $517 amounts to ($150, $1.50, $15).

4. A commission of 12% on sales of $2450 amounts to ($300, $30, $250).

5. If an article priced at $40 is sold for $29.50, the rate of discount is (10%, $33\frac{1}{3}\%$, 25%, 20%).

6. A trade discount of $33\frac{1}{3}\%$ is allowed on an article priced at $89.50. The net price is ($30, $60, $56.17).

7. A profit of $18 based on a selling price of $59.75 represents a profit of ($33\frac{1}{3}\%$, $41\frac{3}{4}\%$, 30%).

8. If a merchant's expenses are $18\frac{1}{2}\%$ of his sales, find his expenses when the sales are $15,500. ($300, $3000, $5000)

9. A trade discount of 25% on a list price of $89 amounts to ($30, $22, $25, $60).

10. A. 5% of $51 is ($25, $.25, $2.50, $250)
    B. 200% of $5000 is ($10,000, $100, $2500, $500)
    C. $2\frac{1}{2}\%$ of $78 is ($20, $2, $32, $200)
    D. $\frac{1}{10}$ of 1% of $340 is ($.03, $3.40, $34, $.34)

11. A. .64 ÷ 3.2 equals (20, 2, .2, .02)
    B. .75 ÷ .15 equals (50, 5, .5, .05)

How Much Is a Dollar Worth?

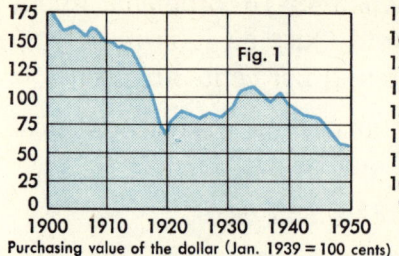

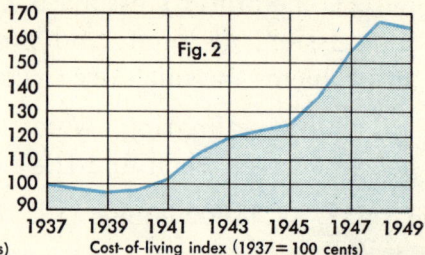

Fig. 1 — Purchasing value of the dollar (Jan. 1939 = 100 cents)

Fig. 2 — Cost-of-living index (1937 = 100 cents)

Things cost much more today than they did when Dad was a boy. Today our dollar will buy only about a third as much as it did in 1900.

How much a dollar is worth depends upon how much it will buy. To be sure, if wages increase, the wage earner has more dollars to spend. But if prices also increase, he may not be able to buy any more than he could before—perhaps even less.

1. If a dollar today buys $\frac{1}{3}$ of what it did in 1900, the cost of living is about __?__ times as great now as in 1900.

2. In 1937, a dollar was worth 100¢ (Fig. **2**). By 1947 it took $1.55 to buy what $1 bought in 1937. The number 155 is an *index number.* It means that things cost, on the average, 1.55 times as much in 1947 as in 1937. In 1951 the index number was 185. This is what per cent increase over 1937?

3. If in a certain period of time the cost of living rises 60%, an article costs 160% of what it did before, or __?__ times as much. If the article costs $\frac{8}{5}$ of what it did before, the dollar is worth only __?__ of what it was.

4. While the cost of living rose 60%, a man's salary was increased 20%. He received $1\frac{1}{5}$ or $\frac{6}{5}$ times as much as before, but can buy only $\frac{120}{160}$ or __?__ as much as he could before the increases.

Family Incomes

Family incomes differ in size as you can see from the chart below, which shows the distribution of incomes by size for a recent year.

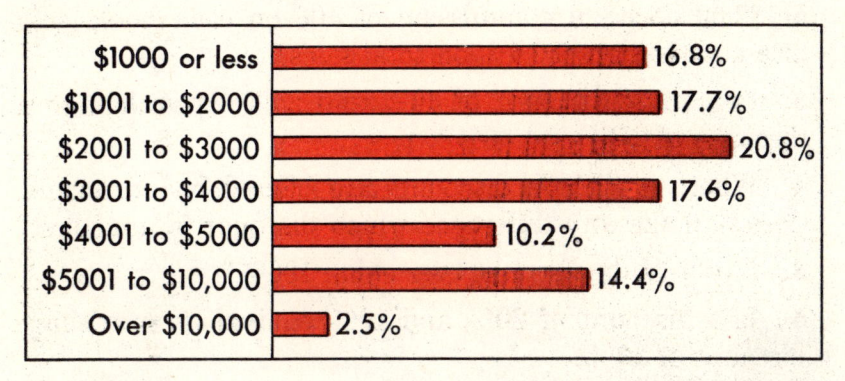

Income	Percent
$1000 or less	16.8%
$1001 to $2000	17.7%
$2001 to $3000	20.8%
$3001 to $4000	17.6%
$4001 to $5000	10.2%
$5001 to $10,000	14.4%
Over $10,000	2.5%

1. What per cent of all the families had incomes of less than $3000?

2. About how much per week is $3000 a year? $1000?

3. What per cent of all families received about $20 a week or less?

4. In what two income groups on the chart do you find the highest per cents of all families?

5. When the cost-of-living index was 100, a man's salary was $2500. Some years later the cost-of-living index was 140. **A.** By what per cent would his salary need to be increased in order to "break even," that is, to be able to buy the same things he could before the cost of living rose? **B.** How much increase would he need? **C.** What salary would he need to receive in order to "break even"?

6. A man's salary was $3200 when the cost-of-living index was 140. To "break even," by what per cent would his salary have to be increased if the cost-of-living index rose to 160? to 180?

Understanding What You Have Learned

1. A weekly wage of $60.80 for a 40-hour week is equivalent to an hourly wage rate of __?__.

2. Which gives a greater income on the sale of 200 books at $2.50 each: a commission of 40¢ on each book sold or a commission of 15% on total sales?

3. Is a trade discount of 40% and 25% equivalent to a discount of 25% and 40%?

4. When two trade discounts are offered on an article, does it make any difference which discount is used first?

5. Can a trade discount ever equal 100%?

6. Is a discount of 20% and 10% equivalent to a single discount of 30%?

7. Is it ever possible to have a trade discount of 60% and 40%? of 60% and 60%?

8. If both a trade and a cash discount are allowed on the same article, which is computed first?

9. Explain the difference between a *cash discount,* a *retail discount,* and a *trade discount.*

10. What three items, together, make up the sales dollar?

11. If you know the amount of sales, the cost of the goods sold, and the expenses, how do you find the amount of the profit?

12. A shopkeeper's expenses are greater than his margin. Is he making a profit?

13. If you know the amount of a dealer's margin and the amount of his expenses, how can you find his profit?

14. Is it possible for a shopkeeper to sell his goods for more than they cost him, and yet lose money in his business? Explain.

Making Sure

1. A watch costing $27 is sold for $45. What is the per cent profit based on the cost? What is the per cent profit based on the selling price? 281

2. Boys' sweaters are offered to Mr. Brown's shop at $36 a dozen, less 30%. What is the net cost of one sweater? 276

3. A man's salary was increased from $4200 to $4725 in a period when the cost-of-living index rose from 155 to 167. Was the salary increase greater or less than the rise in the cost of living? 284, 285

4. The sales of a store were $18,000 and the cost of merchandise sold was $8200. Find the profit if the operating expenses were 25% of the sales. 280

5. Goods costing $1445 were sold for $2570 during a period when the operating expenses amounted to $712. What was the margin? the profit? 278, 279

6. A merchant buys a dress for $12, and wants to sell it at a profit of 25%. His expenses are $6; at what price should he sell the dress? 282

7. A bill for merchandise amounting to $350 is subject to a trade discount of 40% and 10%. With 2% for cash, what is the net amount of the bill? 275, 277

8. A shipping clerk receives $168 monthly. If $1\frac{1}{2}\%$ of his salary is deducted for social security tax and $20.22 for federal income tax, how much does he actually receive each month? 269

9. A salesman was offered an annual salary of $4500, or a commission of 6% on sales. He accepted the latter, and sold $95,000 worth of goods that year. How much more did he earn by accepting the second offer? 272

New York Stock Exchange © Ewing Galloway

9

BORROWING AND INVESTING MONEY

Borrowing from a Bank

Mr. Taylor, a retail merchant, needed extra money for new equipment in his shop. He borrowed it from his bank. To get the money, he signed a **note,** or a promise to pay, such as the one shown below.

$ __450.00__   Madison, Wis. __April 3__ , 19__52__

   __Sixty days__   after date __I__ promise to pay to the order of __First National Bank__ $ __450.00__
   __Four hundred fifty and no/100__   dollars
Payable at __First National Bank of Madison, Wis.__
VALUE RECEIVED
Due __June 2, 1952__   *Frank Taylor*

---

1. Who is the **maker** of the note—that is, who signed it?

2. What is the amount of the loan? This is called the **principal,** or the face value of the note.

3. Who is the borrower? How much did he borrow? From whom did he borrow the money?

4. What is the date of the note? On what date is the note due—that is, when must the loan be repaid? This is the **date of maturity.**

5. What is the time of the loan—that is, for how long is the money to be borrowed? Do you see that from April 3 to June 2 is 60 days?

When Mr. Taylor signed the note he received the money.

Discounting a Note

When Mr. Taylor signed the note for $450, he did not receive $450. The bank figured the interest charge on $450 for 60 days at 5%, deducted this charge at the time the money was loaned, and gave him the remainder. The amount received by Mr. Taylor is called the **proceeds of the note**.

P = $450   60 da. = $\frac{60}{360} = \frac{1}{6}$ yr.
r = 5% $\frac{1}{6} \times $22.50 = 3.75, discount
.05 × $450 = $22.50 $450 − $3.75 = $446.25, proceeds

An interest charge which is collected when a loan is made instead of when it is repaid is called **bank discount**. The bank *discounted* Mr. Taylor's note. What is the amount of the bank discount? Why must Mr. Taylor pay the bank $450 when he repays the loan?

Find the bank discount and the proceeds for each loan:

1. $500 at 4% for 90 da.
2. $375 at 6% for 120 da.
3. $700 at 5% for 3 mo.
4. $1000 at $5\frac{1}{2}$% for 60 da.
5. $800 at 6% for 4 mo.
6. $1600 at $4\frac{1}{2}$% for 60 da.
7. $2000 at 6% for 75 da.
8. $5000 at 6% for 3 mo.
9. $3600 at $5\frac{1}{2}$% for 30 da.
10. $2500 at 5% for 2 mo.

If the time of a note is expressed in days, the date of maturity is found by counting the actual number of days. For example, a note dated August 20 is due in 60 days. The date of maturity is found as follows: days remaining in August = 31 − 20 = 11; days in September = 30; 11 + 30 = 41; 60 − 41 = 19. Then the date due, or date of maturity, is October 19.

Find the date of maturity of each of these notes:

11. 60 da.; date, April 10
12. 90 da.; date, Sept. 18
13. 90 da.; date, Mar. 24
14. 30 da.; date, Jan. 3

Finding the Rate of Interest

The interest on $1000 at 5% for 1 year is simply 5% of $1000, or $50. In other words, for one year, *interest* equals *rate* times *principal*.

If we know that the interest on $1000 for 1 year is $50, and we want to find the interest rate, we must find what fractional part (or what per cent) of the principal the interest is. That is,

$$r = \frac{\$50}{\$1000} = \frac{5}{100} = .05 = 5\%$$

Then, $r = \dfrac{\text{interest due}}{\text{principal}}$, or $r = \dfrac{I}{P}$

Example 1. The interest due in 1 year on a principal of $800 amounts to $36. What is the rate of interest?

$$r = \frac{I}{P} = \frac{\$36}{\$800} = \frac{9}{200} = .045 = 4\tfrac{1}{2}\%$$

Example 2. The interest on $600 for $2\tfrac{1}{2}$ years is $45. What is the rate of interest?

Interest for 1 yr. = $45 \div 2\tfrac{1}{2}$ = $18

$$r = \frac{I}{P} = \frac{\$18}{\$600} = \frac{3}{100} = .03 = 3\%$$

Example 3. The interest on $400 for 3 months is $5. What is the rate of interest?

Interest for 1 yr. = $4 \times \$5 = \$20$

$$r = \frac{I}{P} = \frac{\$20}{\$400} = \frac{1}{20} = .05 = 5\%$$

Find the rate of interest:

	PRINCIPAL	INTEREST	TIME		PRINCIPAL	INTEREST	TIME
1.	$3000	$135	1 yr.	4.	$1800	$45	6 mo.
2.	$800	$72	3 yr.	5.	$2400	$120	$2\tfrac{1}{2}$ yr.
3.	$1600	$108	$1\tfrac{1}{2}$ yr.	6.	$1600	$30	9 mo.

Bank Discount and the Interest Rate

You have learned that when a note is discounted, the bank collects an interest charge at the time that the loan is made. This charge, called bank discount, is paid by the borrower when the loan is made.

Example. A 6-month note for $800 is discounted at 5%. However, the actual rate of interest paid is a little more than 5%.

The bank discount = $.05 \times \frac{1}{2} \times \$800 = \$20$

Since this $20 is deducted from the face value of the note, the borrower receives only $780. He has the use of $780 for 6 months, although he "borrows" $800. Actually, he pays $20 interest for the use of $780 for $\frac{1}{2}$ year, or $40 (2 × $20) for 1 year. So, we find the interest rate on $780.

$$r = \frac{I}{P} = \frac{\$40}{\$780} = .0513 = 5.13\%, \text{ rate of interest}$$

You see that a discount rate of 5% is equivalent to an interest rate of 5.13%.

▶ The rate of interest paid on a discount loan is always slightly higher than the rate of interest stated in the note.

Find the equivalent rate of interest:

1. $400 note for 6 mo., discounted at 5%
2. $1000 note for 90 da., discounted at 4%
3. $500 note for 4 mo., discounted at 6%
4. $600 note for 2 mo., discounted at 5%

5. Find the equivalent interest rate on a $1200 note for 1 year, if discounted at 6%; on $1200 for 1 month, if discounted at the same rate.

Personal Loans

Mr. Parker needed $200 to pay for repairs on his house. He was unable to borrow the money from a bank on a note. But he could borrow the money from the personal loan department of a bank, or a personal loan company.

On such loans, the rate of interest paid is much higher than on ordinary loans. The borrower repays the loan in small, equal amounts (installments); each installment payment includes a part of the principal together with a part of the total interest.

The table shows typical payments charged by personal loan companies:

CASH YOU GET	YOU REPAY MONTHLY			
	6 PAYMENTS	12 PAYMENTS	15 PAYMENTS	20 PAYMENTS
$ 50	$ 9.08	$ 4.87	$ 4.04	$ 3.21
100	18.15	9.75	8.08	6.41
200	36.13	19.33	15.98	12.65
300	54.02	28.82	23.80	18.80

1. If Mr. Parker borrowed $200 for 6 months, how much did he have to pay each month? What was the total amount he had to pay? How much interest did he have to pay for this loan?

2. Mr. King borrowed $100, repaying the loan in 12 equal amounts. What was the amount of each payment? What was the total of all the payments?

3. How much interest did Mr. King pay for the loan? Did he have the use of $100 for the entire year?

4. Mr. King can get a personal loan from a bank, for which he must make 12 monthly payments of $8.86. How much less interest will he pay on a bank loan?

Credit Unions

In order to secure small loans at a reasonable rate of interest, the employees of a large business, or of a large city, or a group engaged in the same occupation, often form a **credit union**. For example, there are credit unions among farmers, policemen, firemen, teachers, and workers in large factories.

Credit union loans are made from money paid in by members. Some members of the union put money into the union's funds in order that their money may earn interest. Interest received by the union from its loans is distributed to the members according to the amount of money they have invested in the union.

To borrow from a credit union one must be a member. Loans are usually repaid in 12 monthly installments.

1. A member of a credit union, made up of the employees of a certain large city, can borrow $300 and repay the loan in 12 installments of $25.78 each. What is the total amount paid by the borrower?

2. This credit union, over a period of more than 25 years, has made about 200,000 loans totaling $55,000,000. What is the average amount of a loan?

3. Another credit union found that the loans were used for the following purposes: Home repairs, taxes, and mortgage payments, 30%; medical expenses 20%; repayment of debts, 20%; household expenses, 15%; all other, 15%. Draw a divided bar graph to show these facts.

4. There are about 9,000 credit unions in the United States. At the end of a recent year, the total loans outstanding were about $400,000,000, as compared with $280,000,000 the preceding year. What was the per cent of increase?

The Language of Business

We need to understand the meaning of certain business terms in order to solve problems concerning business. Indicate the correct answer:

1. *Trade discount* means
   A. a bargain sale reduction
   B. any reduction to the consumer
   C. an allowance for paying bills promptly
   D. a reduction to the merchant when he buys goods

2. *Retail merchants* are
   A. manufacturers of merchandise
   B. commission merchants
   C. storekeepers who sell goods to the public

3. *Commission* refers to
   A. expenses
   B. salary
   C. net proceeds
   D. amount paid to selling agent

4. The trade *list price* means
   A. net price
   B. retail price
   C. catalog price
   D. wholesale cost

5. The *margin* equals
   A. amount of profit
   B. difference between selling price and cost
   C. per cent of profit
   D. operating expenses

Complete the following:

6. Selling price = __?__ + __?__ + __?__.
7. Margin = selling price − __?__.
8. Margin = expenses + __?__.
9. Profit = selling price − __?__ − __?__.
10. Profit = margin − __?__.

Buying on the Installment Plan

Many articles are purchased on the **installment plan,** or by making **time payments.** This means that a certain part of the price, called the **down payment,** is paid at the time the article is bought. The remainder is called the **unpaid balance.** For the privilege of spreading the cost over a period of time, or paying "on time", a charge called a **carrying charge** is added to the unpaid balance.

The sum of the unpaid balance and the carrying charge is paid in monthly installments. All these payments are equal in amount except perhaps the last payment.

Example. Mr. Becker bought a home freezer priced at $247.50, making a down payment of $33\frac{1}{3}\%$ of the cash price. The carrying charge amounted to $16.50, and the regular monthly payments were $10.50. How many payments will he have to make? What will be the amount of the last payment? How much will the freezer cost him?

$33\frac{1}{3}\%$ of $247.50 = $82.50, down payment
$247.50 − $82.50 = $165, unpaid balance
$165 + $16.50 = $181.50, amount to be paid on time

For equal monthly installments of $10.50, we divide $181.50 by $10.50. Answer, 17, with a remainder of $3. Therefore Mr. Becker must make 18 payments in all, — 17 installments of $10.50 each, and a final payment of $3.

The home freezer cost Mr. Becker:
$$\$82.50 + (17 \times \$10.50) + \$3 = \$264$$

Check: cash price + carrying charge = total cost
$$\$247.50 + \$16.50 = \$264$$

1. If a down payment of 15% is required on furniture (bookcase, bedroom set), and 25% for the other items listed, find the missing quantities:

ARTICLE	CASH PRICE	DOWN PAYMENT	UNPAID BALANCE	CARRYING CHARGE	MONTHLY PAYMENT	TOTAL NO. OF PAYMENTS	AM'T OF LAST PAYMENT
A Refrigerator	$209.95	—	—	$14.25	$11.00	—	—
B Television set	$349.95	—	—	$26.50	$16.50	—	—
C Bookcase	$ 55.00	—	—	$ 5.00	$ 5.00	—	—
D Washing machine	$124.95	—	—	$ 9.50	$ 9.00	—	—
E Bedroom set	$185.00	—	—	$16.50	$12.00	—	—
F Vacuum cleaner	$ 59.95	—	—	$ 3.50	$ 5.00	—	—

2. What advantages are there to the consumer when purchasing on the installment plan? what disadvantages?

3. Why does one usually pay more when buying on the installment plan?

4. Which is it probably wiser to buy on time, a pleasure car or a truck to be used in one's business? In general, it is wiser to buy on the installment plan only those things that are immediate needs or that are not "used up" quickly.

5. Do you think that merchants are likely to sell fuel or food on the installment plan? Explain.

Buying a House

1. Mr. and Mrs. Thorpe have saved $3600 toward the purchase of a house costing $9000. What per cent of the purchase price do they have in cash?

2. At a local bank they can borrow $5400 for 6 years at 5%. The interest is payable semiannually. How much interest would they have to pay every 6 months?

3. What total amount of interest would they pay during the 6 years? How much would they still owe at the end of the 6 years?

4. The banker suggested that the Thorpes arrange to pay off $450 of the principal every 6 months. **A.** If they repay $450 every 6 months in addition to the interest due, how much will be due at the end of the first 6 months? **B.** What would be the balance of the loan at the end of the first 6 months? **C.** How much interest would be due at the end of the first year? **D.** What amount of principal remains to be paid at the end of 5 years? 6 years?

To get his loan Mr. Thorpe signed an agreement, or pledge, by which he promised to forfeit the house — his **security** for the loan — if he failed to make payments of principal and interest when due. Such an agreement is a **mortgage**. The loan is called a **mortgage loan**.

5. Find the annual interest due on each of these loans:

COST OF HOUSE	AMOUNT OF LOAN	INTEREST RATE
A. $15,000	$10,500	$4\frac{1}{2}\%$
B. $12,500	$ 8,500	4%
C. $10,000	60% of cost	$4\frac{3}{4}\%$

6. Mr. Clark pays $140 every 6 months on a mortgage loan of $7000. What annual rate of interest is he paying?

Banks, insurance companies, and building and loan associations usually make loans to home owners under an arrangement by which the principal is repaid gradually in installments over a period of years.

This table shows typical monthly payments required on a $1000 mortgage loan for various periods of time. These payments include interest and part of the principal. At the end of the period, the loan has been completely repaid. Such an arrangement is called **amortization**.

AMORTIZATION PLAN FOR $1000 LOAN			
TIME REQUIRED	MONTHLY PAYMENT	TIME REQUIRED	MONTHLY PAYMENT
7 years	$13.91	15 years	$7.65
10 years	10.37	17 years	7.03
13 years	8.48	20 years	6.33

John Cole buys a house for $11,500, making a cash payment of $4500. He obtains a mortgage loan for the remainder, under the above plan, for a period of 15 years. What monthly payments must he make?

$11,500 − $4500 = $7000, amount of loan
$7.65 = monthly payment per $1000 for 15-yr. period
7 × $7.65 = $53.55, monthly payment on $7000

7. How much would Mr. Cole have to pay each month if he amortized his loan over a period of 20 years?

8. What is the monthly payment required to amortize (pay off) a loan of $8,500 in 17 years?

The Hobbycraft Corporation

The members of the Craft and Hobby Club wanted to sell the things they made — book ends, tie racks, games, and toys. They needed $300 for equipment and materials.

They formed the Hobbycraft Corporation, and offered 150 shares of stock for sale at $2 a share. This price is called the **par value** of a share. Each person who bought one or more shares became a **stockholder,** which meant that he owned a part of the business. The amount of money raised in this way is called the **capital.** All the shares, whether sold or not, are the **capital stock.**

1. The Hobbycraft Corporation sold 120 of the shares. How much capital (money) was received?

2. What per cent of the capital stock was sold?

3. Henry Miller bought 6 shares. How much did he pay for his stock? What per cent of the capital of the business does he own?

4. Three months later, the profit from sales was $28.50. The profit was divided on the basis of 20¢ for each share of stock held by the stockholders. This is called **declaring a dividend.** How much did Henry receive on his shares? What per cent of the par value of each share was the dividend?

5. What was the total dividend declared? How much of the profit remained in the treasury?

6. The next time the profit was divided, the corporation declared a dividend of 5% on the par value. How much was the dividend per share? What was the total dividend paid?

7. Henry sold his 6 shares at a profit of 50¢ each. His profit is what per cent of the cost of his shares?

© *American Telephone and Telegraph, Ewing Galloway*

Stocks in Modern Business

The young people of the Craft and Hobby Club did not have the money they needed when they began. They raised $240 by forming a corporation and selling stock.

In the world of business today, no one person is likely to have enough money to build a huge factory or operate a railroad. Therefore, a group of businessmen may form a corporation and raise the large amount of money needed by issuing shares of stock.

A stock certificate (see above) may represent 1, 2, 5, 10, 50, 100, or some other number of shares of stock. Many stocks have a par value of $100; some have a par value of $25 or $50. Sometimes a stock has no par value.

A stockholder, since he actually owns a share of the corporation's property, shares in the profits and the risks of the business. Another name for stockholder is **shareholder**.

Stocks are of two kinds: **preferred** and **common**. Owners of preferred stock receive a set, or fixed, rate of income (dividend) based on the par value of the stock. The owner of common stock is not limited to a set dividend rate; the greater the corporation's earnings, or profits, the greater are his dividends; the smaller the earnings, the smaller are his dividends.

When earnings are divided, the specified dividend to holders of preferred stock is paid first; then whatever remains of the earnings to be divided is shared by the holders of common stock.

1. Mr. Baker owns 5 shares of a preferred stock having a par value of $100, and paying a dividend of 6%. How much does he receive annually on each share?

2. If the dividend on Mr. Baker's stock is paid quarterly, how much does he receive every 3 months on 5 shares?

3. If a dividend of $6 per share is declared on a certain stock, how much would the owner receive on 5 shares?

4. A company declares a quarterly dividend of $1.50 per share. How much would a holder of 10 shares of this stock receive every 3 months? What total annual dividend would he receive?

5. If a corporation declares an annual dividend of 4% on shares having a par value of $100 each, what is the annual dividend on each share? on 50 shares?

6. A quarterly dividend of $1.25 a share is paid on shares of $100 par value. What is the annual dividend rate? How much is paid in one year on 25 shares?

7. If a corporation issues 50,000 shares of stock at $40 par value, what is the par value of all the stock?

Buying and Selling Stocks

In many large cities, stocks are sold in a market called a **stock exchange**. (See page 288.) The men who buy and sell stocks for others are called **brokers**.

The **market values** (daily prices) of stocks are published in the daily newspapers; a few are shown in the table below. They are also called **market quotations**.

A stock quoted at $123\frac{1}{2}$ sells for $123.50 a share; a stock quoted at $22\frac{7}{8}$ sells for 22.87\frac{1}{2}$, etc.

SALES	NAME OF CORPORATION	OPEN	HIGH	LOW	CLOSE
9,000	Coca Cola 4	$123\frac{1}{2}$	124	$123\frac{1}{4}$	$123\frac{3}{4}$
45,000	General Electric 2.20	47	$47\frac{3}{8}$	$46\frac{3}{8}$	$47\frac{3}{8}$
120,000	Nat. Biscuit pf. 7%	$180\frac{1}{2}$	182	$180\frac{1}{2}$	182
30,000	Nat. Steel .60	$45\frac{1}{2}$	$46\frac{1}{2}$	$45\frac{1}{2}$	$46\frac{1}{2}$
45,000	Nor. Pacific $1\frac{1}{2}$	$22\frac{7}{8}$	23	$22\frac{3}{8}$	$22\frac{3}{4}$
15,000	Pacific Mills 2	40	$40\frac{3}{4}$	$40\frac{5}{8}$	$40\frac{1}{2}$

1. How many shares of Coca Cola stock were sold on the day these prices were quoted? What was the highest price at which the stock sold that day? the lowest price?

2. What was the opening price per share of Coca Cola stock? the closing price? What was the difference between the high and low price for the day?

3. What is the price of 10 shares of Coca Cola stock if bought at the closing price? the price of 100 shares?

4. Answer the questions in **1-3**, above, for each of the other stocks given in the table.

5. The number "$1\frac{1}{2}$" after the name Northern Pacific means that the stock pays an annual dividend of 1\frac{1}{2}$, or $1.50 per share. What annual dividend is paid to the owner of 50 shares?

6. What is the annual dividend on each share of General Electric stock? on 15 shares? the quarterly dividend on 100 shares?

7. If the par value of National Biscuit preferred (pf.) stock is $100, and the annual dividend rate is 7%, what is the quarterly dividend on 100 shares?

When brokers buy and sell stocks, they charge a **brokerage fee** (commission) for their services. The amount of the brokerage fee depends upon the number of shares bought and upon the price of the stock. Typical rates on the New York Stock Exchange are as follows:

PRICE OF STOCK	BROKERAGE PER SHARE
At $10	15¢
Above $10 but under $90	15¢ + $\frac{1}{4}$ of 1% of price above $10
$90 and above	35¢

Example. Find the cost, including brokerage, of 200 shares of Shell Oil stock if bought at $47\frac{5}{8}$, brokerage $24.41 per 100 shares.

$$\begin{aligned}\text{market price per share} &= \$47.625 \\ \text{price of 100 shares} &= \$4762.50 \\ \text{brokerage per 100 shares} &= \underline{24.41} \\ \text{total cost of 100 shares} &= \$4786.91 \\ \text{cost of 200 shares} = 2 \times \$4786.91 &= \$9573.82\end{aligned}$$

Find the cost including brokerage per 100 shares:

8. 100 shares, Corn Prod., at $64\frac{1}{2}$; brokerage, $28.63
9. 100 shares, Celotex, at $14\frac{3}{8}$; brokerage, $16.09
10. 200 shares, Beth. Steel pf., at $149\frac{1}{4}$; brokerage, $35
11. 500 shares, Gen. Motors, at $94\frac{7}{8}$; brokerage, $35
12. 300 shares, Am. Tel. & Tel., at $151\frac{3}{4}$; brokerage, $35
13. 100 shares, Otis Elevator pf., at $106\frac{1}{8}$; brokerage, $35

Raising Money with Bonds

Railroad companies, electric power companies, and other industrial corporations issue bonds when they need to borrow money. When some unit of government needs to raise money, it may also issue bonds.

Whether issued by a corporation or a government, a **bond** is a special kind of note, or promise to repay borrowed money. A bond differs from an ordinary note in several ways, of which these two are the most important: 1. The length of time for which the money is borrowed is much longer, being 10, 20, or 30 years, instead of a year or less; 2. the principal (face value) is usually larger — $1000, $5000, or $10,000.

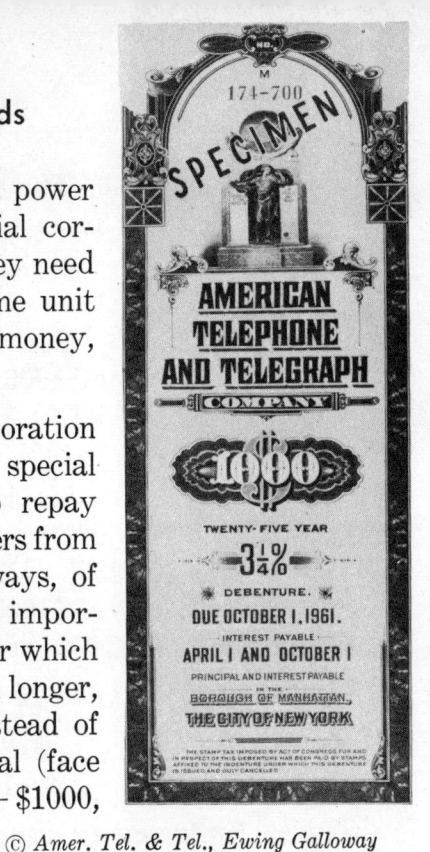

© Amer. Tel. & Tel., Ewing Galloway

1. What is the face value of this corporation bond — that is, the principal, or the amount borrowed? Who is the borrower?

2. What is the interest rate? On what two dates is the interest payable?

3. When must the principal sum be returned?

4. Who receives the interest paid by the company?

5. What is the amount of annual interest paid by this bond?

The face value of a bond is also called its *par value*. The principal is paid, when due, to the owner of the bond, or the **bondholder**.

Buying and Selling Bonds

The **quoted price** of a bond is the price at which it may be bought or sold. This **quotation,** or price, is based upon a face value of $100.

For example, a quotation of 93 on a $1000 bond means 93% of $1000, or $930; a bond quoted at $104\frac{3}{4}$ costs $104\frac{3}{4}$% of $1000, or $1047.50.

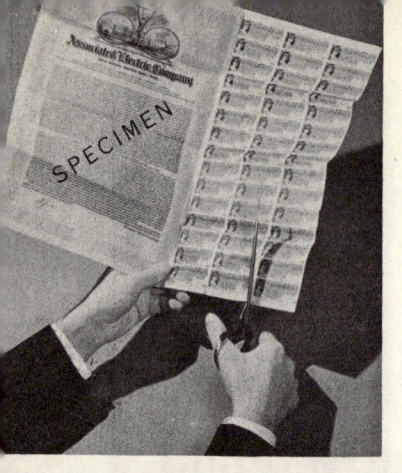

© *Ewing Galloway*
Specimen bond and coupons

Similarly, a quotation of $97\frac{1}{2}$ means $97\frac{1}{2}$% of $1000, or $975; a quotation of $103\frac{1}{4}$ means 103.25% of $1000, or $1032.50. At $96\frac{3}{8}$, a bond costs 96.375% of $1000, or $963.75; at $106\frac{5}{8}$, a bond costs 106.625% of $1000, or $1066.25.

Find the market value of a $1000 bond quoted at:

1. 88
2. 102
3. $101\frac{1}{4}$
4. $87\frac{1}{2}$
5. $98\frac{1}{4}$
6. $103\frac{5}{8}$
7. $106\frac{1}{2}$
8. $99\frac{1}{8}$
9. $92\frac{7}{8}$
10. $102\frac{3}{4}$

Typical brokerage or commission rates are as follows:

Number of $1000 bonds bought or sold	1 or 2	3	4	5 or more
Commission per $1000	$5.00	$4.00	$3.00	$2.50

Example. Find the cost of six $1000 bonds at $86\frac{1}{8}$.

.86125 × $1000 = $861.25, market value of 1 bond
$861.25 + $2.50 = $863.75, cost, including brokerage
6 × $863.75 = $5182.50

Find the cost, including brokerage:

A   B

11. Six $1000 bonds at $92\frac{3}{4}$ Five $1000 bonds at $102\frac{1}{4}$
12. Two $1000 bonds at $113\frac{3}{8}$ Four $1000 bonds at $97\frac{1}{8}$
13. Ten $1000 bonds at $101\frac{5}{8}$ Three $1000 bonds at $105\frac{1}{2}$

Income from Bonds

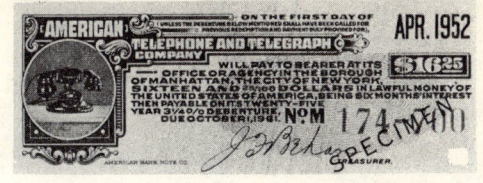

Amer. Tel. & Tel., Ewing Galloway
Bond coupon

The owner of a bond usually collects the interest twice a year (semiannually). Attached to the bond are a number of **coupons**, each of which can be cut off and presented for payment.

The rate of interest paid on a bond is called the **coupon rate**. For example, a $1000 bond bearing $4\frac{1}{2}\%$ interest has a coupon rate of $4\frac{1}{2}\%$. This means that the annual income from the bond is $4\frac{1}{2}\%$ of $1000, or $45. Each semiannual coupon is worth $22.50.

Example. Find the cost of a $1000 bond at $92\frac{1}{2}$, paying $4\frac{1}{2}\%$ interest. What is the annual income? What is the **rate of return** on the money invested?

$$\text{price of bond} = .925 \times \$1000 = \$925$$
$$\text{brokerage} \qquad\qquad\qquad\quad = \$\ \ 5$$
$$\text{total cost of bond} \qquad\quad = \$930$$
$$\text{annual income} = .045 \times \$1000 = \$45$$

$$\text{rate of return} = \frac{\text{annual income}}{\text{market price}} = \frac{\$45}{\$930} = .0484 = 4.84\%,$$

or 4.8%, to the nearest tenth

This rate of return is called the **current yield**.

Find the annual income, and the current yield, on each of the following $1000 bonds; express the yield to the nearest tenth of a per cent:

	COUPON RATE	PRICE		COUPON RATE	PRICE
1.	5%	112	4.	$3\frac{1}{2}\%$	$104\frac{1}{2}$
2.	3%	96	5.	$5\frac{1}{2}\%$	102
3.	4%	$78\frac{1}{4}$	6.	$4\frac{1}{4}\%$	$85\frac{1}{2}$

7. If a bond is bought above par (face value), is the rate of return higher or lower than the coupon rate?

United States Savings Bonds

One of the safest ways for an individual to invest money is to buy United States Savings Bonds. These bonds are backed by the credit and taxing power of our federal government.

United States Savings Bonds Series E are issued for individuals in denominations of $18.75, $37.50, $75, $375, and $750. Interest is received when the bonds are **redeemed** for cash.

Ten years after they are issued the bonds **mature.** The **maturity value,** or the amount received at that time, is shown below.

ISSUE PRICE		MATURITY VALUE
$ 18.75	will increase in 10 years to	$ 25.00
37.50	will increase in 10 years to	50.00
75.00	will increase in 10 years to	100.00
375.00	will increase in 10 years to	500.00
750.00	will increase in 10 years to	1,000.00

1. A. What is the maturity value of a $75 bond? **B.** If held to maturity, how much interest does it earn? **C.** This interest is what per cent of the maturity value?

2. Since the total interest earned in 10 years is $25, what is the average interest earned per year?

3. Using the formula, approximate rate of return = annual income ÷ purchase price, what is the approximate rate of return on a $75 bond?

4. A. What is the maturity value of a $37.50 bond? **B.** If held to maturity, how much interest does this $37.50 bond earn? **C.** The interest received at maturity is what per cent of the maturity value? **D.** The original investment has increased by what per cent?

The table below gives the **redemption values** of certain Series E bonds during half-year periods from the date of issue to the date of maturity.

PERIOD AFTER ISSUE DATE	REDEMPTION VALUE DURING EACH HALF-YEAR PERIOD		
	$25 BOND	$50 BOND	$100 BOND
First $\frac{1}{2}$ year	$18.75	$37.50	$75.00
$\frac{1}{2}$ to 1 year	18.75	37.50	75.00
1 to $1\frac{1}{2}$ years	18.87	37.75	75.50
$1\frac{1}{2}$ to 2 years	19.00	38.00	76.00
2 to $2\frac{1}{2}$ years	19.12	38.25	76.50
$2\frac{1}{2}$ to 3 years	19.25	38.50	77.00
3 to $3\frac{1}{2}$ years	19.50	39.00	78.00
$3\frac{1}{2}$ to 4 years	19.75	39.50	79.00
4 to $4\frac{1}{2}$ years	20.00	40.00	80.00
$4\frac{1}{2}$ to 5 years	20.25	40.50	81.00
5 to $5\frac{1}{2}$ years	20.50	41.00	82.00
$5\frac{1}{2}$ to 6 years	20.75	41.50	83.00
6 to $6\frac{1}{2}$ years	21.00	42.00	84.00
$6\frac{1}{2}$ to 7 years	21.50	43.00	86.00
7 to $7\frac{1}{2}$ years	22.00	44.00	88.00
$7\frac{1}{2}$ to 8 years	22.50	45.00	90.00
8 to $8\frac{1}{2}$ years	23.00	46.00	92.00
$8\frac{1}{2}$ to 9 years	23.50	47.00	94.00
9 to $9\frac{1}{2}$ years	24.00	48.00	96.00
$9\frac{1}{2}$ to 10 years	24.50	49.00	98.00
MATURITY VALUE (10 years from issue date)	$25.00	$50.00	$100.00

5. **A.** What is the total interest earned in 10 years on a bond issued at $18.75? **B.** What average interest per year is earned on this bond? **C.** Would the approximate rate of return be the same on a bond purchased at $37.50 as on a bond purchased at $18.75?

6. Miss Barton bought a $75 bond, and cashed it at the end of 5 years. **A.** What did she receive for her bond? **B.** How much was interest? **C.** What was the average yearly interest earned? **D.** What was the rate of return?

7. Mr. Mason bought a $500 bond and cashed it at the end of 8 years. **A.** How much cash did he receive for his bond? **B.** How much of this was interest? **C.** What was the average yearly interest earned? **D.** What was the approximate rate of return?

8. Mr. Jennings bought a $100 bond. **A.** What was its cash value at the end of 5 years? **B.** How much had it increased in value? **C.** What was the per cent of increase during the first five years? **D.** How much did this bond increase in value during the second five years? **E.** What was the per cent of increase during the second five years, based on its value at the end of the first five years?

9. Mr. Bradley paid $225 for bonds having a total maturity value of $300. When they matured, he reinvested the $300 in more bonds. **A.** Find the maturity value of the new bonds. **B.** By what per cent will his original investment of $225 increase during the entire twenty years?

▶ Owners of Series E bonds who hold their bonds to maturity may now hold them for another 10-year period. If held for the full 10-year extension period, the bonds earn the same rate as the average rate of the first 10-year period.

Compound Interest

When money is left in a savings account, it usually earns interest. The interest is payable at the end of certain intervals, say at the end of a year, or more often at the end of a 6-month or 3-month period.

The interest may be collected at the end of a period, when it is due, or it may be left on deposit. If the interest is left on deposit, it is **automatically added to the principal**. Then for the next period the principal is greater, and so will earn a little more interest than it did during the previous period.

When interest as it falls due is added to the principal, the total interest so earned is called **compound interest**.

Example 1. Find the compound interest on $400 for 3 yr. at 3% a year, compounded annually, and compare it with the simple interest for the same time and rate.

original principal	= $400.00	The simple interest on $400 for 3 years at 3% a year is 3 × $12, or $36.
int. on $400 for 1 yr.	= 12.00	
principal during 2nd yr.	= $412.00	
int. on $412 for 1 yr.	= 12.36	
principal during 3rd yr.	= $424.36	
int. on $424.36 for 1 yr.	= 12.73	
total amount due	= $437.09	
less original principal	= 400.00	
compound interest	= $ 37.09	

Example 2. Find the compound interest on $500 for 16 years at 3%.

From the table, page 313, the amount of $1 at 3% for 16 years is $1.60471.

$500 \times \$1.60471 = \$802.36$, compound amount
$\$802.36 - \$500 = \$302.36$, compound interest

Using the table, page 313, find the compound interest on:

1. $1000 for 8 yr. at 4%
2. $200 for 12 yr. at 3%
3. $2000 for 10 yr. at 1%
4. $500 for 5 yr. at 2½%

Very often the interest is added to the principal twice a year, or semiannually. For example, interest semiannually for 3 years at 4% a year means interest computed for 6 periods (3 × 2) at 2% for each period.

Example 3. What is the interest on $1000 for 2 yr. at 6%, compounded semiannually? This means that interest is added to the principal 4 times (2 periods each year for 2 yr., or 4 periods) at ½ of 6%, or 3%, for each period.

original principal	= $1000.00
int. on $1000 for ½ yr. at 6%	= 30.00
principal for 2nd period	= $1030.00
int. on $1030 for ½ yr. at 6%	= 30.90
principal for 3rd period	= $1060.90
int. on $1069.90 for ½ yr. at 6%	= 31.83
principal for 4th period	= $1092.73
int. on $1092.73 for ½ yr. at 6%	= 32.78
total amount due	= $1125.51
less original principal	= 1000.00
compound interest	= $ 125.51

The same result can be found from the table much more easily. We simply look in the column headed "3%," on the line opposite "4 periods," and find that the compound amount of $1 is $1.12551.

1000 × $1.12551 = $1125.51, compound amount
$1125.51 − $1000 = $125.51, compound interest

In the following problems, use the table on page 313.

5. Find the amount of $600 at 4% compounded semiannually for 5 years. What is the interest?

AMOUNT OF $1 AT COMPOUND INTEREST

YEARS OR PERIODS	1%	1½%	2%	2½%	3%	4%	YEARS OR PERIODS
1	1.01000	1.01500	1.02000	1.02500	1.03000	1.04000	1
2	1.02010	1.03023	1.04040	1.05063	1.06090	1.08160	2
3	1.03030	1.04568	1.06121	1.07689	1.09273	1.12486	3
4	1.04060	1.06136	1.08243	1.10381	1.12551	1.16986	4
5	1.05101	1.07728	1.10408	1.13141	1.15927	1.21665	5
6	1.06152	1.09344	1.12616	1.15969	1.19405	1.26532	6
7	1.07214	1.10984	1.14869	1.18869	1.22987	1.31593	7
8	1.08286	1.12649	1.17166	1.21840	1.26677	1.36857	8
9	1.09369	1.14339	1.19509	1.24886	1.30477	1.42331	9
10	1.10462	1.16054	1.21899	1.28008	1.34392	1.48024	10
12	1.12683	1.19562	1.26824	1.34489	1.42576	1.60103	12
16	1.17258	1.26899	1.37279	1.48451	1.60471	1.87298	16
20	1.22019	1.34686	1.48595	1.63862	1.80611	2.19112	20
24	1.26973	1.42950	1.60844	1.80873	2.03279	2.56330	24
28	1.32129	1.51722	1.74102	1.99650	2.28793	2.99870	28
32	1.37494	1.61032	1.88454	2.20376	2.57508	3.50806	32
36	1.43077	1.70914	2.03989	2.43254	2.89828	4.10393	36
40	1.48886	1.81402	2.20804	2.68506	3.26204	4.80102	40

6. What is the amount of $2000 at 3% compounded semiannually for 8 years? the compound interest?

7. What is the interest on $500 for 6 years at 5%, compounded semiannually? How much more is this than the simple interest on the same principal for the same time?

8. Find the compound interest on $200 for 6 years at 4%, compounded quarterly. (4% quarterly for 6 years is the same as 1% per quarter-year period for 24 periods.)

9. Find the compound interest on:
  A. $400 for 4 yr. at 6% semiannually
  B. $1000 for 5 yr. at 6% quarterly
  C. $300 for 8 yr. at 2% semiannually
  D. $500 for 10 yr. at 4% quarterly

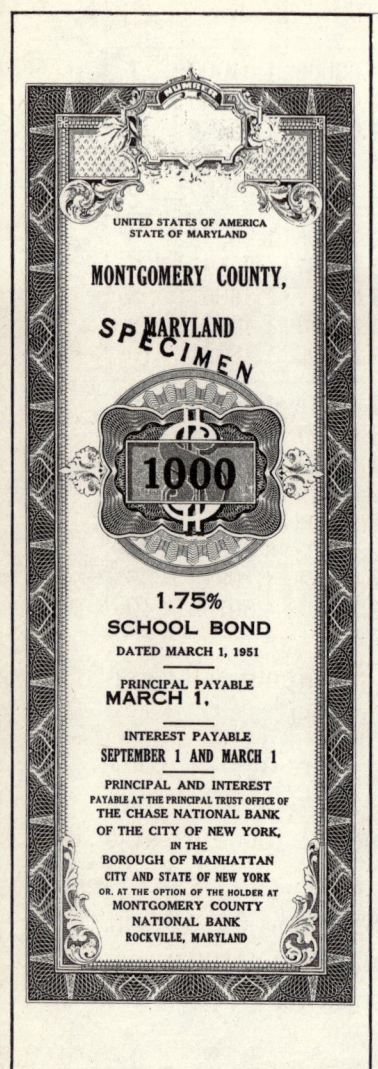

Borrowing for Public Improvements

You have learned that when a city or town or other unit of government needs to raise money to pay for some new construction or other public improvement, it often borrows the money by issuing bonds.

The purchasers of the bonds, whether banks or private individuals, receive interest on their bonds. The interest must be paid by the city or town which borrows the money, or issues the bonds. This means that by the time the borrowed money is repaid, the city or town really has spent more than the actual cost of the new construction. Let us see how this happens.

Suppose that it costs $100,000 to build and equip a new wing to a school building in your town. The town issues $100,000 of 3% school bonds, which it plans to repay gradually over a period of 20 years. Each year, a part of the principal will be repaid, and, in addition, there will also be paid the interest on the principal which has not yet been repaid. A typical schedule of such payments is shown on page 315.

Courtesy Hawkins, Delafield, & Wood

Such a plan for reducing and eventually completely repaying a loan is called an **amortization schedule**.

AMORTIZATION SCHEDULE, $100,000, 3%, 20-YEAR LOAN

YEARS	PRINCIPAL OWING AT BEGINNING OF YEAR	INTEREST FOR YEAR	PRINCIPAL REPAID AT END OF YEAR	TOTAL PAYMENT FOR THE YEAR
1	$100,000	$ 3,000	$ 3,700	$ 6,700
2	96,300	2,889	3,800	6,689
3	92,500	2,775	3,900	6,675
4	88,600	2,658	4,100	6,758
5	84,500	2,535	4,200	6,735
6	80,300	2,409	4,300	6,709
7	76,000	2,280	4,400	6,680
8	71,600	2,148	4,600	6,748
9	67,000	2,010	4,700	6,710
10	62,300	1,869	4,900	6,769
11	57,400	1,722	5,000	6,722
12	52,400	1,572	5,200	6,772
13	47,200	1,416	5,300	6,716
14	41,900	1,257	5,500	6,757
15	36,400	1,092	5,600	6,692
16	30,800	924	5,800	6,724
17	25,000	750	6,000	6,750
18	19,000	570	6,200	6,770
19	12,800	384	6,300	6,684
20	6,500	195	6,500	6,695
TOTALS		$34,455	$100,000	$134,455

1. What is the interest for 1 year on $100,000 at 3%?

2. What is the total amount the town must pay at the end of the first year? How much of this amount is interest? How much of it is principal?

3. How much will the town owe at the end of the first year? How much is one year's interest on this amount? How much of the loan will the town repay at the end of the second year?

4. What is the total amount of interest to be paid during the entire 20-year period?

5. How much will it actually cost the town to build the school wing? How much more is this than the actual cost of construction?

6. About how many times the cost of construction is the total cost of this improvement? Who pays it?

Understanding Investments

1. If a person borrows $1000 from a bank by signing a discounted note, does he receive $1000? Explain.

2. What is the difference between simple interest and bank discount?

3. A 90-day note is dated April 16. What is the date of maturity?

4. Tell how to find the rate of interest when you know the principal, the amount of interest to be paid, and the time of the loan.

5. Complete: The rate of interest is the ratio of the yearly _?_ to the _?_ .

6. Is the price of a stock or a bond always the same as its par value?

7. If the quoted price of a bond is 95, is the price above or below par value?

8. What is meant by the coupon rate of a bond?

9. What is meant by the current yield of a bond?

10. Explain the difference between common stock and preferred stock.

11. When a dividend rate is expressed as a per cent, is it based upon the par value or the market value?

12. How does a bond differ from an ordinary note? In what respects are they alike?

13. Tell what is meant by compounding interest.

14. Explain the meaning of:
   A. Bank discount D. Dividend G. Quarterly
   B. Net proceeds E. Par value H. Capital
   C. Quotation F. Maturity I. Amortize

Making Sure

1. A 2-month note for $750 is discounted at 5%. What is the amount of the discount?   290

2. How much does the borrower actually get if he borrows $500 on a 90-day note discounted at 6%?   290

3. The interest on $300 for 4 months is $6. Find the annual rate of interest.   291

4. The discount on a 60-day note for $2400 is $20. What is the rate of discount? What is the equivalent rate of interest paid?   292

5. A $1000 bond earns $22.50 semiannually. What is the yearly interest rate?   291

6. Mr. Ferris pays the interest on a $6000 mortgage loan in quarterly installments. How much interest does he pay every 3 months, if the annual rate is 5%?   299

7. A corporation declared an annual dividend of $9 a share. What is the quarterly dividend on 50 shares?   302

8. A certain stock pays dividends of 4% a year on a par value of $50. What is the semiannual dividend on one share? on 25 shares?   300, 302

9. Five $1000 bonds are purchased at a market price of $105\frac{3}{4}$. Find the cost, including brokerage at $2.50 per $1000.   306

10. Bonds bearing interest at $3\frac{1}{2}\%$ are quoted at $89\frac{1}{2}$. What is the annual income on $5000 face value of these bonds? If purchased at the price quoted, what is the current yield?   307

11. Find the cash value of two $50 U. S. Savings Bonds, if held for $4\frac{1}{2}$ years. How much of this is interest?   309

12. What is the cost of 300 shares of General Electric stock at $46\frac{3}{4}$, with brokerage at $24.19 per 100 shares?   304

Forest ranger using an alidade to locate a forest fire. By means of this instrument, he can determine the location of the fire. He telephones the location to the fire-fighting crew.

10

SIMPLE WAYS OF USING GEOMETRY

Telling Direction

When two straight lines meet in a point, they form an angle. Figure *AOB* is an angle. It is not the **length** of the lines *OA* and *OB* that is important; it is their **position** that counts. An angle shows a certain **amount of turning**. In this figure, the line *OA* was turned, or rotated, from position *OA* to position *OB*.

The point around which the line is rotated is called the **vertex** of the angle. The two lines are the **sides** of the angle. The amount of rotation is the **size of the angle**.

The angle is used in telling direction by means of a compass. Under what circumstances would one have to depend on a compass to tell direction?

1. The needle on a compass always points in a northerly direction. If you wish to go in a westerly direction, would you have to set out at an angle to the left or right of the direction in which the needle points?

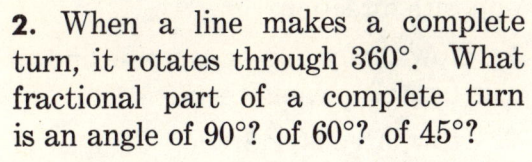

2. When a line makes a complete turn, it rotates through 360°. What fractional part of a complete turn is an angle of 90°? of 60°? of 45°?

3. How many degrees are there between north and east? north and northeast? southeast and southwest?

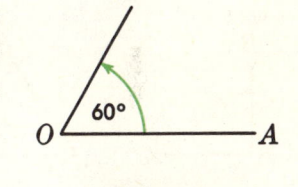

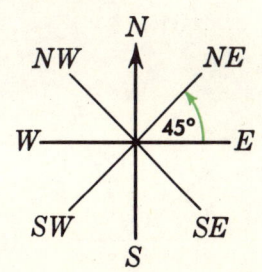

More about Angles

The symbol for an **angle** is ∠. When an angle is named by using three letters, for example, ∠BOA (or ∠AOB), the letter at the vertex of the angle is always the middle letter. Sometimes we name an angle by placing a small letter between the sides, near the vertex. For example, in the diagrams below, ∠AOB can also be written ∠x, or simply by using the letter at the vertex, as ∠O.

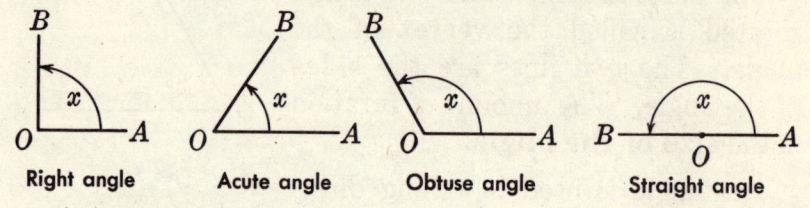

Courtesy Standard Oil Co., (N. J.)
Surveyor using transit

Right angle   Acute angle   Obtuse angle   Straight angle

1. A right angle contains __?__ degrees; a straight angle contains __?__ degrees.

2. An acute angle is always smaller than a __?__ angle.

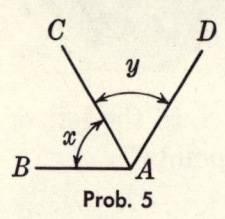

3. An obtuse angle is greater than a __?__ angle, but less than a __?__ angle.

4. Is the size of an angle changed by rotating the same amount, but in the opposite direction?

5. How many angles can you find in this figure? Name them.

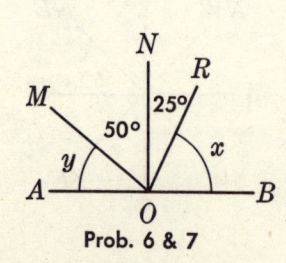

Prob. 5

6. How large is ∠MOR? If ∠AON is a right angle, how large is ∠NOB?

7. Complete: ∠x = __?__°, ∠y = __?__°, ∠AOR = __?__°, ∠BOM = __?__°.

Prob. 6 & 7

320

The direction of a line depends upon the angle that it makes with some standard *reference line.* The north-south line is generally used as the reference line when telling direction. The angle is formed by rotating from the north-south line in the same way that the hands of a clock turn.

8. An airplane pilot leaves Airport A and flies to a city at X. According to his map, the north-south line (AN) runs through A, and $\angle NAX$ is $38°$. He says his "course is 38 degrees." Will he be flying more nearly north or northeast?

9. A pilot flies his plane in the direction of OR. His course is $115°$. How large is $\angle x$? $\angle y$?

10. A plane on course $225°$ is moving in the direction of OP. Which of the angles x and w equals $225°$? How large is $\angle w$? In what compass direction is the plane flying?

11. In this figure could you measure $\angle y$ with a protractor? $\angle x$? If $\angle x = 53°$, how large is $\angle y$?

12. A pilot steers in the direction OP on a course of $39°$. The wind causes the plane to drift so that its actual direction is OR, or along a course of $43°$. What is the "angle of drift"?

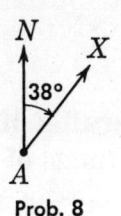

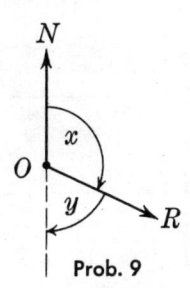

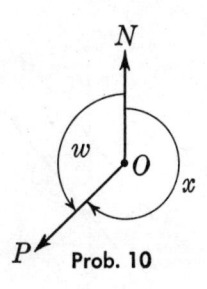

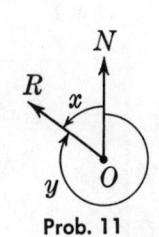

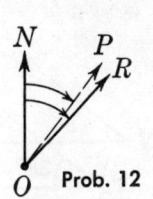

Prob. 8

Prob. 9

Prob. 10

Prob. 11

Prob. 12

Parallel Lines

Parallel lines are lines that have the same direction. The rungs of a ladder, or the rails of a railroad track, are examples of parallel lines. Parallel lines never meet, no matter how far they are extended.

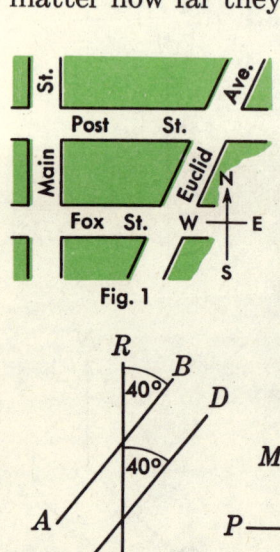

1. In what direction does Post St. run? Fox St.? Do they have the same direction? Are they parallel? Are Main St. and Euclid Ave. parallel? How can you tell?

2. Look at Fig. 2. Do you think AB and CD are parallel? Do AB and CD make equal angles with RS? Do you think that two lines are always parallel if they make equal angles with another line?

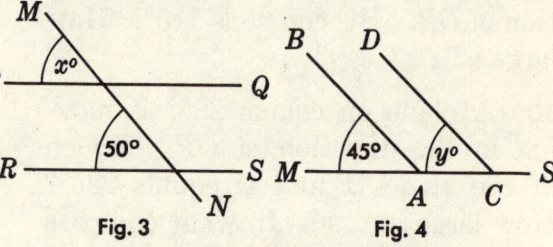

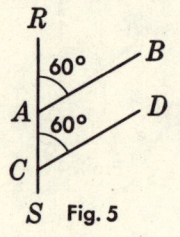

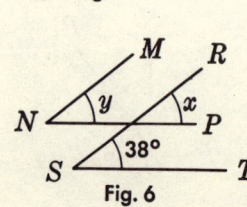

3. In Fig. 3, if PQ is parallel to RS, how many degrees are there in $\angle x$?

4. In Fig. 4, if line CD runs in the same direction as AB, how large is $\angle y$?

5. In Fig. 5, how does $\angle RAB$ compare in size with $\angle RCD$? What can we say, then, about lines AB and CD?

6. In Fig. 6, if MN is parallel to RS, and NP is parallel to ST, what does $\angle x$ equal? $\angle y$?

~ 322 ~

Regular Figures

If a figure with straight sides has all its sides equal in length and all its angles equal, it is called a **regular figure.** A square is a regular figure.

A **regular hexagon** (6 sides) can be made by dividing a circle into 6 equal arcs; start anywhere, and use the compass opened to a distance equal to the radius of the circle (Fig. 1). Each side of the hexagon will equal the radius, as shown.

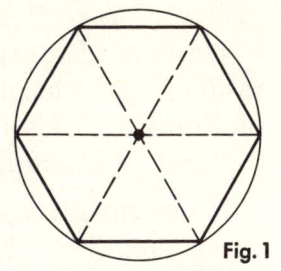

Fig. 1

If you connect every other vertex (corner) of a regular hexagon (Fig. 2), the regular figure so formed is an **equilateral triangle.**

Other regular figures, such as the **pentagon** (5 sides) and the **octagon** (8 sides) can be drawn on a circle by using your protractor to measure the central angles.

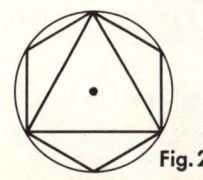

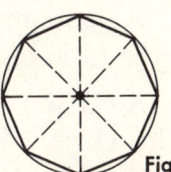

Fig. 2   Fig. 3   Fig. 4

1. How many degrees are there in each of the 5 central angles of a regular pentagon (Fig. 3)? in each central angle of a regular hexagon (Fig. 1)? in each central angle of a regular octagon (Fig. 4)?

2. Copy these designs:

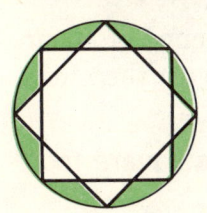

Understanding Ratios

If Carl is 4 ft. tall and Frank is 5 ft. tall, then Carl is $\frac{4}{5}$ as tall as Frank, or Frank is $\frac{5}{4}$, or $1\frac{1}{4}$ times, as tall as Carl.

We may also express these comparisons by saying the ratio of Carl's height to Frank's height is 4:5, or the ratio of Frank's to Carl's height is 5:4. The sign (:) means division; it is simply an abbreviation for ($\div$).

If one quantity is $1\frac{1}{4}$ times, or $\frac{5}{4}$ times as great as another quantity, the ratio of the first quantity to the second is $1\frac{1}{4}$:1, which equals the ratio 5:4.

▶ To express the ratio of two quantities, both quantities must be expressed in the same unit of measure.

1. One book weighs 12 oz.; another weighs 18 oz. Compare the weight of the first with that of the second; the weight of the second with that of the first.

2. A photograph measures $4\frac{1}{2}$ inches by $6\frac{1}{2}$ inches. What is the ratio of its width to its length?

3. A certain bottle holds 1 lb. 2 oz.; another bottle holds 1 lb. 11 oz. What is the ratio of the capacity of the first bottle to that of the second?

4. Compare the first quantity with the second:
   A. 24 in., 18 in.   B. 50¢, $2   C. 2 qt., 6 pt.

5. Compare the second quantity with the first:
   A. 8 oz., $2\frac{1}{2}$ lb.   C. 75¢, $2.25
   B. 16 in., 1 ft.   D. 440 yd., $\frac{1}{2}$ mi.

6. Three cups of flour are mixed with two cups of sugar. What is the ratio of flour to sugar? of flour to the entire mixture? of sugar to the entire mixture?

7. How does a square yard compare with a square foot? a cubic foot with a cubic inch?

Equal Ratios

This man is 6 ft. tall; his shadow is 12 ft. long. The boy is 4 ft. tall, and his shadow is 8 ft. long. The ratio of the man's height to the length of his shadow is 6 to 12, or 6:12. The ratio of the boy's height to the length of his shadow is 4 to 8, or 4:8. Are these two ratios equal? Does 6:12 equal 4:8?

You can see that the two ratios, 6:12 and 4:8, are equal if you write them as fractions. We may write 6:12 as $\frac{6}{12}$ and 4:8 as $\frac{4}{8}$. Does $\frac{6}{12} = \frac{4}{8}$? How do you know?

Then we may say that the man's height has the same relation to the length of his shadow that the boy's height has to the length of his shadow. We may write:

$$\frac{\text{man's height}}{\text{man's shadow}} = \frac{\text{boy's height}}{\text{boy's shadow}} \text{ or,}$$

$$\frac{6}{12} = \frac{4}{8}$$

$$\frac{1}{2} = \frac{1}{2}$$

In other words, 6 is related to 12 in the same way that 4 is related to 8:

6 is $\frac{1}{2}$ of 12, and 4 is $\frac{1}{2}$ of 8

Such a statement, showing that **two ratios are equal,** is called a **proportion**. Here are some examples of proportions:

$\frac{2}{3} = \frac{6}{9}$ $\frac{3}{10} = \frac{12}{40}$ $\frac{6}{2} = \frac{18}{6}$ $\frac{3}{4} = \frac{6}{8}$

$\frac{2}{5} = \frac{20}{50}$ $\frac{6}{2} = \frac{24}{8}$ $\frac{5}{3} = \frac{10}{6}$ $\frac{6}{2} = \frac{3}{1}$

A proportion always shows that two fractions are equal. The numerators and denominators of a proportion are called the **terms** of the proportion.

Understanding Equal Ratios

The proportion $\frac{8}{24} = \frac{4}{12}$ shows that 8 is related to 24 in the same way that 4 is related to 12; 8 is $\frac{1}{3}$ of 24, and 4 is $\frac{1}{3}$ of 12. In other words, the numerator and denominator of the first ratio are related in the same way that the numerator and denominator of the second ratio are related.

The proportion $\frac{8}{24} = \frac{4}{12}$ also shows another relationship: 8 is related to 4 in the same way that 24 is related to 12, since 8 is twice 4 and 24 is twice 12, or two 4's are 8 and two 12's are 24. Then the numerators of the two ratios are related in the same way that the denominators of the two ratios are related.

If we know any three of the four terms of a proportion, we can easily find the missing term.

Example 1. Find the missing term: $\frac{2}{3} = \frac{?}{15}$. The missing term is related to 15 in the same way that 2 is related to 3 in the first ratio. We may think: 2 is $\frac{2}{3}$ of 3, then the missing term must be $\frac{2}{3}$ of 15, or 10; $\frac{2}{3} = \frac{10}{15}$.

Example 2. Find the missing term: $\frac{?}{6} = \frac{9}{18}$. The missing term is related to 6 in the same way that 9 is related to 18 in the second ratio; 9 is $\frac{1}{2}$ of 18. Then the missing term must be $\frac{1}{2}$ of 6, or 3; $\frac{3}{6} = \frac{9}{18}$.

Example 3. Find the missing term: $\frac{5}{3} = \frac{20}{?}$. Since the numerators of two ratios are related in the same way that the denominators are related, we know that the missing term is related to 3 in the same way that 20 is related to 5. $20 = 4 \times 5$. Then the missing term is 4 times 3, or 12; $\frac{5}{3} = \frac{20}{12}$.

Example 4. Find the missing term: $\frac{2}{?} = \frac{10}{35}$. In this proportion the missing term is related to 35 in the same way that 2 is related to 10; 2 is $\frac{1}{5}$ of 10. Then the missing term is $\frac{1}{5}$ of 35, or 7; $\frac{2}{7} = \frac{10}{35}$.

Find the missing term in each of these proportions:

1. $\frac{3}{4} = \frac{?}{28}$
2. $\frac{7}{8} = \frac{?}{32}$
3. $\frac{3}{5} = \frac{?}{30}$
4. $\frac{5}{8} = \frac{40}{?}$
5. $\frac{?}{20} = \frac{4}{5}$
6. $\frac{4}{3} = \frac{?}{9}$
7. $\frac{3}{10} = \frac{9}{?}$
8. $\frac{10}{3} = \frac{30}{?}$
9. $\frac{?}{48} = \frac{5}{6}$
10. $\frac{25}{10} = \frac{5}{?}$
11. $\frac{15}{?} = \frac{3}{7}$
12. $\frac{5}{?} = \frac{15}{9}$

We can use a short cut to find the missing term in a proportion.

In the proportion $\frac{3}{4} = \frac{9}{12}$, the product of the numerator of the first ratio and the denominator of the second ratio equals the product of the denominator of the first ratio and the numerator of the second: $3 \times 12 = 4 \times 9$.

This is called **cross multiplication**: $\frac{3}{4} \diagdown\!\!\!\!\!\!\diagup \frac{9}{12}$

Example 5. A picture $3\frac{3}{4}$ in. wide and $7\frac{1}{2}$ in. long is $2\frac{1}{2}$ in. wide after being reduced in size. What is the new length?

$$\frac{3\frac{3}{4}}{7\frac{1}{2}} = \frac{2\frac{1}{2}}{?}$$ How many $3\frac{3}{4}$'s in $7\frac{1}{2} \times 2\frac{1}{2}$?

$7\frac{1}{2} \times 2\frac{1}{2} = \frac{75}{4}$; $\frac{75}{4} \div 3\frac{3}{4} = 5$, the missing term

The picture after reduction is 5 in. long.

13. A snapshot, measuring $2\frac{1}{4}'' \times 3\frac{1}{4}''$, is enlarged so that its width is $6\frac{3}{4}$ inches. Find its length.

14. A merchant paid $8 for a pair of shoes he sold for $12. If he wants the same ratio of cost to selling price on a pair he bought for $6, at what price must he sell this pair?

15. If $\frac{1}{4}$ lb. of butter weighs 112.5 grams, how many pounds will weigh 675 grams?

Learning to Solve Problems

Relationships in Problems

Understanding ratios and proportions helps us to understand relationships in problems. Solve these problems, using what you know about ratios and proportions.

1. If 3 pieces of candy cost 5¢, how many pieces of this candy can I buy for 35¢?

2. If 4 apples cost 15¢, how many can I buy for 75¢?

3. Helen can fold 7 paper hats in the same length of time that it takes Alice to fold 4. How many hats can Helen fold in the time it takes Alice to fold 20?

4. One machine makes 40 nails in the same length of time that another machine makes 60. How many nails will the first machine make in the time that the second makes 300 nails?

5. The dimensions of a rectangle are in the ratio of 5 to 12. What is its width if the length is 60 inches?

6. The radii of two circles are in the ratio of 3 to 4. If the circumference of the first circle is 24 inches, what is the circumference of the second circle?

7. If 2 pints of lemonade serve 3 persons, how many pints will be needed to serve 21 persons?

8. The circumferences of two circles are in the ratio of 8:5. If the diameter of the second circle is 45 feet, what is the diameter of the first circle?

9. If $1\frac{1}{2}$ qt. of liquid fill eight 6-oz. bottles, how many such bottles will 3 qt. of the liquid fill?

10. A recipe for hot chocolate calls for 5 tablespoons of cocoa, 6 tablespoons of sugar, 2 cups of milk, and $1\frac{1}{2}$ cups of water. These amounts will make 6 servings. What amounts are needed for 8 servings?

Scale Drawings

We often see pictures and drawings which have been drawn "to scale." This means that they are smaller or larger than the things which they represent.

1. In her dictionary, Betty found a drawing of a canvasback, a kind of wild duck. The fraction $\frac{1}{12}$ was printed below the picture. The fraction means that the picture is $\frac{1}{12}$ as long as the duck. If the distance from his bill to his tail in the picture is $1\frac{1}{4}$ in., how long is the canvasback duck?

$\frac{1}{12}$

2. Betty also saw a picture of a snail, with the fraction $\frac{2}{3}$ beside it. In the drawing the snail measured $\frac{7}{8}$ inch in length. How long was the snail?

$\frac{2}{3}$

3. In a book about the weather, Frank found a picture of a snowflake; it was labeled "× 6." This means that the picture is 6 times as wide as the snowflake. If the picture measures $\frac{3}{4}$ inch in width, how wide is the snowflake?

× 6

4. Beside the picture of a mosquito in a science book there is printed: "× $4\frac{1}{2}$." Complete: The picture is _?_ times as long as a real mosquito; the mosquito is _?_ as long as the picture; the ratio of the length of the mosquito to the length of the picture is _?_ : _?_.

5. Tell what these mean when used with a scale drawing:
$\frac{1}{25}$ $\frac{2}{13}$ × 20   × 250 $1\frac{1}{2}$

6. If a picture is life-size, what is the ratio of the dimensions of the object to the dimensions of the picture? the ratio of the dimensions of the picture to those of the object?

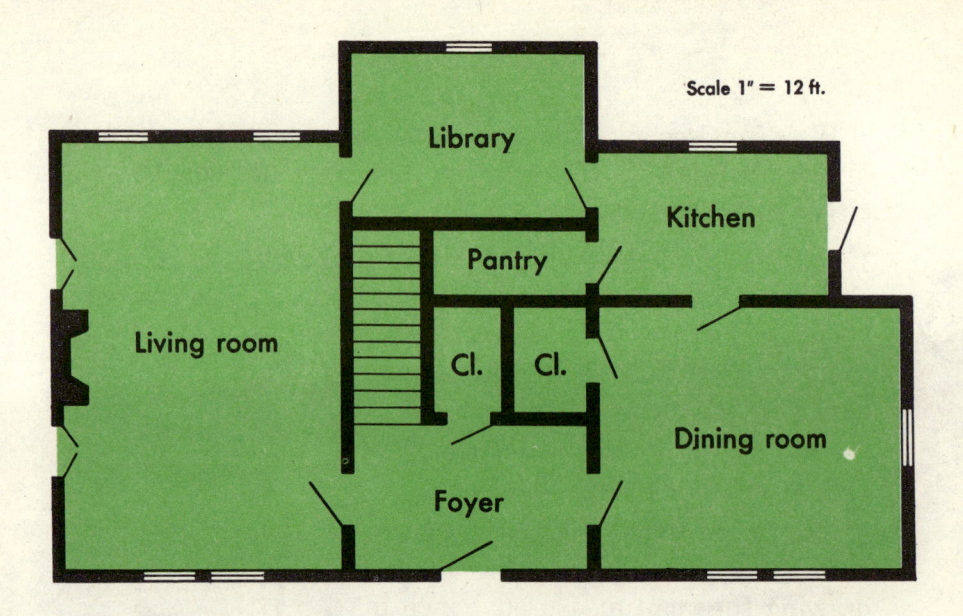

Floor Plans

1. The scale of this floor plan is 1 in. = 12 ft. **A.** Find the dimensions of the kitchen; **B.** the living room; **C.** the dining room; **D.** the foyer; **E.** the library.

2. If a plan is drawn to a scale of $\frac{1}{2}$ in. = 20 ft., a distance of 90 ft. should be how many inches long on the plan? A length of $1\frac{1}{4}$ in. on the plan represents a distance of how many feet?

3. With a scale of $\frac{1}{8}$ in. = 1 ft., an actual distance of 20 ft. is what length on the plan? A length of $3\frac{1}{4}$ in. on the plan represents an actual distance of how many feet?

4. If a line 1 in. long on a blueprint represents an actual distance of 6 ft., a room that is $3\frac{1}{2}$ in. by $1\frac{3}{4}$ in. on the drawing will really be __?__ feet long and __?__ feet wide.

5. In Problem **4**, where the scale is 1 in. = 6 ft., the ratio of any length on the plan to the actual distance it represents is __?__ : __?__.

Reading a Map

Maps are also scale drawings. The distance between two places on a map has a definite relationship to the actual distance between the two places. This relationship is a ratio.

For example, the scale of a map may be given as "1 inch = 25 miles," or "1 inch = 500 miles."

1. A certain map is drawn to the scale of 1 inch = 120 miles. What actual distance is represented by each of the following lengths on this map:

    A. $1\frac{1}{2}$ inches   C. 2 inches   E. $4\frac{1}{4}$ inches
    B. $\frac{3}{4}$ inch   D. $\frac{7}{8}$ inch   F. $3\frac{3}{8}$ inches

2. On another map, the scale is given as 200 miles to the inch. What is the actual distance between two places that are $3\frac{5}{8}$ inches apart on the map? $2\frac{3}{4}$ inches apart? If the air-line distance between two places is actually 1650 miles, how far apart are they on the map?

3. If 1″ represents $\frac{1}{8}$ mile on a map, how many inches on the map represent an actual distance of 440 yards?

JIFFY QUIZ

1. If a certain jar holds $\frac{1}{2}$ pint, how many such jars are needed when canning $3\frac{1}{2}$ quarts?

2. Multiplying by $\frac{1}{10}$ is the same as dividing by __?__.

3. When it is 1:30 P.M. in New York, what time is it in Los Angeles?

4. What decimal part of a quarter is a nickel?

5. The label on a can of peas reads, "Contents, 1 lb. 4 oz. Makes 5 servings." This is how many ounces per serving?

Indirect Measurements

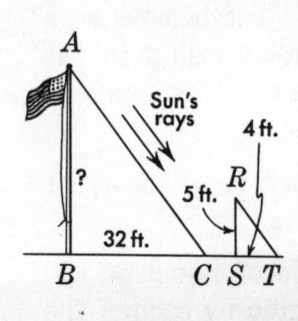

1. Harry and his friend wanted to find the height of this flagpole. They could not measure it **directly** with a tape measure or a yardstick, so they measured it **indirectly** by measuring shadows. Harry is 5 ft. tall. His friend measured Harry's shadow. When it was 4 ft. long, the shadow of the pole was 32 ft. long.

$$\frac{\text{Harry's height}}{\text{Harry's shadow}} = \frac{\text{pole's height}}{\text{pole's shadow}} \quad \text{or,} \quad \frac{5}{4} = \frac{?}{32}$$

So, the pole must be 40 ft. high.

Triangles that have the same shape are called **similar triangles,** even though they differ in size. This means:

A. The corresponding sides are in proportion.
B. The corresponding angles are equal.

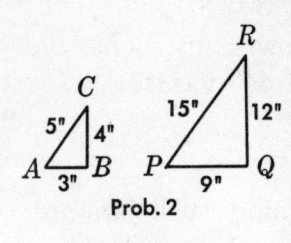

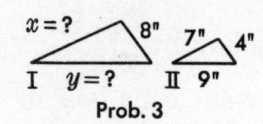

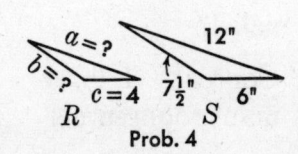

2. In the similar triangles ABC and PQR, side AB corresponds to side PQ; BC corresponds to QR; AC corresponds to PR. Each side of the larger triangle is __?__ times as long as the corresponding side of the smaller triangle. Complete:

$$\frac{9}{3} = \frac{12}{?} \quad \frac{12}{4} = \frac{?}{5} \quad \frac{9}{?} = \frac{15}{5}$$

3. In these two similar triangles, how long is side x? side y? What is the ratio of any side of triangle I to the corresponding side of triangle II?

4. In the similar triangles R and S, find the lengths of the sides a and b.

5. To find the distance PQ across a pond, the following measurements were made after driving stakes in the ground at points A, B, C, P, and Q: $AB = 100$ yd.; $AC = 80$ yd.; $BC = 40$ yd.; $PC = 120$ yd.; and $QC = 240$ yd. Triangles ABC and PQC are similar; find the distance PQ.

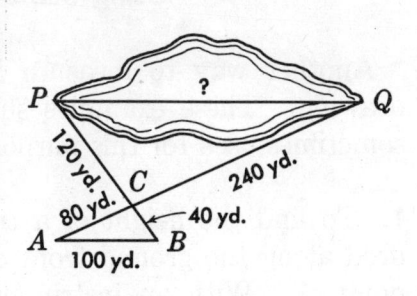

6. To find the distance AB across a river, a surveyor made these measurements. Do you see that RD corresponds to AR? that CD corresponds to AB? If triangle ABR is similar to triangle CDR, how wide is the river?

The symbol for **triangle** is $\triangle$; "$\triangle ABC$" means triangle ABC.

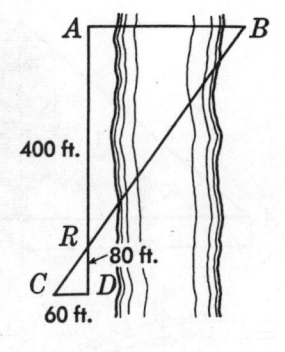

JUST FOR FUN

Each side of the equilateral triangle PAE is 2 in. long. Point B is the middle of AP; D, the middle of PE; C, the middle of AE. Also, R is the middle of AB; T, of BC; L, of CD; N, of DE; and so on. As you first trace the zigzag line $ABCDE$, then the zigzag line $ARSTCLMNE$, etc., these broken lines appear to become more and more like the straight line AE. What is the length of the zigzag line when it has been subdivided 100 times?

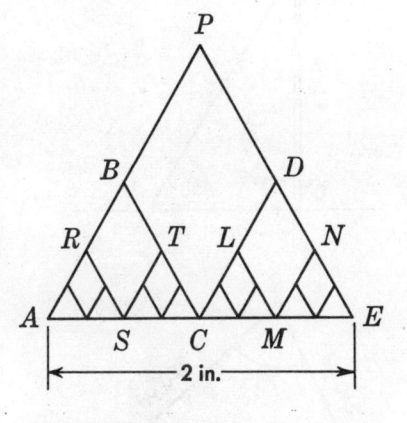

333

Using Scale Drawings

Another way to measure indirectly is to use a scale drawing. These examples show how scale drawings are sometimes used for this purpose.

1. To find the height of a tree, a distance AC is measured along the ground from the base of the tree at C to point A. With an instrument resembling a protractor, the angle BAC is measured and found to be 40°. Using your protractor, draw a right triangle similar to $\triangle ABC$, to a scale of 1 in. = 20 ft. How long is AC on your drawing? CB? Then how high is the tree?

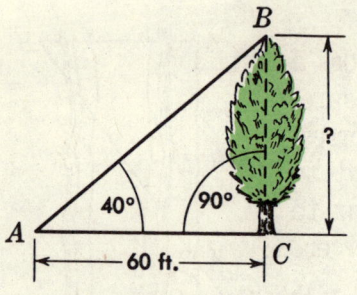

2. A telegraph pole is supported by a wire which reaches from a point 4 ft. from the top of the pole to a point B on the ground 20 ft. from the base of the pole. The angle ABC is 58°. Draw a right triangle similar to $\triangle ABC$, using a scale of 1 in. = 10 ft. How long will you make BC? How long is AC? How high is the pole?

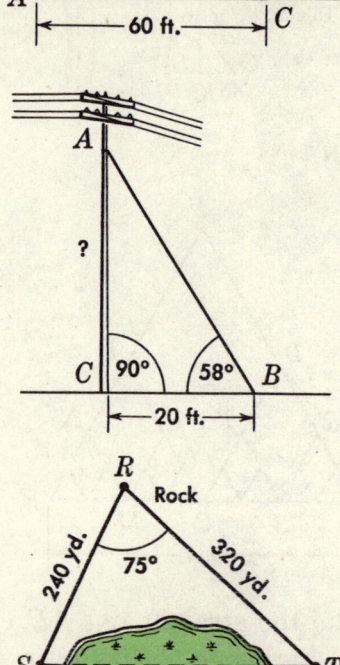

3. Copy $\triangle RST$, using a scale of $\frac{1}{8}$ in. = 10 yd. How long will you make RS? RT? How far is it from S to T?

4. An extension ladder AB is 38 ft. long; leaning against the side of a building, it makes an angle of 70° with the ground. How large is $\angle ABC$? Copy triangle ABC, using a scale of 1 in. = 8 ft. How high above the ground is the point B on the building where the top of the ladder rests?

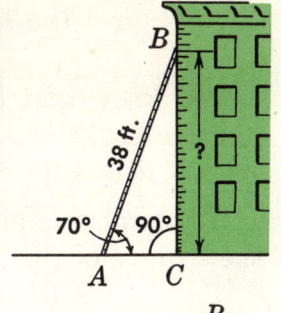

5. A motor boat is to travel from A to B. When it is at A, the angle between a lighthouse at C and the boat's path is 36°; when it is at B, the angle is 50°. The distance from A to B is 3000 yd. Use a scale of 1 in. = 500 yd., and copy the triangle ABC. **A.** What is the distance from A to C? **B.** the distance from B to C?

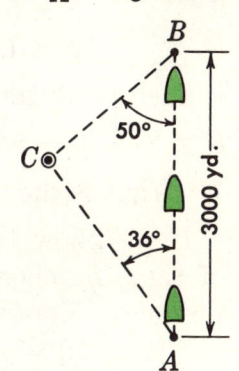

JIFFY QUIZ

1. How many $\frac{1}{4}$-inch squares are there in a $\frac{1}{2}$-inch square?

2. For any particular circle, does $2\pi r = \pi D$? Does πr^2 equal $\frac{\pi D^2}{4}$?

3. Which will carry more water: two 4-inch pipes or one 6-inch pipe?

4. If both a square and a parallelogram have a perimeter of 40 inches, which has the larger area?

5. One solution has 150% the strength of another solution. This is (half again as much; 150 times as much; $1\frac{1}{2}$ times as much; 50% stronger; 150% more; 3 times as much).

The Meaning of Square Root

You know that to find the area of a square we multiply the length of one side by the length of another equal side; $6 \times 6 = 36$, $8 \times 8 = 64$, etc.

If a number is multiplied by itself, the product is called the **square** of the number. For example:

$5 \times 5 = 25$; 25 is the square of 5
$12 \times 12 = 144$; 144 is the square of 12

Such products, or "squares," may be written as follows:
$8 \times 8 = 8^2 = 64 \quad 10 \times 10 = 10^2 = 100 \quad s \times s = s^2$

1. What is the value of: 4^2, 15^2, 20^2, 11^2, 25^2?

If we know the product of two equal numbers, either of these numbers is called the **square root** of the given product. For example:

$10 \times 10 = 100$; then the square root of $100 = 10$
$7^2 = 49$; then the square root of $49 = 7$

The symbol for square root is ($\sqrt{}$); it is read "square root of."

$\sqrt{81} = 9 \quad \sqrt{4} = 2 \quad \sqrt{144} = 12 \quad \sqrt{a^2} = a$

2. Give the square root of: 16, 64, 9, 121, m^2.

3. What is the value of:

$\sqrt{25} \quad \sqrt{36} \quad \sqrt{100} \quad \sqrt{49} \quad \sqrt{1} \quad \sqrt{b^2}$

4. The area of a certain square piece of land is 900 square feet. What is the length of one side?

5. Another square plot contains 2500 sq. yd. What is the length of each side of this plot? the perimeter?

6. Since $6^2 = 36$, and $7^2 = 49$, the value of $\sqrt{40}$ must be greater than _?_ and less than _?_.

7. The value of $\sqrt{85}$ is greater than _?_ and less than _?_.

8. The value of $\sqrt{29}$ lies between _?_ and _?_.

Finding Approximate Square Roots by Trial

The area of a square is 53 square inches. What is the length of one side? The length of one side of the square equals $\sqrt{53}$. But 53 is not a perfect square such as 4, or 9, or 16, or 25.

We know that $7^2 = 49$, and $8^2 = 64$. Since 53 is greater than 49 but less than 64, we see that $\sqrt{53}$ is greater than 7 and less than 8. Since 49 is nearer 53 than 64 is, let us try a number nearer 7 than 8, say 7.3.

$7.3^2 = 7.3 \times 7.3 = 53.29$, which is a little more than 53. Then we try 7.2:

$7.2^2 = 7.2 \times 7.2 = 51.84$, which is less than 53.

Since 53.29 is nearer 53 than 51.84 is, the value of $\sqrt{53} = 7.3$, to the nearest tenth.

1. Between what two perfect squares is each number:
   A. 14, 48, 32, 29, 77?   B. 110, 98, 135, 84, 60?

2. Find by trial the square root of each of the following to the nearest tenth:
   A. 40   C. 28   E. 75   G. 19   I. 88   K. 130
   B. 12   D. 5   F. 10   H. 32   J. 60   L. 115

JIFFY QUIZ

1. At 3 for 5¢, how many pencils can I buy for 50¢?

2. What is the ratio of the circumference of a circle to its diameter?

3. Complete the proportion, 2:3 = 5: ? .

4. When it is 4 P.M. in St. Louis, Missouri, what time is it in Boston, Massachusetts? in San Diego, California?

5. If the sale price of a $12.50 dress is $7.50, what is the per cent of discount?

Table of Squares and Square Roots

N	N²	√N	N	N²	√N	N	N²	√N
1	1	1.00	51	2,601	7.14	101	10,201	10.05
2	4	1.41	52	2,704	7.21	102	10,404	10.10
3	9	1.73	53	2,809	7.28	103	10,609	10.15
4	16	2.00	54	2,916	7.35	104	10,816	10.20
5	25	2.24	55	3,025	7.42	105	11,025	10.25
6	36	2.45	56	3,136	7.48	106	11,236	10.30
7	49	2.65	57	3,249	7.55	107	11,449	10.34
8	64	2.83	58	3,364	7.62	108	11,664	10.39
9	81	3.00	59	3,481	7.68	109	11,881	10.44
10	100	3.16	60	3,600	7.75	110	12,100	10.49
11	121	3.32	61	3,721	7.81	111	12,321	10.54
12	144	3.46	62	3,844	7.87	112	12,544	10.58
13	169	3.61	63	3,969	7.94	113	12,769	10.63
14	196	3.74	64	4,096	8.00	114	12,996	10.68
15	225	3.87	65	4,225	8.06	115	13,225	10.72
16	256	4.00	66	4,356	8.12	116	13,456	10.77
17	289	4.12	67	4,489	8.19	117	13,689	10.82
18	324	4.24	68	4,624	8.25	118	13,924	10.86
19	361	4.36	69	4,761	8.31	119	14,161	10.91
20	400	4.47	70	4,900	8.37	120	14,400	10.95
21	441	4.58	71	5,041	8.43	121	14,641	11.00
22	484	4.69	72	5,184	8.49	122	14,884	11.05
23	529	4.80	73	5,329	8.54	123	15,129	11.09
24	576	4.90	74	5,476	8.60	124	15,376	11.14
25	625	5.00	75	5,625	8.66	125	15,625	11.18
26	676	5.10	76	5,776	8.72	126	15,876	11.22
27	729	5.20	77	5,929	8.77	127	16,129	11.27
28	784	5.29	78	6,084	8.83	128	16,384	11.31
29	841	5.39	79	6,241	8.89	129	16,641	11.36
30	900	5.48	80	6,400	8.94	130	16,900	11.40
31	961	5.57	81	6,561	9.00	131	17,161	11.45
32	1,024	5.66	82	6,724	9.06	132	17,424	11.49
33	1,089	5.74	83	6,889	9.11	133	17,689	11.53
34	1,156	5.83	84	7,056	9.17	134	17,956	11.58
35	1,225	5.92	85	7,225	9.22	135	18,225	11.62
36	1,296	6.00	86	7,396	9.27	136	18,496	11.66
37	1,369	6.08	87	7,569	9.33	137	18,769	11.70
38	1,444	6.16	88	7,744	9.38	138	19,044	11.75
39	1,521	6.24	89	7,921	9.43	139	19,321	11.79
40	1,600	6.32	90	8,100	9.49	140	19,600	11.83
41	1,681	6.40	91	8,281	9.54	141	19,881	11.87
42	1,764	6.48	92	8,464	9.59	142	20,164	11.92
43	1,849	6.56	93	8,649	9.64	143	20,449	11.96
44	1,936	6.63	94	8,836	9.70	144	20,736	12.00
45	2,025	6.71	95	9,025	9.75	145	21,025	12.04
46	2,116	6.78	96	9,216	9.80	146	21,316	12.08
47	2,209	6.86	97	9,409	9.85	147	21,609	12.12
48	2,304	6.93	98	9,604	9.90	148	21,904	12.17
49	2,401	7.00	99	9,801	9.95	149	22,201	12.21
50	2,500	7.07	100	10,000	10.00	150	22,500	12.25

Finding Square Roots from a Table

Square roots of numbers are found conveniently from a table (page 338). To find the square root of any number up to and including 150, we proceed as in Example **1**; to find the square root of a number greater than 150, we proceed as in Examples **2** or **3**.

Example 1. Find the square root of 46. We look down the column headed "N" until we reach the number 46; on the same line, to the right, in the third column, headed "$\sqrt{N}$," we find the square root, 6.78.

Check: $6.78^2 = 6.78 \times 6.78 = 45.9684$, or nearly 46

In the same way, we find:

$\sqrt{62} = 7.87 \qquad \sqrt{113} = 10.63 \qquad \sqrt{140} = 11.83$

Example 2. Find the square root of 484. We look down the column "N^2" until we find 484; directly to the left of 484, in the column "N," we find "22." The square root of 484 equals 22.

Check: $22 \times 22 = 484$

Example 3. Find the square root of 588. When we look down the column "N^2," we do not find the number 588. But 588 is between 576 and 625 in the table; so $\sqrt{588}$ must be between 24 and 25. Since 588 is less than halfway from 576 to 625, $\sqrt{588}$ must be nearer 24 than 25. Study the table at the right. Is 588 nearer to 585.64 than it is to 590.49? Then, the square root of 588 equals 24.2, to the nearest tenth.

$24.1^2 = 580.81$
$24.2^2 = 585.64$
$24.3^2 = 590.49$

Find the square root of:

1. 97
2. 6889
3. 138
4. 16,129
5. 200
6. 920
7. 75
8. 350
9. 462
10. 1700

The Right Triangle Rule

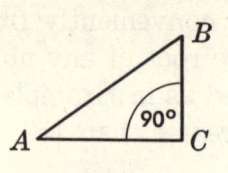

1. What kind of triangle is $\triangle ABC$?

2. Which two sides form the right angle? These are called the **arms** or **legs** of the triangle.

3. Which side lies opposite the right angle? This side is called the **hypotenuse**.

4. If each of the five parts into which AB has been divided represents 1 inch, how long is BC? AC?

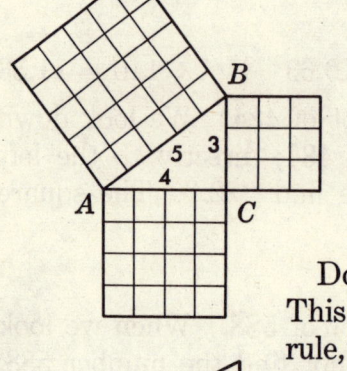

5. What is the area of the square on BC? the square on AC? the square on AB?

6. How does the sum of the areas of the two small squares compare with the area of the square on the hypotenuse?

Do you see that $3^2 + 4^2 = 5^2$? This is known as "the right triangle rule," or "the hypotenuse rule." It is also known as the **Rule of Pythagoras**, after a famous Greek mathematician, who proved it more than 2000 years ago. The rule may be stated:

The square of the length of the hypotenuse equals the sum of the squares of the lengths of the other two sides.

Then, $c^2 = a^2 + b^2$, or, $c = \sqrt{a^2 + b^2}$

Example 1. Find the length of the hypotenuse of a right triangle whose other two sides are 5 in. and 7 in. long.

$$c^2 = 5^2 + 7^2 = 25 + 49 = 74;$$
$$c^2 = 74; \ c = \sqrt{74} = 8.6 \text{ in.}$$

7. Find the length of the hypotenuse of a right triangle whose legs are 5 in. and 12 in. long.

8. The arms of a right triangle are each 6 in. long; how long is the hypotenuse?

9. What is the length of the hypotenuse of a right triangle if the other two sides are 10 in. and 11 in. long?

Example 2. Find the length of the diagonal of a rectangle whose sides are 5 ft. and 8 ft. The diagonal c is the hypotenuse of either of the two right triangles into which the rectangle is divided. Therefore:

$c^2 = 5^2 + 8^2 = 25 + 64 = 89$
$c^2 = 89;\ c = \sqrt{89} = 9.43$, or 9.4 ft.

10. What is the length of the diagonal of a rectangle 6 in. by 8 in.?

11. What is the length of the diagonal of an 8-inch square?

12. Find the diagonal of a rectangle that is 8 ft. wide and 14 ft. long.

13. A baseball diamond is a 90-ft. square. The length of a straight line from home plate to second base is between __?__ feet and __?__ feet.

14. It is 30 ft. to the point on a telegraph pole where a wire cable is fastened. The other end of the cable is fastened to a stake in the ground 16 ft. from the base of the pole. How long is the cable?

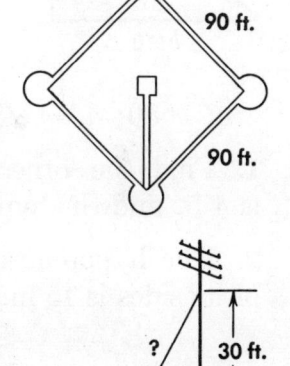

15. What is the length (to the nearest inch) of the longest fishing-rod case that can be laid in a camp locker 36 in. long and 20 in. wide, inside dimensions?

Finding a Side of a Right Triangle

If you know the sum of two numbers, then either one of these numbers equals the difference between their sum and the other number.   For example:

$20 + 30 = 50 \qquad 20 = 50 - 30 \qquad 30 = 50 - 20$

You know from the right triangle rule (page 340) that in this right triangle
$c^2 = a^2 + b^2,$ or, $a^2 + b^2 = c^2$

Then you can also see that
$a^2 = c^2 - b^2,$ and $b^2 = c^2 - a^2$

We can use these last two formulas to find one side of a right triangle if we know the hypotenuse and the other side.

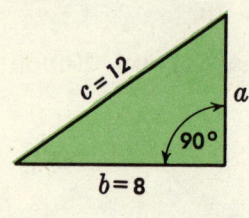

Example. The hypotenuse of a right triangle is 12 in., and one of its sides is 8 in.; find the other side.

Here $b = 8$, and $c = 12$

Since $a^2 = c^2 - b^2,$
$a^2 = 12^2 - 8^2 = 144 - 64 = 80;$
$a^2 = 80;\ a = \sqrt{80} = 8.94$ (from the table, page 338)

1. Find the other side of a right triangle if one side is 4 ft. and the hypotenuse is 8 ft.

2. The hypotenuse of a right triangle is 17 in. and one of its sides is 15 in.; find the other side.

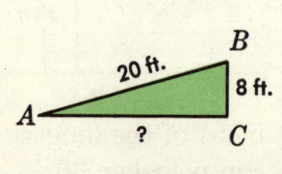

3. If the diagonal of a rectangle is 15 cm., and its length is 10 cm., what is the width of the rectangle?

4. A ramp is 20 ft. long. One end is 8 ft. higher than the other. Find the horizontal distance, AC.

Understanding Ratio and Proportion

1. Write a proportion for each of these statements, and then prove that it is correct:
   A. If 8 crayons cost 20¢, 20 crayons cost 50¢.
   B. At 50¢ an hour, it will cost $1.25 to rent a rowboat for $2\frac{1}{2}$ hours.
   C. At the rate of 6 miles in 2 hours, a man can walk 10 miles in $3\frac{1}{3}$ hours.
   D. If 4 lemons are needed to make 1 quart of lemonade, then 12 lemons will make $\frac{3}{4}$ gallon.

2. At the rate of 25¢ for 2 hours, how much will it cost to park an automobile for 12 hours?

3. If Barbara can read 8 pages in 20 minutes, at the same rate how long will it take her to read 40 pages?

4. What is the ratio of $\sqrt{81}$ to 3^2?

5. A snapshot measures $2\frac{1}{4}'' \times 3\frac{1}{4}''$. It is enlarged so that it is 9 inches wide. How long is the enlarged picture?

6. When an 18-foot pole casts a shadow 24 feet long, how long a shadow will be cast by a boy $4\frac{1}{2}$ feet tall?

7. Is the ratio 4:100 the same as 25%?

8. At the rate of 25¢ for a 10-ounce bar of chocolate, what is the cost of one pound?

9. What is the ratio of the area of a 2-inch square to the area of a 4-inch square?

10. If 1 inch on a map represents $\frac{1}{4}$ mile, what is the distance in feet between two places $\frac{1}{4}$ inch apart on the map?

11. What is the ratio of 24 inches to 2 feet?

12. On a map, $\frac{1}{16}$ inch represents 1 mile. How many miles are represented by $2\frac{1}{4}$ inches?

Making Sure

1. Two ships leave the same place, one sailing northwest, the other, 20° east of north. What is the angle between their courses? 319

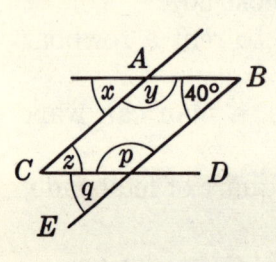

2. If *AB* is parallel to *CD*, and ∠*ABE* = 40°, then ∠*q* = __?__°, and ∠*p* = __?__°. If *AC* is parallel to *BE*, then ∠*x* = __?__° and ∠*y* = __?__°. How large is ∠*z*? What can you say about the opposite angles of any parallelogram? 322

3. The ratio of a quart to a gallon equals __?__. The ratio of a gallon to a pint equals __?__. 324

4. Find the missing terms: $\frac{9}{6} = \frac{?}{42}$; $\frac{?}{36} = \frac{2}{9}$. 327

5. A plan is drawn to a scale of $\frac{1}{4}$ in. = 1 ft. Express this scale as a ratio. 330

6. Write the ratio of 4:5 in two other ways. 324

7. What is the ratio of the side of a square to the perimeter of the square? of the perimeter to the side? 324

8. The scale on a map is 1 in. = 250 mi. What is the actual distance between two places $3\frac{1}{4}$ inches apart on the map? 331

9. Find: $\sqrt{49}$; $\sqrt{144}$; $\sqrt{100}$; $\sqrt{400}$; $\sqrt{10,000}$. 336

10. Find, from the table (page 338), to the nearest tenth, the square root of: 135, 149, 19, 72, 110, 30. 339

11. What is the length of the diagonal of a square 24 inches on a side? 341

12. A kind of nickel silver, often used for tableware, consists of 5 parts copper, 3 parts nickel, and 2 parts zinc. How many ounces of each metal are there in a nickel silver tray weighing 20 oz.? 328

11

A NEW WAY OF USING ARITHMETIC

Getting Acquainted with Algebra

Jerry was fond of asking riddles. Here is one he asked Paul. "If I weighed 10 lb. more than twice as much as I really do, I would be as heavy as my father, who weighs 170 lb. How much do I weigh?"

HOW PAUL SOLVED THE RIDDLE BY ARITHMETIC	HOW JERRY SOLVED IT BY USING A NEW WAY
If 10 more than twice something is 170, then twice something is 10 less than 170, or 160.	Let x = the number of pounds Jerry weighs
If twice a certain number is 160, then that number must be half of 160, or 80.	Then $2x$ = twice Jerry's weight
	But $2x + 10 = 170$
	$2x = 160$
Therefore Jerry's weight is 80 lb.	$x = 80$, Jerry's weight
To prove it, think: Twice 80 = 160; and 10 more, 170.	Check: $2 \times 80 + 10 = 170$

Do you agree that Jerry's way of solving the problem is easier than Paul's? Jerry solved the problem by **algebra**. This is simply a new way of using arithmetic.

In algebra we use *letters* to represent numbers or quantities. Jerry used x to represent his weight. We have already used letters in this way when we studied formulas, such as the formula for the area of a rectangle, $A = lw$, or the interest formula, $I = Prt$, or the time-rate-distance formula, $D = RT$.

Changing from Words to Letters

In arithmetic, we would write the quantity "3 more than the number 5" as 5 plus 3, or $5 + 3$. In algebra, we write the quantity "3 more than the number n" as $n + 3$.

In arithmetic, we express "2 less than 8" as 8 minus 2, or $8 - 2$. In algebra, we express "2 less than the number n" as $n - 2$.

In the same way:
1. A number increased by 10 is written $n + 10$.
2. A number decreased by 5 is written $n - 5$.
3. A number multiplied by 4 is written $4n$.
4. A number divided by 3 is written $\frac{n}{3}$.
5. 6 times a number is written $6n$.
6. $\frac{1}{8}$ of a number is written $\frac{1}{8}n$, or $\frac{n}{8}$.

Express each of the following quantities by using only letters and numbers:
1. 5 times a number.
2. A number increased by 3.
3. A number divided by 2.
4. A number plus 4.
5. One-sixth of a number.
6. 12 more than a number.
7. 8 less than a number.
8. Twice a number.
9. A number minus 10.
10. Three times a number.
11. The sum of a number and 5.
12. Fifteen minus a number.
13. A number multiplied by 9.
14. The quotient of 18 divided by a number.
15. The product of 8 and a number.
16. A number decreased by 16.
17. Twenty increased by a number.

Changing from Letters to Words

You know that in the formulas $A = lw$ and $I = Prt$ the letters represent quantities. In algebra we often use letters in this way. If a quantity is expressed in words, then letters can be used to stand for the words; if it is expressed in letters, then words can be used to stand for the letters. For example:

1. $n + 6$ means 6 more than the number n.
2. $n - 5$ means 5 less than the number n.
3. $\frac{1}{4} n$ means $\frac{1}{4}$ of the number n.
4. $10\,n$ means 10 times the number n.
5. $\frac{a}{3}$ means the number a divided by 3.
6. $2 + x$ means 2 increased by the number x.
7. $8 - b$ means 8 decreased by the number b.

Express each quantity by using only words and numbers:

1. $4\,n$
2. $n + 8$
3. $b - 2$
4. $\frac{x}{10}$
5. $k + 16$
6. $y - 1$
7. $\frac{1}{8} n$
8. $12 + b$
9. $3\,x$
10. $6 - n$
11. $\frac{1}{10} r$
12. $100 + c$
13. $\frac{2\,x}{3}$
14. $3\,n + 4$
15. $4\,a - 5$
16. $\frac{2}{3} n$
17. $a + n$
18. $a - b$

Think before you answer:

19. Does $a + 5$ equal $5 + a$? Does $n - 3$ equal $3 - n$?
20. Does $\frac{1}{5} n$ equal $\frac{n}{5}$? Does $\frac{2}{3} n$ equal $\frac{2\,n}{3}$?
21. How much is $n + 0$? $0 + n$? How much is $n - 0$?
22. What does rt mean?
23. What does $x \times 0$ equal? $0 \times x$? $0 \div x$?

Reading and Writing Equations

If Ted weighs 85 lb. and Henry weighs 15 lb. more than Ted, or 100 lb., then the quantity (85 + 15) and the quantity 100 are **equal quantities;** $85 + 15 = 100$. If t represents Ted's weight, we may write $t + 15 = 100$.

Such a statement, telling us that two quantities are equal, is called an **equation.** An equation is like the scales shown here; when the total weights on each side are equal, the scales **balance.** When two quantities are equal, they balance and form an equation.

Write an equation for each of the following statements, letting n represent the unknown number:

1. A number increased by 4 equals 12.
2. Ten times a number equals 75.
3. 8 less than a number equals 15.
4. 12 more than a number equals 20.
5. A certain number subtracted from 12 leaves 5.
6. 18 increased by another number is 22.
7. One-third of a number is 17.
8. A certain number divided by 10 equals 6.
9. When 6 is added to $\frac{1}{2}$ a number, the result is 14.
10. If 8 is subtracted from $\frac{1}{2}$ a number, the result is 20.

Tell what each equation means:

11. $n - 12 = 30$
12. $3x = 15$
13. $a + \frac{1}{2} = 10$
14. $b - 20 = 10$
15. $\frac{2}{3}n = 12$
16. $2n + 8 = 14$
17. $3x - 6 = 21$
18. $15 + 4x = 23$
19. $18 - 3y = 6$

Using Division to Solve Equations

The perimeter of this regular hexagon is 48 in. How long is each side?

Since the 6 sides of a regular hexagon are equal, we know that the perimeter, p, equals 6 times one side s; that is, $p = 6 \times s$, or $p = 6s$. Therefore, $6s = p$.

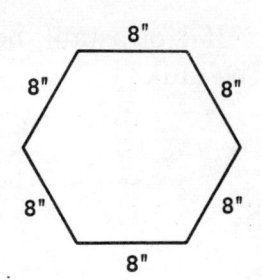

Substituting the value 48 for p, we obtain the equation, $6s = 48$.

$6s = 48$ means 6 times $s = 48$; then $s = \frac{1}{6}$ of $48 = 8$. In $6s = 48$, we can divide both $6s$ and 48 by 6. Then we have: $6s \div 6 = 48 \div 6$
that is, $1s = 8$
or $s = 8$

Each side of the hexagon is 8 inches long.

Check: $6 \times 8 = 48$

When we divide one of two equal quantities by a number, we must also divide the other by the same number to keep the two quantities equal.

Solve these equations by dividing by the appropriate number; check your answers.

1. $3a = 27$
2. $7x = 56$
3. $5n = 30$
4. $2k = 98$
5. $140 = 5t$
6. $6y = 20$
7. $4h = 3.2$
8. $3x = 1$
9. $20a = 15$
10. $9x = 162$
11. $55p = 220$
12. $288 = 6r$

13. How much does 1 ton of coal cost if 8 tons cost $128? if 8 tons cost n dollars? if n tons cost $128?

14. How far will a car travel in 1 hour if it travels 120 miles in 4 hours? if it travels n miles in 4 hours? if it travels 120 miles in n hours?

Using Multiplication to Solve Equations

If $\frac{1}{5}$ of a tank holds 40 gallons, what is the capacity of the tank?

Let us say the tank holds g gallons. Then $\frac{1}{5}$ of g, or $\frac{1}{5}g$, equals the number of gallons in the tank.

Therefore, $\frac{1}{5}g = 40$.

We multiply each of the equal quantities by 5, because we have only $\frac{1}{5}$ of g:

$$\frac{1}{5}g = 40$$
$$5 \times \frac{1}{5}g = 5 \times 40$$
$$\frac{5}{5}g = 200$$
$$g = 200$$

The tank holds 200 gallons.   Check: $\frac{1}{5}$ of $200 = 40$

If we multiply one of two equal quantities by a number, we must also multiply the other by the same number.

Solve these equations by multiplying each of the equal quantities by the appropriate number. Check your answers.

1. $\frac{x}{3} = 8$
2. $\frac{k}{12} = 3$
3. $\frac{m}{20} = 5$
4. $72 = \frac{y}{4}$
5. $\frac{a}{8} = 1$
6. $\frac{b}{5} = 2.4$
7. $\frac{r}{100} = .3$
8. $\frac{1}{6}p = 12$
9. $\frac{t}{9} = 4.5$
10. $\frac{x}{4} = 3\frac{3}{4}$
11. $0.1\,r = 2.8$
12. $\frac{n}{6} = \frac{5}{3}$

13. A family spends $24, or $\frac{1}{4}$ of its weekly income, for food. What is its weekly income? Here $\frac{1}{4}i = 24$; why?

14. A man spends $75, or $\frac{1}{5}$ of his monthly income, for rent; what is his monthly income?

15. If a saving of $2.40 is $\frac{1}{6}$ of the original price, what was the original price?

Using Both Multiplication and Division to Solve Equations

Sometimes we use both multiplication and division to solve an equation.

If $\frac{3}{4}$ of the time required for a certain trip is 12 hours, find the length of time required for the entire trip.

Let t = number of hours for the entire trip.

Then $\frac{3}{4} t$, or $\frac{3t}{4}$ = number of hours for $\frac{3}{4}$ of the trip.

Therefore, $\frac{3t}{4} = 12$

We multiply by 4: $4 \times \frac{3t}{4} = 4 \times 12$; or, $3t = 48$

We divide by 3: $t = 16$

The entire trip required 16 hours. Check: $\frac{3}{4}$ of 16 = 12

Solve the following equations:

1. $\frac{2x}{5} = 10$
2. $\frac{2n}{3} = 24$
3. $\frac{5a}{6} = 15$
4. $\frac{3n}{10} = 30$
5. $\frac{3y}{4} = 1$
6. $\frac{4b}{3} = 8$
7. $\frac{7x}{4} = 28$
8. $\frac{3x}{2} = 10$
9. $\frac{n}{8} = \frac{1}{4}$
10. $\frac{3}{8} k = 6$
11. $\frac{p}{10} = \frac{9}{2}$
12. $\frac{5}{14} = \frac{n}{28}$

13. If $\frac{2}{3}$ of a can holds 20 ounces, what is the capacity of the can? Here $\frac{2n}{3} = 20$.

14. If $1\frac{1}{2}$ lb. of cheese cost 84¢, what is the cost of one pound? Here $1\frac{1}{2} x = 84$.

15. If $\frac{7}{10}$ of a certain number is 105, find the number.

16. If $\frac{3}{4}$ doz. cookies cost 54¢, find the cost of a dozen.

Using Subtraction to Solve Equations

Evelyn has 8 more long-playing records than Susan. If Evelyn has 19 records, how many does Susan have?

Let n = the number of records Susan has: then $n + 8$ = the number Evelyn has. Why? So, $n + 8 = 19$; this means that we add 8 to n to get 19. Now if we subtract 8 from $(n + 8)$, the remainder is n; if we subtract 8 from 19, the remainder is 11.

$$\begin{array}{r} n + 8 = 19 \\ 8 = 8 \\ \hline n = 11 \end{array} \qquad \begin{array}{c} n + 8 - 8 = 19 - 8 \\ n = 11 \end{array}$$

Susan has 11 records.

Check: $11 + 8 = 19$, substituting 11 for n.

We may subtract any number from one of two equal quantities, provided we also subtract the same number from the other quantity.

Solve these equations by subtracting the appropriate number from each of the equal quantities:

1. $n + 6 = 18$
2. $x + 10 = 25$
3. $a + 4 = 36$
4. $y + 9 = 10$
5. $p + 2\frac{1}{2} = 8$
6. $12 + k = 40$
7. $25 = b + 15$
8. $33 = 11 + p$
9. $h + 4 = 12\frac{1}{4}$
10. $t + 3.2 = 14$
11. $48 = 22 + k$
12. $m + 4.3 = 9.1$

13. In a garden there are 18 more rose bushes than lilac bushes. If there are 26 rose bushes, how many lilac bushes are there? Here $n + 18 = 26$.

14. The length of a rectangle is $8\frac{1}{2}$ feet greater than its width. If the length is 20 feet, what is the width?

15. The girls in a cooking class made 7 more cakes than pies. If they made 19 cakes, how many pies did they make?

16. Mr. Hutchin's income tax is $24 more this year than last. His tax this year is $76. What was it last year?

Using Addition to Solve Equations

At a sale, a shopkeeper sold an article for 69¢, which was 19 cents less than it cost. How much did it cost?

Let x = the number of cents the article cost.
Then $x - 19$ = the number of cents he sold it for.
Therefore, $x - 19 = 69$. (Why?)
Add 19 to each of these equal quantities:

$$\begin{array}{r} x - 19 = 69 \\ 19 = 19 \\ \hline x = 88 \end{array} \qquad \begin{array}{r} x - 19 + 19 = 69 + 19 \\ x = 88 \end{array}$$

Do you see that if we subtract 19 from x, and then add 19 to this result, the answer will be x?

The article cost 88¢. Check: 88¢ − 19¢ = 69¢

We may add any number to one of two equal quantities, provided we also add the same number to the other quantity.

Solve these equations by adding the appropriate number to each of the equal quantities; check your results.

1. $n - 4 = 16$
2. $x - 13 = 28$
3. $y - 25 = 5$
4. $k - 8 = 1$
5. $x - 4\frac{1}{2} = 12$
6. $15 = n - 3$
7. $p - 6 = 4\frac{1}{2}$
8. $24 = r - 1$
9. $m - 0.9 = 2.3$
10. $n - 12 = 0$
11. $x - 3\frac{1}{2} = 5\frac{1}{4}$
12. $5\frac{1}{2} = t - 2$

13. After Ruth spent 45 cents for a cake, she had 23 cents left. How much did she have at first? Here, $n - 45 = 23$.

14. At the end of the winter season, an overcoat was sold for $27.50, which was $12.25 less than the regular price. What was the regular price?

15. A stock closed at $89\frac{3}{4}$, which was $3\frac{1}{2}$ points lower than the highest price of the day. What was the highest price?

Practice with Equations and Formulas

Solve each of these equations for x:

	A	B	C
1.	$x + 9 = 15$	$\frac{1}{10}x = 13$	$5 = \frac{x}{4}$
2.	$5x = 70$	$60 = 10x$	$144 = 6x$
3.	$x - 2 = 8$	$25 = \frac{x}{5}$	$x + 30 = 70$
4.	$\frac{x}{3} = 12$	$16 = x + 4$	$x - 24 = 32$
5.	$x - 18 = 4$	$4x = 120$	$960 = 3x$

Solve each of these equations for the unknown quantity:

6.	$\frac{a}{6} = 15$	$\frac{3n}{4} = 48$	$6h = 4\frac{1}{2}$
7.	$k + 4\frac{1}{2} = 10$	$4r = 6.4$	$\frac{5p}{4} = 60$
8.	$s - 2\frac{1}{4} = 8$	$n + 2\frac{1}{2} = 6\frac{1}{4}$	$72 = 0.6m$
9.	$\frac{2}{3}n = 24$	$4.1 + t = 9.6$	$2\frac{1}{2}x = 45$
10.	$p - 2.5 = 6.3$	$\frac{2x}{5} = 40$	$0.3n = 7.5$

Find the missing quantity in each of the following:

	A	B	C	D	E
11.	$\frac{x}{6} = \frac{5}{12}$	$\frac{2}{3} = \frac{n}{18}$	$\frac{2}{9} = \frac{p}{15}$	$40 = \frac{n}{2}$	$\frac{a}{8} = 16$
12.	$\frac{a}{8} = \frac{3}{4}$	$\frac{5}{6} = \frac{k}{24}$	$\frac{m}{4} = 1$	$\frac{y}{3} = \frac{5}{7}$	$100 = \frac{r}{5}$

13. In the formula $V = lwh$:

 A. when $l = 8$, $w = 6$, and $V = 192$, find h.
 B. when $V = 400$, $l = 10$, and $h = 4$, find w.

14. In the formula $A = \frac{1}{2}bh$, find h when $A = 56$ and $b = 14$.

15. If $P = 2l + 2w$, find l when $w = 8$ and $P = 56$.

Using Equations in Problems

Some problems in arithmetic can be solved more easily by using simple equations, as these examples will show.

Example 1. A farmer sold $\frac{3}{4}$ of his crop for $975. At this rate, find the value of the entire crop.

Let x represent the value of the entire crop.

Then $\frac{3x}{4} = 975$

$3x = 3900$

$x = 1300$

Check:

$\frac{3}{4}$ of $1300 = $975

Example 2. Tom wishes to cut a board 14 ft. long into two pieces, but he wants one of the pieces to be 3 times as long as the other. How long should he make each piece?

Let x represent the length, in feet, of the shorter piece.

Then $3x$ represents the length, in feet, of the longer piece. But the two pieces together must equal 14 feet.

$x + 3x = 14$

$4x = 14$

$x = 3\frac{1}{2}$

$3x = 10\frac{1}{2}$

Check:

$3\frac{1}{2} + 10\frac{1}{2} = 14$

1. If $\frac{2}{3}$ of your vacation is over and you have already had 12 days of vacation, how long is your whole vacation?

2. A mechanic was paid $42 for working $3\frac{1}{2}$ days. How much did he receive per day?

3. An orchard contains 120 acres. The part planted in apple trees is 3 times as large as the part planted in peach trees. How many acres are there in each part?

4. A man paid $2400, or 40%, toward the purchase price of a house. What did the house cost?

Changing the Subject of a Formula

A formula shows how two or more quantities are related. In many ways it is like an equation, since the quantity on one side of the equal sign always balances or equals the quantity on the other side. Any formula can always be written in more than one way.

Example 1. If $A = lw$, write a formula that tells how to find l if we know A and w.

Using division, we "solve the formula" for l by dividing each "side" by w.

$$\frac{A}{w} = \frac{lw}{w}, \quad \text{or} \quad \frac{A}{w} = l; \quad \text{that is,} \quad l = \frac{A}{w}$$

This may be called *changing the subject of a formula.* In the formula $A = lw$, the subject of the formula is A. What is the subject in $l = \frac{A}{w}$? in $w = \frac{A}{l}$?

Example 2. Change the formula $A = \frac{1}{2} bh$ so that h is the subject of the formula instead of A.

Multiplying by 2: $2A = bh$

Dividing by b: $\frac{2A}{b} = h$, or, $h = \frac{2A}{b}$

Change the subject of each of the following formulas as indicated:

1. $A = lw$; $w = ?$
2. $P = 4s$; $s = ?$
3. $V = lwh$; $h = ?$
4. $D = RT$; $R = ?$
5. $C = \pi D$; $D = ?$
6. $A = \frac{bh}{2}$; $b = ?$
7. $C = 2\pi r$; $r = ?$
8. $D = RT$; $T = ?$
9. $I = Prt$; $r = ?$
10. $I = Prt$; $P = ?$
11. $V = \frac{1}{3} Bh$; $B = ?$
12. $A = \pi r^2$; $r^2 = ?$

Making Sure

Solve these equations:

A	B	C
1. $7 + y = 21$	$\dfrac{x}{3} = 6$	$.4\,k = 28$
2. $b - 12 = 20$	$3 = \dfrac{x}{6}$	$.8\,p = 3.2$
3. $18 = n - 8$	$\dfrac{x}{3} = 0$	$.6\,t = .18$
4. $x + 12 = 35$	$\dfrac{x}{6} = 6$	$.05\,n = 20$

Write an equation for each of these statements:

5. Four times a certain number is 16.
6. If a number is increased by 10, the result is 27.
7. Two-thirds of a number equals 24.
8. If a number is decreased by 6, the result is 15.
9. Four more than twice a number equals 12.
10. Half a certain number increased by 3 equals 7.
11. Twice a number decreased by 4 equals 18.

Solve these problems by using equations:

12. Two numbers are in the ratio of 5:7. If the larger number is 21, what is the smaller number?
13. The interest on a certain principal for one year at 4% is $10. What is the principal?
14. If the interest on $600 for 1 year is $21, what is the rate of interest?
15. What length of time will be required for $200 to earn $9 interest at 6% annually?
16. Find the radius of a circle having a circumference of 33 feet.

REMEDIAL PRACTICE

Addition of Whole Numbers

I.
A	B	C	D	E	F	G	H	I	J
6	5	4	9	3	4	8	4	8	5
9	7	7	5	6	8	5	4	8	9
6	8	9	8	4	9	9	9	6	6
8	8	4	2	8	2	3	5	4	3
2	3	3	9	3	9	9	6	9	2
1	9	8	1	5	7	8	4	1	4
4	6	6	4	5	4	2	3	7	9

II.
A	B	C	D	E	F	G
32	78	36	62	57	93	62
69	80	48	45	77	45	67
44	26	82	36	94	84	79
58	67	38	46	63	57	86
64	41	96	58	24	94	57
43	88	60	22	48	65	87
81	66	13	87	45	66	59
25	41	89	58	95	26	65

III.
A	B	C	D	E
$96.85	$12.22	$11.16	$82.57	$93.97
27.08	33.54	91.95	22.89	22.53
51.77	50.34	28.33	13.92	18.12
64.52	71.59	25.39	32.67	57.11
29.37	36.87	26.57	90.87	55.47
16.18	73.78	98.47	21.89	39.55

IV.
A	B	C	D
$ 24.88	$ 98.38	$ 8.71	$ 6.89
315.62	80.77	377.99	42.99
46.75	9.84	61.18	678.69
230.64	419.72	961.66	8.67
309.49	76.79	48.58	90.67

Subtraction of Whole Numbers

I. | | A | B | C | D | E | F | G |
    |-----|----------|----------|----------|----------|----------|----------|------|
    | 1. | 835 | 486 | 974 | 859 | 495 | 877 | 668 |
    | | 612 | 432 | 831 | 216 | 374 | 864 | 163 |
    | 2. | 856 | 759 | 964 | 389 | 728 | 849 | 651 |
    | | 404 | 35 | 402 | 52 | 500 | 703 | 350 |

II. | 1. | 641 | 827 | 563 | 838 | 984 | 353 | 829 |
    | | 317 | 194 | 248 | 766 | 935 | 182 | 251 |
    | 2. | 928 | 739 | 386 | 698 | 592 | 973 | 316 |
    | | 178 | 597 | 327 | 559 | 346 | 544 | 296 |
    | 3. | 719 | 434 | 813 | 427 | 855 | 594 | 444 |
    | | 260 | 309 | 620 | 408 | 49 | 507 | 380 |

III.| 1. | 430 | 6408 | 1500 | 7746 | 9270 | 6525 | 810 |
    | | 282 | 5567 | 698 | 7077 | 2581 | 1287 | 739 |
    | 2. | 820 | 916 | 680 | 9222 | 9562 | 3008 | 6347 |
    | | 545 | 179 | 194 | 6133 | 1164 | 1462 | 5068 |

IV. | | A | B | C | D | E | F |
    |-----|------|------|------|------|------|------|
    | 1. | 8720 | 8522 | 7852 | 8743 | 9530 | 5930 |
    | | 6892 | 4039 | 988 | 7408 | 3975 | 5041 |
    | 2. | 6000 | 5123 | 2657 | 7094 | 8754 | 6402 |
    | | 2179 | 1064 | 743 | 2397 | 5016 | 3985 |

V. | | A | B | C | D |
    |-----|---------|---------|---------|---------|
    | 1. | 738,461 | 999,041 | 987,080 | 358,150 |
    | | 678,298 | 42,352 | 579,817 | 61,140 |
    | 2. | 400,328 | 644,752 | 620,071 | 776,255 |
    | | 196,676 | 33,523 | 52,334 | 248,457 |

Multiplication of Whole Numbers

I.

	A	B	C	D	E	F	G	H
1.	29 8	54 3	46 4	73 6	93 2	57 9	68 5	38 7
2.	32 19	51 42	84 63	27 75	35 94	56 82	48 28	64 71

II.

	A	B	C	D	E
1.	216 8	312 3	165 6	481 9	154 5
2.	519 7	743 8	287 4	235 7	679 3

III.

	A	B	C	D	E
1.	328 32	175 61	913 49	892 17	249 68
2.	139 53	262 69	724 26	246 15	764 97
3.	809 90	308 18	170 24	310 70	105 84

IV.

	A	B	C	D	E
1.	370 503	405 310	907 109	600 321	589 500
2.	308 640	103 123	510 320	730 805	206 304
3.	900 604	240 440	700 800	540 700	504 900

V.

	A	B	C	D	E
1.	4900 1200	1402 5008	6700 7012	6008 6005	860 4800
2.	8006 9030	9300 6500	5600 5060	9080 3700	8009 2004

Division of Whole Numbers

I.   A   B   C   D   E   F

1. 6)486   9)549   8)328   3)216   9)810   7)560

2. 7)637   4)368   8)720   4)872   3)246   6)540

     A   B   C   D   E

3. 8)6424   6)4224   7)4921   8)5648   9)3672

4. 7)2842   4)2428   9)2763   6)1836   3)1839

II.

1. 6)5591   7)4490   4)2299   9)2550   8)3087

2. 3)556   8)1395   4)1077   6)1724   5)2862

3. 6)5419   9)3334   3)9029   4)3883   7)1123

4. 7)6444   5)2049   8)3261   3)3190   9)5760

III.

1. 40)722   90)1092   70)694   60)1631   80)2080

2. 20)689   50)730   80)615   30)644   90)710

IV.

1. 41)107   82)1067   52)1668   11)483   91)2972

2. 12)1376   31)1085   22)1388   61)4410   72)8359

V.

1. 62)3093   12)1186   71)2838   32)612   51)4020

2. 32)3170   91)3629   11)201   42)2898   81)1600

VI.

1. 22)1421   41)817   52)1508   61)2568   21)987

2. 81)2744   72)6554   92)8116   31)908   12)918

		A	B	C	D	E
VII.	1.	28)412	49)1040	79)3479	38)448	99)2624
	2.	59)2814	68)4500	19)1640	89)3204	48)3540
VIII.	1.	18)928	69)6298	78)6398	39)3173	88)1956
	2.	38)1940	28)1991	58)1154	29)899	49)2995
IX.	1.	29)2650	89)2760	38)2323	79)6399	98)4255
	2.	68)3200	19)1788	59)1585	48)3408	18)696
X.	1.	34)1770	56)1542	94)1303	23)1035	35)2200
	2.	87)3580	73)2858	47)888	66)6130	65)2796
XI.	1.	13)714	14)373	16)3500	15)951	17)1442
	2.	15)1100	16)538	17)820	14)5866	13)1188
XII.	1.	95)3808	27)2441	84)4280	26)1839	53)12200
	2.	67)20109	33)8592	77)13912	58)17995	76)47120
XIII.	1.	24)2462	86)26490	75)15370	63)44457	97)29310
	2.	43)26097	64)32245	36)28888	82)8310	37)33602
XIV.	1.	93)1000	25)41000	96)20000	44)2000	57)5000
	2.	54)200	45)800	83)6000	46)3000	55)9000

		A	B	C	D
XV.	1.	121)7860	611)249711	407)48238	549)774839
	2.	298)6953	704)228179	851)259856	346)796509

Addition of Fractions and Mixed Numbers

I.
A	B	C	D	E	F	G	H
$\frac{2}{3}$	$\frac{7}{10}$	$\frac{5}{6}$	$\frac{7}{8}$	$\frac{4}{5}$	$\frac{3}{4}$	$\frac{5}{12}$	$\frac{9}{16}$
$\frac{2}{3}$	$\frac{9}{10}$	$\frac{1}{6}$	$\frac{5}{8}$	$\frac{3}{5}$	$\frac{3}{4}$	$\frac{11}{12}$	$\frac{5}{16}$

II.
$\frac{1}{5}$	$\frac{1}{4}$	$\frac{1}{2}$	$\frac{2}{5}$	$\frac{3}{8}$	$\frac{1}{5}$	$\frac{2}{3}$	$\frac{3}{8}$
$\frac{3}{4}$	$\frac{2}{3}$	$\frac{3}{5}$	$\frac{1}{3}$	$\frac{1}{5}$	$\frac{5}{6}$	$\frac{1}{2}$	$\frac{2}{3}$

III.
$\frac{1}{2}$	$\frac{3}{4}$	$\frac{5}{12}$	$\frac{3}{5}$	$\frac{2}{3}$	$\frac{1}{2}$	$\frac{1}{6}$	$\frac{3}{4}$
$\frac{5}{6}$	$\frac{3}{8}$	$\frac{1}{4}$	$\frac{9}{10}$	$\frac{5}{6}$	$\frac{7}{8}$	$\frac{7}{12}$	$\frac{1}{2}$

IV.
$\frac{3}{8}$	$\frac{2}{3}$	$\frac{3}{5}$	$\frac{1}{2}$	$\frac{5}{8}$	$\frac{2}{3}$	$\frac{5}{12}$	$\frac{4}{5}$
$\frac{1}{6}$	$\frac{3}{4}$	$\frac{5}{6}$	$\frac{1}{3}$	$\frac{3}{4}$	$\frac{5}{6}$	$\frac{1}{4}$	$\frac{3}{10}$
$\frac{2}{3}$	$\frac{1}{8}$	$\frac{3}{10}$	$\frac{1}{4}$	$\frac{1}{2}$	$\frac{1}{2}$	$\frac{2}{3}$	$\frac{3}{4}$

V.

	A	B	C	D	E	F
1.	$8\frac{5}{6}$	$5\frac{3}{8}$	$12\frac{1}{3}$	$16\frac{1}{3}$	$10\frac{3}{4}$	$12\frac{5}{6}$
	$6\frac{2}{3}$	$2\frac{3}{4}$	$7\frac{1}{4}$	$4\frac{1}{2}$	$8\frac{2}{3}$	$16\frac{5}{8}$
2.	$6\frac{2}{3}$	$5\frac{1}{3}$	$3\frac{3}{8}$	$16\frac{5}{6}$	$18\frac{1}{5}$	$8\frac{3}{8}$
	$12\frac{1}{2}$	$16\frac{1}{4}$	$10\frac{3}{4}$	$6\frac{1}{4}$	$8\frac{1}{2}$	12
	$13\frac{2}{3}$	$4\frac{1}{3}$	$8\frac{5}{8}$	$12\frac{3}{8}$	15	$16\frac{5}{16}$

VI.

	A	B	C	D	E
1.	$\frac{2}{5} + \frac{1}{2}$	$\frac{2}{3} + \frac{3}{4}$	$\frac{3}{8} + \frac{5}{6}$	$\frac{7}{8} + \frac{3}{10}$	$\frac{9}{16} + \frac{3}{8}$
2.	$\frac{7}{8} + \frac{3}{4}$	$\frac{2}{3} + \frac{5}{8}$	$\frac{7}{10} + \frac{5}{12}$	$\frac{1}{12} + \frac{5}{8}$	$\frac{3}{4} + \frac{5}{16}$

VII.

	A	B	C
1.	$\frac{1}{2} + \frac{1}{3} + \frac{1}{4}$	$\frac{2}{3} + \frac{3}{4} + \frac{1}{6}$	$\frac{1}{6} + \frac{1}{3} + \frac{4}{5}$
2.	$2\frac{1}{2} + 3\frac{1}{4}$	$3\frac{1}{4} + 1\frac{2}{5}$	$5\frac{3}{4} + 1\frac{1}{8}$

Subtraction of Fractions and Mixed Numbers

I.   A   B   C   D   E   F   G   H

1. $\frac{9}{10} - \frac{3}{10}$ $\frac{5}{6} - \frac{1}{6}$ $\frac{7}{8} - \frac{1}{2}$ $\frac{5}{6} - \frac{1}{3}$ $\frac{3}{4} - \frac{1}{2}$ $\frac{1}{2} - \frac{1}{8}$ $\frac{3}{4} - \frac{3}{8}$ $\frac{1}{2} - \frac{1}{6}$

2. $\frac{1}{2} - \frac{2}{5}$ $\frac{2}{3} - \frac{1}{4}$ $\frac{1}{2} - \frac{1}{3}$ $\frac{2}{3} - \frac{2}{5}$ $\frac{3}{4} - \frac{1}{6}$ $\frac{5}{6} - \frac{3}{8}$ $\frac{7}{10} - \frac{1}{4}$ $\frac{5}{12} - \frac{1}{8}$

II. 1. $8\frac{3}{4} - 6\frac{1}{2}$ $5\frac{7}{8} - 1\frac{1}{4}$ $10\frac{3}{4} - 4\frac{1}{8}$ $8\frac{2}{5} - 3\frac{2}{5}$ $3\frac{2}{3} - 1\frac{1}{4}$ $6\frac{5}{12} - \frac{3}{8}$ $4\frac{1}{2} - 2\frac{1}{8}$ $9\frac{7}{10} - 3\frac{2}{5}$

2. $7\frac{2}{3} - 5\frac{1}{2}$ $6\frac{3}{4} - 6\frac{2}{3}$ $4\frac{4}{5} - \frac{1}{2}$ $3\frac{1}{4} - 2\frac{1}{2}$ $10\frac{3}{4} - 8\frac{3}{10}$ $6\frac{5}{6} - 1\frac{1}{4}$ $9\frac{5}{6} - 9\frac{5}{8}$ $8\frac{7}{12} - 3\frac{1}{8}$

III. 1. $8\frac{1}{3} - 4\frac{2}{3}$ $6\frac{1}{4} - 2\frac{1}{2}$ $5\frac{1}{8} - 3\frac{5}{8}$ $9\frac{1}{2} - 8\frac{3}{4}$ $4\frac{1}{6} - \frac{2}{3}$ $8\frac{2}{5} - 2\frac{4}{5}$ $12\frac{3}{8} - 11\frac{3}{4}$ $9\frac{1}{2} - 4\frac{7}{8}$

2. $6 - 1\frac{2}{3}$ $8 - \frac{5}{6}$ $5 - 2\frac{7}{8}$ $10 - 4\frac{3}{4}$ $9 - 3\frac{4}{5}$ $7 - 6\frac{3}{8}$ $15 - 5\frac{3}{10}$ $9 - 8\frac{5}{6}$

3. $6\frac{1}{2} - 2\frac{1}{4}$ $5\frac{1}{4} - 4\frac{3}{8}$ $9\frac{2}{3} - 6\frac{5}{6}$ $12 - 8\frac{1}{3}$ $8\frac{1}{8} - 7\frac{1}{4}$ $16\frac{3}{4} - \frac{1}{8}$ $7\frac{5}{12} - 4\frac{1}{3}$ $12\frac{5}{16} - 10\frac{3}{4}$

IV.   A   B   C   D   E

1. $\frac{3}{4} - \frac{5}{8}$ $\frac{5}{6} - \frac{1}{2}$ $\frac{9}{16} - \frac{1}{4}$ $\frac{4}{5} - \frac{2}{3}$ $\frac{7}{10} - \frac{3}{5}$

2. $\frac{4}{5} - \frac{1}{2}$ $\frac{7}{8} - \frac{1}{4}$ $\frac{2}{3} - \frac{1}{2}$ $\frac{7}{12} - \frac{3}{8}$ $\frac{5}{6} - \frac{5}{8}$

V.   A   B   C

1. $2\frac{1}{2} - 1\frac{1}{4}$ $6\frac{3}{8} - 4\frac{3}{4}$ $12\frac{2}{3} - 4\frac{1}{6}$

2. $4\frac{1}{4} - 2\frac{1}{2}$ $5\frac{1}{2} - 2\frac{3}{8}$ $10\frac{1}{4} - 7\frac{7}{8}$

Multiplication of Fractions and Mixed Numbers

	A	B	C	D	E
I. 1.	$\frac{2}{3} \times 10$	$\frac{5}{8} \times 5$	$\frac{2}{9} \times 4$	$\frac{3}{8} \times 13$	$\frac{4}{15} \times 8$
2.	$\frac{1}{4} \times 27$	$\frac{3}{10} \times 7$	$\frac{3}{4} \times 15$	$\frac{5}{12} \times 11$	$\frac{7}{8} \times 35$
3.	$\frac{3}{5} \times 8$	$\frac{1}{3} \times 10$	$\frac{2}{5} \times 9$	$\frac{11}{16} \times 3$	$\frac{5}{6} \times 23$
II. 1.	$\frac{1}{6} \times 20$	$\frac{9}{16} \times 12$	$\frac{5}{6} \times 27$	$\frac{4}{5} \times 80$	$\frac{3}{16} \times 2$
2.	$\frac{3}{4} \times 30$	$\frac{7}{12} \times 12$	$\frac{3}{8} \times 4$	$\frac{11}{12} \times 18$	$\frac{2}{15} \times 90$
3.	$12 \times \frac{3}{5}$	$10 \times \frac{5}{6}$	$42 \times \frac{7}{8}$	$12 \times \frac{3}{7}$	$9 \times \frac{1}{6}$
4.	$20 \times \frac{1}{8}$	$56 \times \frac{3}{4}$	$23 \times \frac{1}{2}$	$60 \times \frac{5}{12}$	$15 \times \frac{5}{9}$
III. 1.	$3\frac{1}{2} \times 18$	$1\frac{3}{4} \times 50$	$4\frac{1}{8} \times 16$	$3\frac{1}{7} \times 28$	$2\frac{1}{2} \times 64$
2.	$2\frac{1}{4} \times 24$	$2\frac{2}{3} \times 36$	$12\frac{1}{2} \times 52$	$4\frac{1}{6} \times 54$	$3\frac{7}{8} \times 48$
3.	$39 \times 5\frac{1}{3}$	$108 \times 4\frac{1}{2}$	$4 \times 6\frac{5}{8}$	$80 \times 6\frac{3}{8}$	$30 \times 2\frac{3}{10}$
IV. 1.	$\frac{3}{4} \times \frac{4}{5}$	$\frac{7}{8} \times \frac{2}{3}$	$\frac{3}{8} \times \frac{5}{6}$	$\frac{7}{12} \times \frac{6}{7}$	$\frac{1}{8} \times \frac{7}{8}$
2.	$\frac{3}{16} \times \frac{1}{2}$	$\frac{2}{5} \times \frac{3}{5}$	$\frac{5}{8} \times \frac{2}{15}$	$\frac{2}{3} \times \frac{9}{16}$	$\frac{4}{9} \times \frac{9}{10}$
V. 1.	$2\frac{1}{2} \times \frac{3}{5}$	$1\frac{1}{4} \times \frac{2}{3}$	$1\frac{2}{3} \times \frac{7}{10}$	$5\frac{1}{2} \times \frac{4}{5}$	$3\frac{1}{8} \times \frac{1}{2}$
2.	$\frac{1}{2} \times 1\frac{1}{2}$	$\frac{3}{4} \times 1\frac{2}{3}$	$\frac{2}{3} \times 4\frac{1}{2}$	$\frac{3}{5} \times 7\frac{1}{2}$	$\frac{1}{4} \times 5\frac{1}{3}$
3.	$1\frac{1}{2} \times 1\frac{1}{2}$	$1\frac{1}{4} \times 1\frac{3}{4}$	$6\frac{1}{2} \times 1\frac{1}{2}$	$2\frac{2}{3} \times 1\frac{7}{8}$	$1\frac{2}{3} \times 2\frac{1}{3}$
4.	$2\frac{1}{4} \times 1\frac{1}{4}$	$3\frac{1}{2} \times 1\frac{1}{3}$	$5\frac{1}{4} \times 3\frac{1}{7}$	$2\frac{1}{2} \times 2\frac{1}{2}$	$4\frac{1}{2} \times 2\frac{3}{4}$

	A	B	C
VI. 1.	$\frac{2}{3} \times \frac{1}{2} \times \frac{1}{4}$	$\frac{1}{2} \times \frac{1}{2} \times \frac{1}{2}$	$\frac{1}{4} \times \frac{1}{2} \times \frac{3}{4}$
2.	$\frac{3}{8} \times \frac{2}{5} \times \frac{4}{9}$	$\frac{3}{5} \times \frac{1}{2} \times \frac{2}{3}$	$\frac{3}{8} \times \frac{5}{6} \times 1$
3.	$1\frac{1}{2} \times \frac{1}{3} \times 120$	$2\frac{1}{2} \times 12 \times 1\frac{1}{4}$	$400 \times \frac{9}{200} \times \frac{8}{12}$

Division of Fractions and Mixed Numbers

	A	B	C	D
I. 1.	$\frac{8}{9} \div 2$	$\frac{4}{5} \div 4$	$\frac{2}{3} \div 8$	$\frac{6}{5} \div 8$
2.	$\frac{9}{10} \div 3$	$\frac{12}{13} \div 6$	$\frac{8}{3} \div 4$	$\frac{15}{16} \div 5$
II. 1.	$12 \div \frac{3}{4}$	$30 \div \frac{1}{2}$	$24 \div \frac{6}{7}$	$9 \div \frac{9}{16}$
2.	$10 \div \frac{2}{5}$	$16 \div \frac{4}{5}$	$18 \div \frac{2}{3}$	$40 \div \frac{5}{8}$
III. 1.	$\frac{1}{2} \div \frac{3}{8}$	$\frac{3}{5} \div \frac{9}{10}$	$\frac{4}{9} \div \frac{5}{6}$	$\frac{2}{3} \div \frac{3}{2}$
2.	$\frac{5}{6} \div \frac{1}{3}$	$\frac{3}{4} \div \frac{3}{8}$	$\frac{7}{8} \div \frac{3}{4}$	$\frac{7}{12} \div \frac{3}{8}$
IV. 1.	$24 \div 2\frac{2}{3}$	$35 \div 2\frac{1}{2}$	$30 \div 3\frac{1}{3}$	$9 \div 2\frac{1}{4}$
2.	$14 \div 1\frac{3}{4}$	$52 \div 2\frac{3}{5}$	$44 \div 1\frac{3}{8}$	$10 \div 1\frac{1}{5}$
V. 1.	$6\frac{1}{4} \div 15$	$1\frac{7}{8} \div 3$	$2\frac{4}{5} \div 7$	$3\frac{1}{7} \div 22$
2.	$2\frac{2}{3} \div 8$	$6\frac{3}{4} \div 9$	$1\frac{2}{3} \div 5$	$3\frac{1}{3} \div 20$
VI. 1.	$2\frac{1}{2} \div \frac{1}{2}$	$2\frac{2}{3} \div \frac{4}{5}$	$4\frac{1}{2} \div \frac{2}{9}$	$3\frac{1}{5} \div \frac{2}{5}$
2.	$1\frac{1}{4} \div \frac{5}{8}$	$6\frac{1}{4} \div \frac{5}{16}$	$5\frac{1}{4} \div \frac{7}{8}$	$2\frac{2}{5} \div 1\frac{2}{5}$
3.	$2\frac{1}{4} \div \frac{3}{5}$	$5\frac{1}{3} \div \frac{4}{9}$	$7\frac{1}{2} \div \frac{1}{10}$	$1\frac{1}{3} \div \frac{3}{16}$
VII. 1.	$\frac{1}{2} \div 1\frac{1}{2}$	$\frac{5}{9} \div 2\frac{2}{3}$	$\frac{7}{8} \div 3\frac{1}{2}$	$\frac{1}{2} \div 1\frac{3}{4}$
2.	$\frac{1}{3} \div 1\frac{2}{3}$	$\frac{7}{8} \div 1\frac{1}{4}$	$\frac{4}{9} \div 1\frac{1}{3}$	$\frac{1}{4} \div 3\frac{1}{5}$
3.	$\frac{3}{8} \div 2\frac{1}{4}$	$\frac{5}{6} \div 4\frac{1}{2}$	$\frac{2}{5} \div 2\frac{1}{2}$	$\frac{3}{4} \div 3\frac{3}{8}$
VIII. 1.	$4\frac{1}{2} \div 1\frac{1}{2}$	$5\frac{1}{3} \div 2\frac{2}{3}$	$6\frac{1}{4} \div 1\frac{2}{3}$	$2\frac{1}{4} \div 2\frac{3}{4}$
2.	$3\frac{1}{2} \div 2\frac{1}{3}$	$4\frac{1}{2} \div 2\frac{1}{4}$	$5\frac{1}{4} \div 2\frac{5}{8}$	$10\frac{1}{2} \div 2\frac{1}{4}$
3.	$1\frac{1}{2} \div 2\frac{1}{4}$	$1\frac{2}{3} \div 2\frac{1}{3}$	$4\frac{2}{3} \div 3\frac{1}{2}$	$6\frac{1}{8} \div 1\frac{3}{4}$

Addition of Decimals

I.

	A	B	C	D	E	F	G	H
1.	5.9	3.7	17.8	29.4	0.5	8.7	42.3	65.2
	0.6	16.4	8.6	15.3	9.7	.5	4.6	76.7
	3.8	8.5	5.2	13.9	0.6	3.4	6.9	.8
2.	.026	.365	.039	.439	.857	.419	.538	.693
	.285	.883	.875	.889	.027	.980	.408	.599
	.307	.549	.064	.974	.746	.837	.967	.908

II.

	A	B	C	D	E	F
	0.653	4.839	2.948	7.506	4.009	54.768
	0.325	0.358	9.878	2.979	39.386	94.184
	7.007	5.769	0.686	4.527	22.579	1.099

III.

	A	B	C	D	E
	$35.64	$25.98	$ 5.75	$ 2.79	$35.78
	1.19	4.30	.52	74.78	9.85
	20.33	2.39	26.58	22.07	13.40
	4.12	14.68	4.86	1.80	7.95

Subtraction of Decimals

I.

	A	B	C	D	E	F	G
1.	5.28	14.84	6.30	13.82	9.04	10.60	8.03
	0.53	7.26	4.50	0.56	4.70	7.83	3.97
2.	.694	.081	.634	.090	.900	.062	.811
	.283	.007	.245	.005	.260	.038	.804

II.

	A	B	C	D	E	F
1.	4.899	18.935	86.020	8.353	19.262	38.046
	2.523	6.941	62.054	4.796	7.873	1.299
2.	$46.70	$13.76	$70.24	$140.27	$106.60	$288.16
	13.48	9.87	56.68	85.99	49.69	78.36

Multiplication of Decimals

I.	A	B	C	D	E	F	G
1.	.6 .3	.8 .8	.43 .5	.52 .7	.76 .4	9.4 .6	.71 .9
2.	4.6 .9	34.7 .2	.28 .6	3.05 .4	13.7 .8	2.09 .3	.825 .5

II.							
1.	37 .6	74 .03	38 .7	62 .18	24 4.1	49 .78	35 9.2
2.	61 .5	28 .9	56 .06	38 .13	59 2.9	27 .017	75 5.8

III.							
1.	.9 .4	.05 .1	.6 .7	.1 .1	.08 .4	.01 .2	.9 .5
2.	.06 .2	.15 .3	.08 .2	2.7 .3	.04 .6	.92 .1	.18 .3

IV.							
1.	.901 .4	.037 .5	.261 .2	.346 .03	.008 .06	.046 .8	.124 .9
2.	.056 .01	.504 .3	.729 .2	.486 .05	.208 .004	.036 .09	.314 .07

V.							
1.	.361 1.4	4.08 .012	1.63 .06	.417 4.6	.708 .91	1.39 7.8	50.8 .48
2.	.857 .07	9.52 .06	20.9 .03	.129 .05	1.06 .07	.09 .09	42.1 .08

VI.	A	B	C	D	E	F
1.	5.3 10	.568 10	7.294 1000	.63 100	.924 100	58.72 1000
2.	.093 100	37.2 10	.0685 1000	59.4 100	273.5 1000	.037 10

Division of Decimals

	A	B	C	D	E
I. 1.	4)6.4	11).77	25)12.5	88)1.76	13).052
2.	9).027	6).192	8)9.68	15).75	22)5.5
3.	3).084	14)4.2	27).27	35).7	61).0549
4.	5).12	12)28.8	7)2.87	16).08	18)10.8
II. 1.	.6).54	1.6)25.6	.11).088	.8)1.12	6.3).126
2.	.14).84	.9)1.08	4.5)1.8	.33).33	1.2)4.8
3.	1.1)13.2	1.8)1.44	.55)2.2	1.5).75	.13).65
4.	.25)1.25	.5).205	.7)49.07	.48).096	7.5)4.5
III. 1.	.08)9.6	.05).06	.3).015	.08).0056	.19)1.9
2.	.07).0042	.03)2.1	1.7).034	.09)5.4	.44)2.2
3.	.9).0036	.4).012	.006)2.4	.36)7.2	.16)6.4
IV. 1.	.011)11	.005)2	.06)72	.16)8	.25)5
2.	.9)180	.24)6	.002)10	.08)4	2.4)12
3.	.004)8	.7)14	.8)480	.05)10	.3)45
V. 1.	4)1	36)24	12)3	32)16	5)2
2.	8)10	10)8	16)14	8)5	40)1
3.	25)15	12)1	54)9	16)1	10)1

Percentage

I.   **1.** Find 25% of: 40, 96, 2, 120, 8000.
      2. Find $33\frac{1}{3}$% of: 75, 66, 225, 4500, 1.
      3. Find 20% of: 50, 125, 10,000, 5, 20.
      4. Find 75% of: 24, 100, 4, 1800, 160.

II.

	A	B	C
1.	10% of $39 = ?	$1\frac{1}{2}$% of 500 = ?	12% of $320 = ?
2.	85% of $200 = ?	92% of 70 = ?	55% of $1000 = ?
3.	3% of $1200 = ?	60% of 400 = ?	17% of $300 = ?
4.	24% of $20 = ?	8% of 19.5 = ?	$4\frac{1}{2}$% of $800 = ?

III. **1.** A. 16 is _?_% of 64   B. 80 is _?_% of 80
      2. A. 30 is _?_% of 48   B. 9 is _?_% of 12
      3. A. _?_% of 40 is 16   B. _?_% of 20 is 18
      4. A. _?_% of 30 is 24   B. _?_% of 40 is 24

IV. **1.** A. 20% of _?_ = 16   B. 10% of _?_ = 3
      2. A. 75% of _?_ = 180   B. 60% of _?_ = 54
      3. A. 18 is 50% of _?_   B. 180 is 90% of _?_
      4. A. 24 is 40% of _?_   B. 82 is $66\frac{2}{3}$% of _?_

V. Express as decimals: VI. Express as per cents:
1. 10%, 27%, 94%, 6%   **1.** .4, .03, .88, .60
2. $3\frac{1}{2}$%, $5\frac{1}{4}$%, $6\frac{3}{4}$%, $\frac{3}{10}$%   **2.** .015, .002, .0325, .046
3. $\frac{1}{2}$%, 2.4%, 0.8%, $\frac{1}{10}$ of 1%   **3.** 1.0, .1, .01, 0.10

VII.
1. A. $\frac{3}{4}$% of $1200 = ?   B. $\frac{9}{10}$% of $20,000 = ?
2. A. $\frac{1}{2}$ of 1% of $600,000 = ?   B. .2% of $5000 = ?

VIII.
1. A. 150% of $600 = ?   B. 300% of $125 = ?
2. A. 110% of $440 = ?   B. 225% of $800 = ?
3. A. 40% more than 15 = ?   B. 20% more than 200 = ?
4. A. 50% more than 40 = ?   B. 20% less than 200 = ?

Tables for Reference

MEASURES OF LENGTH

12 inches (in.) = 1 foot (ft.)
3 feet = 1 yard (yd.)
5½ yards = 16½ feet = 1 rod (rd.)

320 rods = 1 mile (mi.)
1760 yards = 1 mile
5280 feet = 1 mile

MEASURES OF SURFACE

144 square inches (sq. in.) = 1 square foot (sq. ft.)
9 square feet = 1 square yard (sq. yd.)
30¼ square yards = 1 square rod (sq. rd.)
160 square rods = 1 acre (A.)
640 acres = 1 square mile (sq. mi.)

MEASURES OF VOLUME

1728 cubic inches (cu. in.) = 1 cubic foot (cu. ft.)
27 cubic feet = 1 cubic yard (cu. yd.)

MEASURES OF CAPACITY

Liquid Measure
4 gills (gi.) = 1 pint (pt.)
2 pints = 1 quart (qt.)
4 quarts = 1 gallon (gal.)

Dry Measure
2 pints = 1 quart (qt.)
8 quarts = 1 peck (pk.)
4 pecks = 1 bushel (bu.)

MEASURES OF WEIGHT

16 ounces (oz.) = 1 pound (lb.)
100 pounds = 1 hundredweight (cwt.)
20 hundredweight = 1 ton (T.)
2000 pounds = 1 ton
2240 pounds = 1 long ton

MONEY
10 mills = 1 cent
10 cents = 1 dime
10 dimes = 1 dollar

COUNTING
12 units = 1 dozen
12 dozen = 1 gross
12 gross = 1 great gross
20 units = 1 score

KITCHEN MEASURES

3 teaspoons = 1 tablespoon
16 tablespoons = 1 cup
2 cups = 1 pint
(all measures level full)

---

1 cup flour = $\frac{1}{4}$ lb.*
1 cup sugar = $\frac{1}{2}$ lb.*
1 cup butter = $\frac{1}{2}$ lb.*
1 cup lard = $\frac{1}{2}$ lb.*
1 cup chopped meat = $\frac{1}{2}$ lb.*

MEASURES OF COMMON THINGS

1 pt. water weighs 1 lb.*
1 gal. water weighs $8\frac{1}{3}$ lb.*
1 cu. ft. water weighs $62\frac{1}{2}$ lb.*
1 cu. ft. ice weighs $57\frac{1}{2}$ lb.*
1 bbl. flour weighs 196 lb.*
1 ton coal = 35 cu. ft.*

MISCELLANEOUS MEASURES

1 gallon = 231 cu. in.
1 cu. ft. = $7\frac{1}{2}$ gal.*
1 bushel = 2150.4 cu. in.

*Items starred are approximate values.

WEIGHT OF A BUSHEL IN MOST STATES

ARTICLE	LB.	ARTICLE	LB.
Apples	50	Oats	32
Barley	48	Onions	57
Beans	60	Peaches	48
Clover seed	60	Peas	60
Coal	80	Potatoes	60
Coke	40	Rye	56
Corn (shelled)	56	Tomatoes	56
Corn (on cob)	70	Wheat	60

APPROXIMATE METRIC EQUIVALENTS

Metric to English

1 centimeter (cm.) = 0.4 inch (in.)
1 meter (m.) = 39.37 in. = 1.1 yards (yd.)
1 kilometer (km.) = 0.62 mile (mi.)
1 kilogram (kg.) = 2.2 pounds (lb.)
1 liter (l.) = 1.06 liquid quarts (qt.)

English to Metric

1 inch (in.) = 2.54 centimeters (cm.)
1 yard (yd.) = 0.9 meter (m.)
1 mile (mi.) = 1.6 kilometers (km.)
1 pound (lb.) = 0.45 kilogram (kg.)
1 liquid quart (qt.) = 0.95 liter (l.)

Index

Abacus, 5
Acre, 163
Acute angle, 169
Acute triangle, 170
Addition, 4, 5, 9, 10, 11, 27, 88, 353
Air pressure, 52
Air travel, 1, 51
Algebra, introduction to, 345–355
Altitude
  of trapezoid, 174
  of triangle, 165
Amortization, 299
  schedule, 314, 315
Angle
  acute, 169, 170
  everyday problems about, 321
  meaning of, 169, 319
  obtuse, 169, 170
  right, 169
  straight, 169
  symbol for, 320
  vertex of, 169, 319
Area
  everyday problems with, 161, 163–164, 181, 196
  making sure of, 188
  of circle, 180
  of cylinder, 197
  of parallelogram, 172, 175
  of prism, 193, 194–195
  of rectangle, 38, 158, 160, 172, 173
  of sphere, 210
  of square, 38, 158, 159, 162
  of trapezoid, 174–175
  of triangle, 165, 166–167, 173
  understanding, 38
Assessed valuation, 150
Automobile driving, speed and, 82–83, 136

Balance, bank, 124
  unpaid, 296
Bank checks, 111, 112, 113
Bank discount, 290, 292

Bank note, 289
Banks, and banking, 111, 112, 115, 117, 118, 123, 124, 125, 289–290, 292, 293, 298–299
Barometer, 52
Base, in percentage, 70, 71, 93, 94, 100
Base, or bases
  of cylinder, 204
  of prism, 193
  of a solid, 192
  of trapezoid, 174
  of triangle, 165
Baseball, per cents in, 72
Billion, 2–3
Bills, paying, 275
Blueprints, reading, 21, 330
Board foot, 202
Bonds
  buying and selling, 305, 306
  income from, 307
  maturity value of, 308
  raising money with, 305, 314–315
  redemption value of, 309
  United States Savings, 308–310
Borrowing money, 289–294, 298–299
Broker, 303
Brokerage fee, 304, 306
Budget
  family, 98–99, 107–108
  government, 145
Bulk, 40
Business, problems about, 68, 73, 74, 80–81, 94, 123, 235, 271, 272, 273, 274, 275, 276, 277, 278, 279, 280, 281, 282, 300 301, 302, 303–304
  language of, 100, 295

Calculating machines, 5
Calories, 230, 231
Cancellation, 13
Capacity, measures of, 40, 41, 42, 200, 206, 371

Capital, 300
Capital stock, 300
Carrying charge, 296
Cash, 110
Cash discount, 275
Centimeter, 44–45
Checking
  in addition, 88
  in division, 7, 89
  in multiplication, 6, 88
  in subtraction, 88
Checks
  bank, 111, 112, 113
  endorsing, 112
  things to remember about, 113
  travelers, 115
Circle
  area of, 180
  circumference of, 177–178
  diameter of, 177
  everyday problems about, 181, 184
Clothing and the clothing industry, 233–234, 235, 236
Commission, 80–81, 272, 273
  rate of, 80
Commission merchant, 273
Common denominator, 9
Compound interest, 311–313
Cone, 191, 208–209
Corporation, 300, 301
Cost of living, 225, 236, 284, 285
Coupon rate, 307
Coupons (bond), 307
Credit instruments, 110
Credit union, 294
Cross multiplication, 327
Cube, 42, 191, 195, 198, 199
Cubic contents, 42
Cubic foot, 42
Cubic inch, 42
Currency, 110
Current yield on bonds, 307
Customs revenues, or duties, 147, 154
Cylinder, 191
  capacity of, 206
  surface, or lateral area of, 197
  volume of, 204–205

Decimal equivalents
  of fractions, 24–25, 26
  of per cents, 63
Decimal fraction, 24
Decimal point, 24, 30, 33, 63
Decimals, 24
  addition of, 27
  changing common fractions to, 24, 26
  changing per cents to, 63
  changing to per cents, 62
  division with, 31, 32, 33
  estimating answers in, 283
  everyday problems with, 46–47, 52, 53, 56
  in science, 53
  making sure of, 59
  multiplication with, 28–29, 30
  practice with, 25, 26, 27, 29, 30, 32, 33, 63
  rounding, 25, 33, 55
  subtraction of, 27
  understanding, 24–25
  units of measure, and, 44
Decimeter, 44, 45
Denominator, 9
Deposit slip, 111
Diameter, 177
Dimensions, 158, 200
Direction, telling, 319, 321
Discount, 73
  bank, 290, 292
  cash, 275
  retail, 73
  trade, 276, 277, 295
Disk, 191
Distance, measuring, 37, 44–45, 46, 265, 371
Dividends, 143, 300
Division, 7, 16, 17, 18, 19, 31, 32, 33, 89, 349, 351
Dollar, value of, 284
Down payment, 296
Dry measure, 40, 49, 371

Earning a living, 80–81, 268–287
Earth, as a globe, 258, 259, 260
Electric power, 241, 243, 244–245
Energy, measuring, 240–241

374

Equations, 348–355
Equilateral triangle, 168, 323
Error of measurement, 36
Estimating answers in problems, 43, 55, 232, 283
Excise tax, 147
Expenses, in selling, 279, 280, 281, 282

Faces, of a solid, 192
Farms and farming, 220–221, 222, 223, 271
Federal Deposit Insurance Corporation (F.D.I.C.), 125
Fixed charge, 98
Flat surface, 210
Floor plans, 330
Fluid ounce, 41
Food, and food processing, 224, 225, 226–227, 228–229, 230, 231
Foot, 37
  board, 202
  front, 163
Forests, conservation of, 223
Formula, for finding,
  area of circle, 180
  area of parallelogram, 172, 175
  area of rectangle, 158
  area of sphere, 210
  area of square, 159
  area of trapezoid, 175
  area of triangle, 165
  circumference and diameter of circle, 177
  interest, 121, 291
  interest rate, 291
  lateral area of prism, 193
  lateral surface of cylinder, 197
  per cent, percentage, base, 249
  rate of interest, 291
  side of right triangle, 342
  volume of cone, 208
  volume of cylinder, 204
  volume of prism, 198–199
  volume of pyramid, 208–209
  volume of sphere, 211
Formulas, practice in using, 173, 354

Fractions, 8–20, 22–26, 59, 62, 64, 65
Front foot, or frontage, 163

Geometric figures and measurement
  angles, 169, 170–171, 319, 320, 321
  area of circle, 180
  area, lateral, of cylinder, 197
  area of parallelogram, 172
  area of rectangle, 38, 158, 160
  area of rectangular prism, 193, 194–195
  area of square, 38, 159, 162
  area of trapezoid, 174–175
  area of triangle, 165, 166, 173
  finding side of right triangle, 342
  floor plans, 330
  hexagon, 323
  indirect measurements in, 332–333, 334–335
  parallel lines, 322
  pentagon, 323
  ratios, 324, 325, 326–327
  right triangle rule, 340, 341
  scale drawings, 329–331, 334–335
  square root, 336, 337, 338, 339
  volume of cone, 208–209
  volume of cube, 191, 198, 199
  volume of cylinder, 204–205
  volume of prism, 198–199
  volume of pyramid, 208–209
  volume of sphere, 211

Government, cost of, 144, 145, 252–253, 314–315
Graduations, on a scale, 35
Gram, 48
Graphs, 96–97

Hexagon, 323
Home, cost of owning a, 153, 298
Horsepower, 240, 241
Hospitalization, 137
Hydroelectric power, 243

Hypotenuse, 340
Import duties, or customs revenues, 154
  ad valorem, 154
  specific, 154
Income tax, 148–149
Incomes, family, 285
Index number, 221, 284
Indirect measurements, 332–333, 334–335
Installment buying, 296–297
Insurance
  accident, 139
  automobile, 134–135
  collision, 134
  dividends on, 143
  endowment, 142
  everyday problems in, 132, 135, 137, 139, 141, 142, 143
  face value of policy, 131, 141
  fire, 132–133
  hospitalization, 137
  life, 140–141, 142
  making sure of, 157
  policy, 131, 134
  premiums, 132
  term, 142
  understanding, 156
Interest
  compound, 311–313
  everyday problems in, 123, 124, 126, 293, 298, 299, 315
  formula for, 121, 291
  making sure of, 129, 317
  meaning, 116
  rate of, 116, 118, 121, 291, 292, 293
  simple, 117–123
  understanding, 127
Internal revenue, 147
International date line, 262
Investments, 301–313, 316
Isosceles triangle, 168

Jiffy quiz, 30, 50, 95, 122, 171, 185, 196, 203, 215, 275, 331, 335, 337
Just for fun, 19, 58, 104, 128, 164, 185, 333

Keeping in practice, 47, 58, 81, 87, 99, 104, 113, 120, 128, 175, 178, 213, 248
Kilogram, 48
Kilometer, 45
Kilowatt, 241, 244
Kilowatt-hour, 244
Knot, 265

Land measures, 163, 265
Lateral area
  of cylinder, 197
  of prism, 193
Learning to solve problems, see Problem solving
Length, measures of, 37, 44–45, 371
Liability, automobile insurance and, 134
License fees, 144
Lines
  parallel, 172, 322
  reference, 321
Liquid measure, 40, 41, 49, 371
List price, 276, 295
Liter, 49
Loans
  mortgage, 298–299
  personal, 116, 117, 118, 293
Longitude, 258
Lumber, measuring, 202–203

Maker, of note, 289
  of check, 112
Making sure tests
  areas, 188
  buying and selling, 287
  equations, 357
  geometric figures and measurement, 188, 344
  insurance, 157
  measures, 59, 267
  money, borrowing and investing, 317
  money and interest, 129
  per cents, 105, 129, 287
  solid figures, measuring, 217
  square root, 344
  surfaces, measuring, 188

Making sure tests—*continued*
 taxes, 157
 whole numbers, fractions, decimals, 59
Margin, 278, 279, 280, 281, 295
Market values, or quotations, of stocks, 303
Maturity date of note, 289
Maturity value of bonds, 308
Measurement and measuring
 capacity, 40, 41, 42, 200, 206, 371
 distance, 37, 44–45, 46, 265, 371
 dry things, 40, 49, 371
 energy, 240–241, 244–245
 error of, 36
 estimating with, 232
 indirect, 332–333, 334–335
 land, 163, 258, 265
 length, 37, 44–45, 371
 liquids, 40, 41, 49, 371
 lumber, 202–203
 precision in, 34
 surfaces, 38, 187, 193, 194–195, 197, 371
 time, 259–263
 understanding, 35
 weight, 39, 371
Measures
 dry, 40, 49, 371
 everyday problems about, 37, 39, 40, 41, 43, 45, 46–47, 56, 186, 195, 196, 197
 liquid, 40, 41, 49, 371
 metric units of, 44–45, 48, 372
 tables of, 371–372
Meridians, 258, 259
Meter, 44, 46–47, 372
Metric system, 44–45, 46–47, 48, 49, 372
Metric ton, 48
Micrometer, 36
Mill, 151
Milliliter, 49
Millimeter, 44, 45
Million, 2–3
Money, 106, 110, 116, 127, 284, 289–294
Mortgage, 298–299

Multiplication, 6, 13–15, 28–30, 59, 88, 350, 351
 cross, 327

National resources, 220–221, 222, 223, 233–234, 242, 246
Nautical mile, 265
Net cost, 275, 276, 277
Net price, 73
Net proceeds, 80, 100, 273
Note, bank, 289, 290
Number system, 2–3
Numbers
 mixed, 11, 12, 14, 16, 18
 periods in, 2
 place-holder in, 2
 place value in, 2
 reading, 2, 3
 Roman, 57
 rounding, 54, 219, 220, 222, 223
 whole, 2, 4–5, 6, 7, 13, 16, 17, 54, 219

Obtuse angle, 169, 170
Obtuse triangle, 170
Octagon, 323

Parallel lines, 172, 322
Parallelogram, area of, 172, 175
Par value, 300, 305
Passbook, 124
Pentagon, 323
Per cents
 as rates, 70
 as ratios, 85
 changing fractions and decimals to, 62
 changing to decimals, 63
 changing to fractions, 64
 estimating answers in, 283
 everyday uses of, 61, 67, 72, 74, 75, 76, 77, 85, 90, 91, 94, 95, 98–99, 103, 107–108, 233, 234, 235, 236, 272, 273, 276, 277, 281, 282
 finding a per cent of a number, 66
 finding the base, 70, 93, 94, 249
 finding the rate, 69, 70, 249, 291

Per cents—*continued*
  fractional, 62, 86–87
  greater than *100%*, 78–79
  in baseball, 72
  in business, 68, 90, 91, 94, 95, 221, 235
  making sure of, 105
  of increase or decrease, 75–76
  of profit, 281, 282
  practice with, 62, 63, 64, 65, 66, 69, 71, 73, 78, 81, 85, 87, 92, 93, 99, 101, 102, 103
  understanding, 101
  uneven, 71
Periods, in a number, 2
Pi (π), 176
Pitching average, 72
Place-holder, 2
Place value, 2
Postal money order, 114
Postal savings, 126
Practice, *see* Keeping in, Making sure tests, Remedial
Premium, insurance, 132, 135, 140–143
Prime meridian, 258
Principal, 116, 118, 121
  of a note, or face value, 289
Prisms
  bases of, 193
  everyday problems about, 201
  rectangular, 191, 194–195
  surface of, 193, 194, 195
  volume of, 198–199
Problem solving
  checking answers in, 88–89
  deciding what process to use, 50
  estimating answers in, 43, 283
  facts missing in, 183, 207
  practice in, 43, 50, 77, 84, 88–89, 100, 103, 182, 183, 207, 214, 232, 266, 283, 295, 328, 355
  relationships in, 328
  understanding language in, 100, 286, 295, 316
Proceeds of a note, 290
Profit, 279, 280, 281, 282
Promissory note, 289, 290

Proportion, 325, 326–327, 328, 343
  terms of, 325
Pyramid, volume of, 208–209
Pythagoras, rule of, 340

Quotation, of a bond, 306
  of a stock, 303

Radius, 177
Rate, 70
  annual interest, 116, 118, 291
  of commission, 80
  of profit, 281
  premium, 132
  tax, 148, 149, 150, 151
  understanding, 84
Ratio, 22–23, 25, 324, 325, 326, 328, 343
Ratios, equal, 325, 326
Reaction time, 82–83
Real estate tax, 150–151
Rectangle, area of, 38, 158, 160, 172, 173
Rectangular prism, 191, 194–195
  everyday problems with, 201
  volume of, 198
Redemption value of bonds, 309
Reference line, 321
Regular figures, 323
Remedial practice, 358–370
Retail merchant, 274, 295
Right angle, 169
Right triangle, 170, 342
Right triangle rule, 340
Roman numbers, 57
Rounding
  decimals, 25, 33, 55
  whole numbers, 54, 219

Salary, 269
Savings accounts, 124, 311
Scale drawings, 329, 330, 331, 334–335
Science, using decimals in, 53
Section, of land, 164
Sector, 180
Selling price, 278, 279, 280, 281, 282
Shipping goods, 237–238

Similar triangles, 332, 334–335
Solids, 191, 192, 193–217
   base of, 192
   everyday problems about, 212–213
   faces of, 192
   understanding, 216
Sphere
   surface of, 210
   volume of, 211
Square, area of, 38, 158, 159, 162
Square foot, 38
Square inch, 38
Square of a number, 336
Square root, 336–339
Square yard, 38
Standard time, 260–263
Statute mile, 265
Stock exchange, 303
Stockholder, 300
Stocks, 300, 301, 302, 303–304
   common, 302
   preferred, 302
Subtraction, 4, 5, 12, 27, 88, 352
Surface, measure of, 38, 187, 193, 194, 197, 371

Tariff, 154
Taxes, 147
   benefits from, 144
   consumer and, 155
   customs duties, 147, 154
   excise, 147
   everyday problems about, 146, 147, 149, 152, 155
   import duty, or tariff, 154
   income, 147, 148–149
   internal revenue, 147
   license fees, 144
   making sure of, 157
   rate of, 148, 149, 150, 151
   real estate, 150, 152
   sales, 147
   understanding, 156
   withholding, 149
Thrift, 109
Time, 259, 260–261, 263
Time payments, 296–297
Timetable, 264

Ton-mile, 237
Township, 164
Trade discount, 276, 277, 295
Trapezoid, area of, 174–175
   altitude of, 174
Travelers checks, 115
Triangles
   acute, 170
   altitude of, 165
   angles of, 170
   area of, 165, 166, 173
   arms or legs of, 340
   base of, 165
   equilateral, 168, 323
   everyday problems with, 341
   isosceles, 168
   obtuse, 170
   right, 170, 340, 342
   sides of, 168, 340
   similar, 332, 334–335
   symbol for, 333

United States Savings Bonds, 308–310

Valuation, assessed, 150
Vertex
   of angle, 319
   of a solid, 192
Volume, 40
   of cone, 208–209
   of cube, 42, 198, 199
   of cylinder, 204–205
   of prism, 199
   of pyramid, 208–209
   of rectangular prism, 198
   of a solid, 200
   of sphere, 211

Wages, 270
Watt, 241
Weight, measures of, 39, 48, 371
Whole numbers, *see* Numbers

Zero
   as place-holder, 2
   in division of decimals, 32, 33
   in multiplication of decimals, 28–29

References to Life Situations

Air transportation, 1, 51
Atmospheric pressure, 52
Banks and banking, 111–113
Baseball averages, 72
Blueprints, 21
Bonds, 305, 306, 307, 308–309, 310
Borrowing money, 116, 289–294, 314–315
Budgets, 98–99, 107–109, 145
Buying at a discount, 73–76
Calculating machines, 5
Clothing and the clothing industry, 233–234, 235, 236
Communication in our world, 254–257
Conservation, 223
Cost of living, 106, 225, 236, 244, 284–285
Credit unions, 294
Earning a living, 269–285
Education, public, 250–253
Farms and farming, 220–221, 223, 271
Floor plans, 330
Food and food processing, 224, 225, 226–227, 228–229, 230, 231
Highways, 146
Home, buying a, 153, 298–299
Installment buying, 296–297
Insurance, 131–143
Interest on money, 116, 123
Measuring, precision in, 34–36
Measuring bulk, 40, 200
Measuring capacity, 42, 49, 200
Measuring distance and length, 37, 44

Measuring energy, 240–241
Measuring land, 163–164
Measuring liquids, 41, 49
Measuring lumber, 202–203
Measuring surfaces, 158–162, 165, 172–175, 180
Measuring volume, 198–199, 200, 204, 208–209, 211
Measuring weight, 39, 48
Money, borrowing, 116, 289–294, 314–315
Money, earning, 269–274, 276, 279, 281, 282
Motion pictures and television, 256–257
Per cents in everyday life, 67, 68, 90, 91, 95, 98–99, 106
Postal money orders, 114
Profit in business, 279–282
Reaction time, 82
Safety, 82–83, 136
Savings accounts, 124, 311
Scale drawings, 334–335
Science, 53
Shop work, 20
Solids, in everyday life, 196, 212–213
Sports, 46–47, 72
Stocks, 301–302, 303–304
Taxes, 147, 149, 150, 152, 155
Time, 258–263
Timetables, 264
Transportation, 228, 237–238, 239
Travelers checks, 115
Turbines, steam, 179
United States Savings Bonds, 308–310